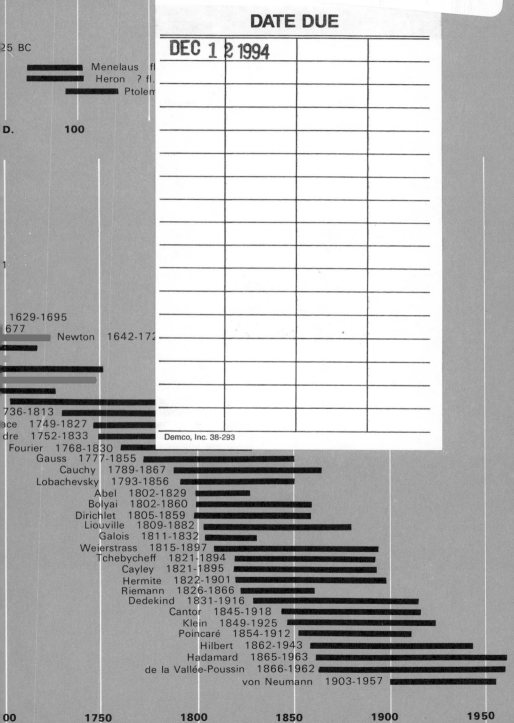

GREEK

25 BC

Menelaus fl.
Heron ? fl.
Ptolem

D. 100

1629-1695
677
Newton 1642-172

736-1813
ace 1749-1827
dre 1752-1833
Fourier 1768-1830
Gauss 1777-1855
Cauchy 1789-1867
Lobachevsky 1793-1856
Abel 1802-1829
Bolyai 1802-1860
Dirichlet 1805-1859
Liouville 1809-1882
Galois 1811-1832
Weierstrass 1815-1897
Tchebycheff 1821-1894
Cayley 1821-1895
Hermite 1822-1901
Riemann 1826-1866
Dedekind 1831-1916
Cantor 1845-1918
Klein 1849-1925
Poincaré 1854-1912
Hilbert 1862-1943
Hadamard 1865-1963
de la Vallée-Poussin 1866-1962
von Neumann 1903-1957

00   1750   1800   1850   1900   1950

Mathematics: *Its Spirit and Evolution*

MATHEMATICS
Its Spirit and Evolution

JOHN R. DURBIN

The University of Texas at Austin

Allyn and Bacon, Inc.   Boston

119438

TO MY MOTHER AND FATHER

Contents

Preface

Mathematics has been an elemental pursuit of the collective human intellect for at least twenty-five hundred years; its place in any definition of liberal education is secure. This leads to the question of how the spirit of mathematics can best be conveyed to those with limited background in the subject. This book is the author's answer to that question.

Notice that we are after nothing less than the spirit of mathematics, however difficult that might be to capture. Our primary goal is not to survey all of mathematics, or even that part of mathematics that is easily accessible. We shall concentrate at first on becoming familiar with a few significant ideas, following the principle that it is better to pursue a few topics carefully than many topics superficially. In the final chapter we shall abandon that principle in trying to gain a view of some general characteristics of modern mathematics.

The reader is assumed to have a knowledge of minimal high school mathematics (a course in each of geometry and algebra). Beyond that the only prerequisites are curiosity and an open mind, one which accepts the possibility that just as music is something more than scales and simple tunes, mathematics may be something more than what is reflected in either elementary mathematics or everyday applications. Some specific suggestions for use of the book follow this preface.

Of the many persons to whom I am indebted, I would like especially to acknowledge the advice I have received from Professors Sterling K. Berberian (The University of Texas at Austin), Carl B. Boyer (Brooklyn College, CUNY), Underwood Dudley (DePauw University), Robert A. McGuigan (University of Massachusetts), and Kenneth O. May (University of Toronto). Most of all I am grateful to my wife, Jane. Both her encouragement and her criticism have been valuable; it is difficult to imagine the existence of the book without her.

JOHN R. DURBIN

Suggestions

The book has been written to accommodate varied mathematical backgrounds and interests. In particular, the chapters can be read in an order other than that in which they appear, and the level of the material within chapters can be adjusted by selective omission. The choice of problems can also be used to adjust the level of difficulty: many are routine, but some are not.

The chapters, after the first, are nearly independent of one another. The notable exceptions are some terminology about sets from Chapter III (Section 17) which is used in Chapter IV, references to Chapter IV in the discussion of isomorphism in Chapter V, and references to earlier chapters to illustrate general remarks in Chapter VI. Even within chapters it is sometimes possible to read sections in an order other than that given. This is especially true in Chapter II, where the material in Sections 8 through 13 can be omitted and a view of the significance of the chapter gained from Sections 6, 7, and 14. A similar comment applies to Chapter VI: see the introductory remarks given there.

Section 48 (Distribution of Primes) furnishes an example of how the level can be adjusted through choice of stopping-place. The first half of the section requires almost no special preparation. The next portion, a discussion of the Prime Number Theorem, requires an acquaintance with the logarithmic function (Section 36) and a general idea about limits (Section 39). The section then closes with a brief exposition of the history surrounding the Riemann Hypothesis, which demands much more from earlier portions of the chapter.

It is suggested that at least one part of the book be covered carefully, to avoid the evils of a mere survey. On the other hand reading at least part of each chapter should help give a broader view. In any event a minimal first reading should include all of Chapter I, Sections 6, 7, and 14 in Chapter II, Section 33 in Chapter VI, and the introductory remarks for each chapter.

Each chapter has its own list of references, and any number in square brackets, such as [1], refers to the list of references at the end of the chapter in which it is found. The symbol $\square$ is used to denote the end of each proof.

Mathematics: *Its Spirit and Evolution*

An Introduction

§1. A Remarkable Theorem

If we are to take our subject at all seriously, then we must let it speak for itself. We begin, therefore, by considering a specific piece of mathematics. It should be familiar to anyone who has studied geometry, and we shall use it to introduce a number of essential ideas and questions, some of which will recur at different levels throughout the book.

PYTHAGOREAN THEOREM
In any triangle containing a right angle, the square on the side opposite the right angle is equal to the sum of the squares on the sides containing the right angle.

It will be instructive for us to look at two different interpretations of this theorem, and then to trace its origins.

There is a strictly geometric interpretation that given a triangle ABC with right angle at C (Figure 1.1), it is somehow possible to cut up the squares I and II (constructed on the legs CB and AC), and arrange

Figure 1.1

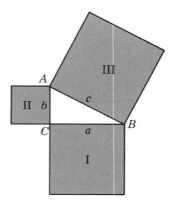

the pieces in such a way that they will exactly cover square III (constructed on the hypotenuse AB). We can make this interpretation more functional, without changing its essential spirit, if we allow ourselves not only to cut and rearrange but also to alter the figures we want to compare by adding to them, or subtracting from them, pieces of the same shape. In other words, we simply allow ourselves the freedom gained from assuming that equals added to equals are equal and that equals subtracted from equals are equal. Granted this, we can put together a short geometric proof of the theorem.

Geometric Proof

Consider the two drawings shown in Figure 1.2, where sides labelled with the same letter in Figures 1.1 and 1.2 are meant to be equal. The two large squares shown in Figure 1.2 are equal, each having sides equal to the sum of the legs of the right triangle given in Figure 1.1. Each of the four triangles shown in Figure 1.2(a) is equal to the given right triangle, and each of the four triangles shown in Figure 1.2(b) is also equal to the given right triangle. Thus when we remove these triangles from the large squares, the remaining parts must be equal. But in Figure 1.2(a), the part remaining is equal to the sum of I and II, and in Figure 1.2(b), the part remaining is a quadrilateral

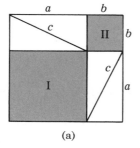

(a)

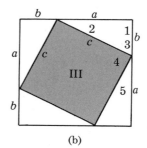

(b)

Figure 1.2

(four-sided figure) of side c. We shall be finished once we show that this quadrilateral is a square, as III in Figure 1.1. That is, we must verify that each of its angles is a right angle. (Problem 1.13 shows why this is necessary.) We shall verify that the angle we have labelled 4 is a right angle, and the other angles of the quadrilateral will be right angles by similar reasoning.

      We make use of the fact that the sum of the angles of a triangle is two right angles (Problem 1.12). Thus

$$\text{angle } 1 + \text{angle } 2 + \text{angle } 3 = \text{two right angles,}$$

so

$$\text{angle } 2 + \text{angle } 3 = \text{one right angle.}$$

But angle 2 = angle 5, because they are corresponding angles of triangles each just like the one originally given. Therefore

$$\text{angle } 5 + \text{angle } 3 = \text{one right angle.}$$

But

$$\text{angle } 4 + \text{angle } 5 + \text{angle } 3 = \text{two right angles,}$$

since the side of the large square is straight. Therefore angle 4 must be a right angle. $\square$

      Now we consider a second way of looking at the theorem. Before doing so, however, it is important to notice that nowhere in the first interpretation or in the geometric proof did we say anything about length or area or any other numerical measure of the geometric figures involved. We did speak of lines as being 'equal', but this can be taken to mean that they could be made to coincide if moved about appropriately. For our second interpretation we shall permit the use of numbers. Thus we assume that lines can be measured according to some common unit of length (inches, if you like), and that figures such as squares and triangles can be measured according to a corresponding square unit (square inches, then). If we accept the fact that the area of a square is the square of the length of one of its sides, the conclusion of the theorem now becomes a statement about numbers, saying that $a^2 + b^2 = c^2$. In these terms we can give a different proof of the theorem.

Algebraic-Geometric Proof

      This time we think of a as denoting the number giving the length of a side of the triangle in terms of some common unit, rather than just a label used to denote different equal lines; similarly for b and c. We begin with a square having each side of length c, and put copies of our triangle on the inside of this square, one on each side (Figure 1.3). We assume a to be larger than b (otherwise we just interchange a and b), and use the fact that the area of a right triangle is one-half the product of its two legs (that is, one-half base times altitude). The

Figure 1.3

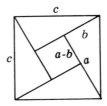

area of the large square is c^2, and this is equal to the sum of the areas of the four triangles added to the area of the small square in the middle (which disappears if $a = b$). Thus

$$\text{Area of large square} = \text{Area of four triangles} + \text{Area of small square}$$
$$c^2 = 4(\tfrac{1}{2}a\,b) + (a - b)^2$$
$$c^2 = 2ab + a^2 - 2ab + b^2$$
$$c^2 = a^2 + b^2. \quad \square$$

As we have said, there is a basic difference in our two views of the Pythagorean Theorem, in that one is strictly geometric while the other involves both geometry and arithmetic (or algebra, through the use of letters to denote unspecified numbers). The act of associating numbers with geometric entities, something which is done unconsciously now, is both crucial and subtle. It is crucial because most of the power of mathematics in applications rests ultimately on the ability to establish correspondences between numbers and things like line segments and time intervals; this can be seen in the mundane (measuring heights of people), or the dramatic (the technology involved in putting men on the moon). And the association of numbers with line segments is subtle in ways that were not appreciated by the people who first did it well over 3,000 years ago, or for that matter even by most nonmathematicians today; we shall return to this point in Section 4.

We complete this section by recording the converse of the Pythagorean Theorem. The theorem itself states that *if* a triangle satisfies a certain premise (the triangle contains a right angle), *then* a certain conclusion can be deduced (the squares of the sides of the triangle are related in a particular way). By the *converse* of the theorem (any theorem, for that matter) is meant the statement that results from interchanging the premise and conclusion. Explicitly:

CONVERSE OF THE PYTHAGOREAN THEOREM
If the square on a side of a triangle is equal to the sum of the squares on the remaining two sides of the triangle, then the angle contained by these remaining two sides is a right angle.

Thus, referring again to triangle ABC in Figure 1.1, if $c^2 = a^2 + b^2$ then the angle at C must be a right angle; the geometric version is similar. We shall not give a proof of this converse here, but one is outlined in Problem 6.1. It must be emphasized that although this converse is true, the converse of a true statement may very well be false (Problem 1.15).

With the Pythagorean Theorem and its converse in hand, we shall next look at what is known of the origins of mathematics, and in particular at how these results fit into those origins.

PROBLEM SET 1

PROBLEM 1.1. Simplify each of the following numbers, recalling that $x^2 = x \cdot x$, $x^3 = x \cdot x \cdot x$, and so forth, and that $x^{-n} = (1/x)^n$.

(a) 3^2

(b) 2^6

(c) 5^6

(d) 3^{-2}

(e) $(2^{-3})^2$

(f) $(\frac{1}{2})^{-5}$

(g) $(3^{-2})^{-3}$

(h) $1/(3^{-2})$

PROBLEM 1.2. Simplify each of the following numbers, recalling that if x is a positive number then $\sqrt{x}$ (square root of x) denotes that positive number whose square is x; that is, if $y = \sqrt{x}$ then $y^2 = x$.

(a) $\sqrt{4}$

(b) $\sqrt{25}$

(c) $(\sqrt{2})^2$

(d) $(\sqrt{3})^4$

(e) $(\sqrt{2})^6$

(f) $\sqrt{\frac{1}{4}}$

(g) $(\sqrt{16})^{-2}$

(h) $\sqrt{2^{-4}}$

PROBLEM 1.3. Which of the following numbers is nearest $\sqrt{5}$: 2, 2.2, 2.5, 3? Find a number nearer $\sqrt{5}$ than any of these.

PROBLEM 1.4. In the second proof of the Pythagorean Theorem, we used the identity $(a - b)^2 = a^2 - 2ab + b^2$. Verify this for $a = 5$, $b = 2$; $a = 3$, $b = 3$; $a = 1$, $b = 3$. (That this is an identity means it is true for all pairs of numbers a and b. Here we have verified it only for some pairs. Problem 1.19 indicates how this and some other useful identities can be proved to be identities.)

PROBLEM 1.5. What is the length of the hypotenuse c of a right triangle with legs as follows?

(a) 3 and 4

(b) 5 and 12

(c) 1 and 1

(d) 1 and 2

(e) 2 and $\sqrt{3}$

(f) $\sqrt{2}$ and $\sqrt{3}$

PROBLEM 1.6. What is the length of the second leg of a right triangle with hypotenuse and one leg as follows?

(a) 5 and 4

(b) 3 and 2

(c) 13 and 12

(d) 4 and $\sqrt{7}$

(e) $\sqrt{8}$ and 2

(f) $\sqrt{3}$ and $\sqrt{2}$

PROBLEM 1.7. (a) What is the length of a diagonal of a rectangle 6 units long and 2 units wide?
(b) What are the dimensions of a square with diagonal of length 4?

PROBLEM 1.8. (a) Is a triangle with sides 20, 21, 29 a right triangle? Why?
(b) Is a triangle with sides 16, 30, 33 a right triangle? Why?

PROBLEM 1.9. If a ladder of length 10 feet, originally standing flat against a vertical wall, is moved so that its top slides down 4 feet, how far along the floor will the bottom move? Why?

PROBLEM 1.10. (a) A baseball diamond is a square with sides of length 90 feet. What is the straight-line distance from home plate to second base?
(b) A diagram in a baseball rule book shows the straight-line distance from home plate to second base to be 127 feet $3\frac{3}{8}$ inches. Is this value exact or too short or too long?

PROBLEM 1.11. (a) Show that a square with side s units long has diagonal $s\sqrt{2}$ units long.
(b) What are the dimensions of a square with diagonal of length d?
(c) If the length of a rectangle is s and the width $\frac{1}{2}s$, what is the length of the diagonal?

PROBLEM 1.12. Prove that the sum of the interior angles of a triangle is two right angles (180°). (Suggestion: Given triangle ABC, pass a line through B parallel to AC. Use the fact that opposite interior angles, determined by a transversal cutting parallel lines, are equal: in Figure 1.4, angle 2 = angle 5 and angle 3 = angle 4. Also angle 5 + angle 1 + angle 4 = two right angles.)

Figure 1.4

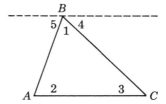

PROBLEM 1.13. A *rhombus* is a quadrilateral without right angles, having its four sides of equal length (such as $ABDC$ below). In the geometric proof of the Pythagorean Theorem, we took pains to show that the figure in the interior of Figure 1.2(b) was actually a square. This was necessary because a square of side s has an area different from that of a rhombus of side s. Verify this by showing that the area of a rhombus is hs, where h is the height and s the length of a side (Figure 1.5).

Figure 1.5

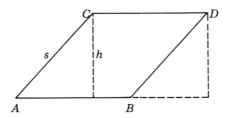

PROBLEM 1.14. (a) Verify that the area of a right triangle is $\frac{1}{2}hb$, where b is the length of one leg (base) and h is the length of the other leg (height). (Suggestion: Consider Figure 1.6(a)).

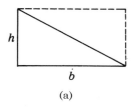
(a)

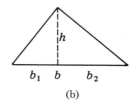
(b)

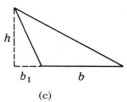
(c)

Figure 1.6

(b) Prove that the area of any triangle is $\frac{1}{2}hb$, where b is the length of a side (base) and h is the length of the altitude (height) to that side. (Suggestion: Consider (a) and the other two cases shown, once adding areas and once subtracting areas.)

PROBLEM 1.15. The converse of a true statement may be false.

Statement (true): If x and y are each greater than 5, then x + y is greater than 10.
Converse (false): If x + y is greater than 10, then x and y are each greater than 5.

Write the converse of each of the following statements, and determine which statements are true and which converses are true. You may want to rewrite some of these in an 'If____, then____' form; such statements are called *implications* or *conditional statements*.

(a) If today is Saturday, then this is a weekend.
(b) If m is odd and n is even, then mn is even (m, n numbers).
(c) If m is less than n, then n is greater than m.
(d) If m is less than n, then n is at least as great as m.
(e) If a statement is true, then its converse is true.
(f) If $x = y$, then $x^2 = y^2$ (x, y numbers).
(g) If x is positive, then x^2 is positive (x a number).
(h) If $x = 2$, then $x^2 - 5x + 6 = 0$.
(i) If $x = 2$, then $x^2 - 4x + 4 = 0$.
(j) If two angles of a triangle are each greater than 60°, then one angle of the triangle is less than 60°. (Angle sum of a triangle is 180°.)
(k) Similar triangles are necessarily congruent. (Two triangles are *similar* if their vertices can be made to correspond in such a way that corresponding angles are equal; if the corresponding sides are equal also, then the triangles are *congruent*.)
(l) Every right triangle is equilateral (has three equal sides).

PROBLEM 1.16. Figure 1.7 suggests an algebraic-geometric proof of the Pythagorean Theorem different from that already given. Write out the proof. (Suggestion: Area of large square is equal to area of tilted inside square plus area of four triangles.)

PROBLEM 1.17. (a) The Pythagorean Theorem can be thought of as giving a formula for the length of a diagonal of a rectangle (see Problem 1.7(a)).

Figure 1.7

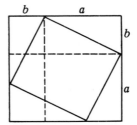

Generalize this to three dimensions by showing that the length w of a diagonal of a box (technically: rectangular parallelopiped) of sides x, y, and z satisfies $x^2 + y^2 + z^2 = w^2$ (Figure 1.8). (Suggestion: Use the Pythagorean Theorem twice.)

(b) A room is 20 feet wide, 40 feet long, and 10 feet high. How far is it from one top corner to the most distant bottom corner?

(c) What if the room were 9 feet by 12 feet by 36 feet?

Figure 1.8

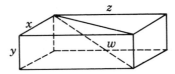

PROBLEM 1.18. (This problem assumes acquaintance with properties of similar triangles.) Here is a generalization of the Pythagorean Theorem for triangles containing an obtuse angle (angle greater than a right angle): Let ABC be a triangle with obtuse angle at C, and draw lines from C intersecting AB at D and E so that angles CDA and CEB are equal to angle ACB. Then $\overline{AC}^2 + \overline{BC}^2 = \overline{AB}(\overline{AD} + \overline{EB})$. (Figure 1.9.)

Figure 1.9

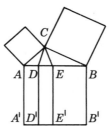

(a) Fill in all of the missing details in the following sketch of a proof of this theorem.

(1) Construct the square $AA'B'B$ as shown, with D', E' denoting the feet of the obvious perpendiculars.

(2) $\overline{AC}/\overline{AB} = \overline{AD}/\overline{AC}$ and $\overline{BC}/\overline{AB} = \overline{EB}/\overline{BC}$.

(3) $\overline{AC}^2 + \overline{BC}^2 = \overline{AB}(\overline{AD} + \overline{EB})$.

(b) If the angle at C is a right angle, this theorem becomes the Pythagorean Theorem. Why? (There is a corresponding theorem for a triangle each of whose angles is acute ([2], p. 259). Also see Propositions 12 and 13 of Book II of the *Elements* [10].)

PROBLEM 1.19. In the algebraic-geometric proof of the Pythagorean Theorem, we used algebra to prove a theorem about geometry. Use Figure 1.10(a) through (d) to give geometric proofs of the accompanying algebraic identities.

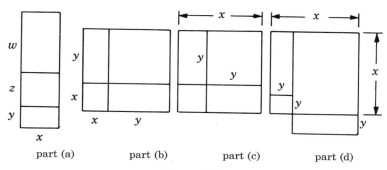

part (a)   part (b)   part (c)   part (d)

Figure 1.10

(a) $x(y + z + w) = xy + xz + xw$.
(b) $(x + y)^2 = x^2 + 2xy + y^2$.
(c) $(x - y)^2 = x^2 - 2xy + y^2$.
(d) $x^2 - y^2 = (x + y)(x - y)$.

§2. Mathematics Through Euclid

Mathematics has not always been what it is today, having changed at various times in at least three different ways. One change has to do simply with an increase in the number of facts known about geometric and other kinds of mathematical objects—the Pythagorean Theorem is an example. A second change concerns the kinds of mathematical objects and problems studied by mathematicians, and can be caused by forces either external or internal to mathematics, such as problems arising from science or new problem-solving techniques developed within mathematics itself. Finally, there have occasionally been more fundamental changes, ones involving the very idea of what does and what does not constitute mathematics. A working mathematician is most likely to be concerned with the first kind of change: at any given time he will be trying to solve a particular problem or prove a particular theorem, and he will be operating under a fixed set of notions about what mathematics is and about what mathematical tools are available to him. For our purposes, however, it will be advantageous to keep a broader view, remembering of course to avoid superficiality by staying in touch with specific examples of mathematics. In this section and in Chapter II we shall be concerned with two fundamental changes of particular significance to mathematics, the first of which took place over two thousand years ago, the second during the last century. With the first, we distinguish that period when mathematics took on its most characteristic feature. Thus we now take up the development of mathematics from prehistory until approximately 300 B.C.

Early mathematics can be divided into four parts: prehistoric, Egyptian, Babylonian (or Mesopotamian), and early Greek, the latter consisting, for our present purposes, of the development of the subject as a deductive science during the sixth, fifth, and fourth centuries B.C. There was activity independent of this in other parts of the world, notably China and India, but as it does not bear directly on the more significant achievements of the Greeks, we shall not discuss it. Our division is, we should make clear, mainly a convenience; each period is part of some more or less continuous chain beginning in darkness.

Little can be said with confidence about prehistoric mathematics, except that processes such as counting and working with simple geometric figures must date back thousands of years before the oldest known written documents. And the development of systematic notations for writing whole numbers, even the most primitive such systems, must have taken place only gradually over very long periods of time.

When we get to the Egyptian and Babylonian civilizations, the extant documents give a basis for more definite conclusions and conjectures. Although even here much is left to guesswork, historians have been able to reconstruct the overall level of mathematical achievement.

What is known about the mathematics of ancient Egypt is based primarily on the content of several papyri which date from the period 1800–1600 B.C. The largest of these is the Ahmes, or Rhind, Papyrus, now in the British Museum (Ahmes copied it about 1650 B.C., Rhind found it in A.D. 1858). It contains about 85 problems, most of them very practical—such as calculations of areas and volumes and distribution of wages among laborers—and altogether it gives a good idea of the geometry of the Egyptians and the level of arithmetic they were able to perform. Two points stand out: their arithmetic was essentially additive, and their handling of fractions was totally inadequate for more sophisticated applications such as astronomy. The fact that their arithmetic was essentially additive means that multiplication and division were reduced to repeated addition and subtraction. (This method of multiplication is illustrated in Problem 2.3. Problem 2.7 gives a sample of their difficulties with fractions.) Their geometry does not give a hint at what was to emerge later from the Greeks. The Egyptians were concerned primarily with specific cases; there is no evidence of general geometric facts such as the Pythagorean Theorem, or of systematic derivations or proofs. Briefly, the absence of generality, abstractness, and logical content reveals that the Egyptians, however far they had advanced, were still some way from the kind of thought that eventually came to characterize mathematics.

More examples are known of Babylonian than Egyptian mathematics, for the simple reason that the clay tablets of the former (roughly 2000–600 B.C.) have survived better than the papyri of the latter. Of these two civilizations from which the Greek mathematicians of the sixth century, and later, were to borrow, that of Babylonia had more to offer than that of Egypt. This difference is due largely to the invention in Babylonia of a place-value notation for numbers, one suitable for both whole numbers and fractions. This means that in principle they had a system like the one we use, with numbers written using a units-place, a tens-place, a hundreds-place, and so on, and a tenths-place, a hundredths-place, and so on. Their system was sexagesimal (based on sixty) rather than decimal (based on ten), but again, in basic principle it was like the one in use today (the Hindu-Arabic, perfected roughly a thousand years ago). The importance of the superior numeration system of the Babylonians came from the increased facility it gave them with numerical computations, which in turn contributed to the development of a somewhat elementary level of algebra. We shall not dwell on the technicalities of systems of numeration, but refer to Problem 2.6, where appropriate references are given along with an experiment designed to generate appreciation for a place-value system.

In addition to the algebra mentioned, the Babylonians also possessed more geometrical facts than the Egyptians. For instance, they were using the Pythagorean Theorem as early as 1700 B.C. In general, though, mathematics was still largely an experimental science concerned with special cases, with only traces of what would now be accepted as true mathematics.

What essential features were missing from Egyptian and Babylonian mathematics? To begin with, they did not make consistent distinctions between approximate and precise answers. This would have been acceptable for many applications, but it indicates the presence of an attitude not conducive to the development of an exact science. We can see a second shortcoming by looking at their use of the Pythagorean Theorem. As we stated the theorem, it is a statement which is true about *every* right triangle. There is no record that either the Egyptians or Babylonians stated anything explicitly in this generality. Still, evidence suggests that the Babylonians did believe the statement true about every right triangle, so at least the seeds of generalization were present with them.

More important, though, in neither Egypt nor Babylonia had mathematics evolved as a rational, deductive science. This is the most characteristic feature of mathematics, but it did not appear until the sixth century and later, and then among the Greeks. We shall have much to say about this aspect of mathematics. As a start, we return once more to the Pythagorean Theorem.

We have stated that the Babylonians believed the theorem to be true, but from what we know about them, this can only mean that it was a fact which they had established experimentally from examining many right triangles. It may have been perfectly reasonable for them to believe the theorem on the basis of such experimental evidence, but in doing so they were ultimately relying on something other than the methods of mathematics as we know it; what they were using was more akin to the method of experimental science.

The point to be made here is so central that it must not be allowed to slip away. We must distinguish between *inductive* reasoning, which is the process of discovering general laws from observing special cases*, and *deductive* reasoning, which is the process of proving a statement from other statements previously assumed to be true. In the case of the Pythagorean Theorem, it is likely that the Babylonians discovered the theorem by inductive reasoning, after which it eventually passed to the Greeks who used deductive reasoning to prove it from more self-evident propositions of geometry. Such interplay between inductive reasoning to discover theorems and deductive reasoning to prove them is vital to mathematics. Again, though, it is deductive reasoning which is the decisive feature of our subject, and we turn now to the people who took the final steps in giving it this essence.

Greek mathematics did not start in a vacuum. It obviously drew much from the mathematics from the south and east, where we have already seen the beginnings of algebra and of geometry as an empirical science. Still, for mathematics as for most other activity involving the human mind, it is to the Greeks that we owe the most. Other periods may have produced more mathematics considered as a body of rationally organized and deductively established truths, but it was in ancient Greece that the first examples of such a discipline clearly emerged.

It is difficult to reconstruct the detailed story of Greek mathematics during the sixth, fifth, and fourth centuries B.C. Whatever written mathematical works there may have been are now lost or destroyed, and it is not until the fourth century, in the writings of Plato and Aristotle, that we have even secondary mathematical sources. But although we may not know exactly when certain contributions were made, or who made them, we do have a clear picture of mathematics as it existed in Greece at the end of the fourth century. The source for this is the *Elements* of Euclid, written around 300 B.C. and containing in logically organized form the fundamentals of elementary mathematics as known at that time. This has undoubtedly been the most successful mathematics work ever written, and has been used as a textbook even during the present century. Before looking at just what mathematics the *Elements* contains, however, let's consider briefly the probable way in which its contents took shape over the three hundred years preceding its appearance.

---

* Not to be confused with mathematical induction, a method used to prove certain kinds of propositions in mathematics.

The two names commonly associated with the beginning of Greek mathematics are Thales and Pythagoras. Both date from the sixth century, and almost all that is known about them is the result of tradition rather than direct written evidence. It does seem probable, however, that the emergence of geometry as a logically organized study began with them. It is also likely that much of the geometry and number theory in the *Elements* was first discovered by the Pythagoreans, the scientific and religious order established by Pythagoras and surviving into the fourth century; in particular, the first proof of the Pythagorean Theorem was probably given by them.

During the fifth and fourth centuries, significant advances were made by at least a dozen contributors—we shall avoid an inventory of names. We shall also avoid an inventory of theorems, but do point out that much of the progress resulted from attempts to settle some very far-reaching questions which the Greeks had the insight to ask, questions having to do with the mathematics of motion, area, geometric construction, and the use of numbers to measure physical quantities (and which we shall discuss). Some of the most stimulating of these questions were philosophical in nature. Thus it is not surprising that although Plato was not himself a mathematician, many of the mathematicians of the time seem to have had close association with him and his school; it is believed that Euclid studied with Plato's pupils before founding his own school in Alexandria. What is important, the period leading up to the appearance of the *Elements* was one of exceptional mathematical achievement by the Greeks, during which their faith in the rationality and simplicity and intelligibility of the universe led them to attack problems of the greatest significance for mathematics. And the *Elements* summarizes this achievement.

The *Elements** is a collection of thirteen books, covering plane and solid geometry, the theory of numbers, and incommensurables (which we shall discuss in Section 4). It was not the first systematized treatment of elementary Greek mathematics, but it was probably the best, and in any case the others have been lost. The theorems seem not to have been original with Euclid. However, the arrangement of the material, as well as some of the proofs, was presumably his own.

It would be difficult to overstate the impact the *Elements* has had on mathematics and science. It has been claimed to have had a wider circulation than any book except the Bible. Generations of mathematicians have learned elementary mathematics either from it or from inferior imitations of it. It has been most influential as a model, however: starting from a few very primitive statements which the reader is likely to accept as true, one is led through a chain of simple logical steps to statements that would not have been obvious at the outset. Thus, for

---

* All references to the *Elements* refer to the edition of T. L. Heath [10].

instance, Book I begins with twenty-three definitions and ten basic assumptions about lines and points, and concludes with proofs of the Pythagorean Theorem and its converse. Mathematical treatises have followed this basic pattern ever since, and indeed, the example set by the *Elements* was influential in determining that mathematics became largely concerned with the development of just such deductive systems as it presented. We shall return to Euclid in Chapter II, and to other Greek mathematics—which flourished for at least six hundred years after Euclid—in Chapter VI.

PROBLEM SET 2

The Egyptians used a method of multiplication that relied on two facts: (i) any natural number (1, 2, 3,...) can be expressed as a sum of terms from the sequence 1, 2, 4, 8, 16,..., consisting of powers of 2; (ii) a multiple of any natural number by a power of 2 can be obtained by repeated doubling of the number.

PROBLEM 2.1. Express each of the following numbers as a sum of distinct powers of 2. (Suggestion: First take out the highest possible power of 2, then take the highest power of 2 from what remains, and so forth.)

(a) 13   (b) 5
(c) 12   (d) 60
(e) 593   (f) 3127

PROBLEM 2.2. Compute each of the indicated products by repeated doubling. (In order to multiply a number by 2^n, double n times.)

(a) $9 \cdot 8$ (Solution: 9, 18, 36, <u>72</u>.)   (b) $5 \cdot 64$
(c) $3 \cdot 4$ (d) $12 \cdot 16$
(e) $11 \cdot 8$ (f) $3 \cdot 128$

PROBLEM 2.3. Compute each of the indicated products by combining the techniques in Problems 2.1 and 2.2. (First write the second factor as a sum of required powers of 2, then use Problem 2.2 to compute multiples of the first factor by these required powers, then add.)

(a) $13 \cdot 9$ (Solution: $13 \cdot 9 = 13 \cdot (1 + 8) = (13 \cdot 1) + (13 \cdot 8)$, so we add the terms underlined: <u>13</u>, 26, 52, <u>104</u>. Therefore $13 \cdot 9 = 13 + 104 = 117$.)

(b) $91 \cdot 5$ (c) $15 \cdot 7$
(d) $20 \cdot 15$ (e) $37 \cdot 33$
(f) $23 \cdot 23$

When we write the number 6428, we mean $6 \cdot 1000 + 4 \cdot 100 + 2 \cdot 10 + 8 \cdot 1$, each of the digits corresponding to a different power of ten (10^3, 10^2, 10^1, or 10^0). More generally, $a_n a_{n-1} \cdots a_2 a_1 a_0$ represents

$$a_n 10^n + a_{n-1} 10^{n-1} + \cdots + a_2 10^2 + a_1 10^1 + a_0 10^0,$$

the a's giving the different place-values. (For 6428: $n = 3$, $a_3 = 6$, $a_2 = 4$, $a_1 = 2$, $a_0 = 8$.) We could, and electronic computers do, use 2 instead of 10 here, and thereby obtain a 'binary' system rather than a 'decimal' system. The problem of representing a number in binary rather than decimal form is the same as that considered in Problem 2.1. Thus (using subscript 10 to denote decimal numbers, subscript 2 to denote binary numbers): $13_{10} = 1101_2$, because $13_{10} = 1 \cdot 8 + 1 \cdot 4 + 0 \cdot 2 + 1 \cdot 1$. Counting in binary form looks like 1, 10, 11, 100, 101, 110, 111, 1000, ...

PROBLEM 2.4. Write each of the following in binary form:

(a) 9_{10} (b) 12_{10}
(c) 31_{10} (d) 33_{10}
(e) 593_{10} (f) 2912_{10}

(The only symbols appearing in the answers will be 0's and 1's.)

PROBLEM 2.5. Write each of the following in decimal form:

(a) 1001_2 (b) 10101_2
(c) 111111_2 (d) 1000000_2
(e) $100_2 \cdot 100_2$ (f) $1011_2 \cdot 10_2$
(g) $1011_2 \cdot 100_2$ (h) $1011_2 \cdot 10000_2$

PROBLEM 2.6. The advantages that a place-value system offers in com- putations are often taken for granted. Try to perform the indicated operations with Roman numerals without changing to the decimal system ($L = 50$, $C = 100$, $D = 500$):

(a) XIII + IV   (b) DCL + LIV
(c) XXI · VII

(Reference [6] contains a survey of numeral systems under 'Numerals and Numeral Systems'. The book by Menninger [11] is extensive.)

PROBLEM 2.7. The Egyptians did not use fractions as we know them. With the exception of 2/3, they essentially used only fractions with numerator 1 ('unit fractions'). More general expressions were written using these unit fractions. Thus $1/3 + 1/5 + 1/15$ was used in place of 3/5.

(a) Find m and n (different from 11) such that $2/11 = 1/m + 1/n$.
(b) Find r and s (different from 35) such that $2/35 = 1/r + 1/s$.
(This is intended only to give a hint at the difficulties one faces from the beginning if general fractions are not used. The Rhind Papyrus contains a table expressing $2/n$ as a sum of unit fractions for all odd values of n from 5 to 101. See [2] and [12] for full discussions of Egyptian fractions.)

PROBLEM 2.8. A *prime* number is an integer greater than 1 having no factors other than itself and 1. Thus the primes are 2, 3, 5, 7, 11, 13, 17, ... Goldbach noted in 1742 that

$4 = 2 + 2$	$10 = 5 + 5$	$16 = 11 + 5$
$6 = 3 + 3$	$12 = 7 + 5$	etc.
$8 = 5 + 3$	$14 = 7 + 7$	

and conjectured that every even integer greater than 2 could be written as a sum of two primes. Verify Goldbach's conjecture for even integers through 40. (Although inductive evidence for Goldbach's conjecture is enormous, the conjecture has yet to be proved (or disproved). Section 48 contains more on primes.)

PROBLEM 2.9. Examine the values of the sums

$$1$$
$$1 + 3$$
$$1 + 3 + 5$$
$$1 + 3 + 5 + 7$$
$$1 + 3 + 5 + 7 + 9$$
$$\cdots$$

Guess a general formula. (It will be like $1 + 3 + 5 + \cdots + (2n - 1) =$ something, where the 'something' involves n.)

PROBLEM 2.10. An example of imprecise Babylonian mathematics can be seen from certain volume calculations. The correct formula for the volume of a frustum of a square pyramid (what one gets by cutting off the top of a square pyramid parallel to the base) is

$$V_C = h(x^2 + y^2 + xy)/3,$$

where h is the height, x and y the lengths of the sides of the upper and lower bases (Figure 2.1). The Babylonians used several formulas, including the correct one as well as

$$V_B = h((x + y)/2)^2.$$

Figure 2.1

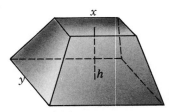

(a) Compare V_C and V_B when $h = 2$, $x = 9$, $y = 10$.
Compare V_C and V_B when $h = 3$, $x = 6$, $y = 8$.
Compare V_C and V_B when $h = 10$, $x = 2$, $y = 10$.
(b) The error in V_B is the amount it differs from V_C, that is, $V_C - V_B$. Show that $V_C - V_B = h(x - y)^2/12$.
(c) Was the Babylonian formula ever correct? For which shapes did it give the best approximation?
(d) Interpret V_B geometrically as the volume of a figure with vertical sides related in a natural way to the original frustum. Now explain why V_B might have seemed to be correct, but also (without using (b)) why it will actually give a volume smaller than that of the frustum. (Suggestion: Locate a line of length of $(x + y)/2$ on the frustum. A slight knowledge of similar geometric figures is necessary to do part (d) in detail.)

PROBLEM 2.11. (a) Figure 2.2 shows, by adding the number of x's in the different L-shaped regions, that $1 + 3 + 5 + 7 = 4^2$. Consider larger squares and get a general formula for the sum of the first n odd integers. (Compare Problem 2.9.)

Figure 2.2

X	X	X	X
X	X	X	X
X	X	X	X
X	X	X	X

(b) Figure 2.3 shows that $1 + 2 + 3 + 4 = \frac{1}{2} \cdot 4 \cdot 5$ (the sum of the number of x's in the rows is half the total number of symbols). Consider larger rectangles and get a general formula for $1 + 2 + 3 + \cdots + n$.

Figure 2.3

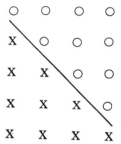

PROBLEM 2.12. Perhaps the most impressive application of mathematics in ancient times was the measurement of the earth's circumference by Eratosthenes (c. 250 B.C.). At the summer solstice, the sun passes directly over Syrene (on the Nile, near the present Aswan Dam), 5,000 stadia south of Alexandria. With the sun overhead, Eratosthenes measured the angle made by the line from the sun to a stake at Alexandria pointing to the earth's center, and got 1/50 of a complete circle (Figure 2.4). He deduced

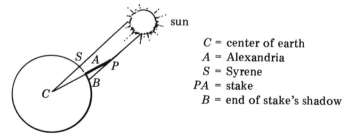

C = center of earth
A = Alexandria
S = Syrene
PA = stake
B = end of stake's shadow

Figure 2.4

that the earth's circumference was 250,000 stadia (compared with a true value of approximately 242,000 stadia). Verify his deductions. (Essentially, PB is parallel to SC, so angle APB = angle ACS.) (The true value for the circumference in terms of stadia may not be precise, but is close. The exact length of a stadium in terms of our units is not known.)

§3. Pythagorean Triples

We discussed the Pythagorean Theorem and its converse as purely geometric facts and as facts about geometry describable in terms of numbers. With the latter interpretation we are given an equation, $a^2 + b^2 = c^2$, which will always be satisfied by the numbers measuring the lengths of the sides of a right triangle. Practical uses of this fact abound. For example, as early as 1700 B.C. the Babylonians were using this relation to determine one leg of a right triangle given the other leg and the hypotenuse (as in Problem 1.6). The theorem is often used today in more technically sophisticated ways, but the fact remains that it is one of the most useful theorems in mathematics for practical applications.

An important point to be made, though, is that however much a mathematician may be pleased by the 'usefulness' of his work, he is often more strongly motivated by questions arising within mathematics itself. Indeed, the word 'useful', as applied to mathematics, is likely to have a different meaning to a mathematician than to someone else, and even among mathematicians it can be a very subjective matter whether a given theorem or subject is useful; this point will be discussed again later. In this section we give an example of a problem considered simply as mathematics for mathematics' sake. It illustrates that the Babylonians possessed the spirit to do such things, to some extent, as early as 1500 B.C.; it also illustrates the kind of questioning attitude that induces much of the progress in mathematics.

Notice that once one knows the Pythagorean Theorem, it is fairly natural (given a minimum of curiosity) to look for triples of numbers that will satisfy $a^2 + b^2 = c^2$. For example, $(3, 4, 5)$ is such a triple: $3^2 + 4^2 = 5^2$. Another triple of natural numbers* satisfying the equation is $(5, 12, 13)$: $5^2 + 12^2 = 13^2$. The significant step, the one revealing the crucial attitude, is to ask, 'What are some other such triples?' Or better still, 'Can we find lots of others?' Or best, 'Can we find them all?' Because we want to spend some time on these triples, we make the formal definition: a triple (a, b, c) of natural numbers is called a *Pythagorean triple* if $a^2 + b^2 = c^2$. Thus $(3, 4, 5)$ and $(5, 12, 13)$ are Pythagorean triples, but $(1, 1, 2)$ and $(1, 2, 3)$ are not. It is to the everlasting credit of the Babylonians that they knew how to answer at least the second of our questions above; we know this because of Plimpton 322, a clay tablet now in the Columbia University Library. Although there is some doubt about the precise purpose of the calculations on the tablet, it does exhibit a scheme that would allow one to compute all Pythagorean triples. We shall describe this scheme, but we should first struggle over the questions ourselves.

---

* The *natural numbers* are the ones we count with: 1, 2, 3, ...

EXERCISE. Find one or more Pythagorean triples in addition to (3, 4, 5) and (5, 12, 13). (Either (4, 3, 5) or (12, 5, 13) is considered cheating. We shall not distinguish between such triples as (3, 4, 5) and (4, 3, 5).)

Even this exercise can require a fair amount of work if attacked by brute force; one good idea can make it much easier. The most direct approach consists in the construction of a list of squares of natural numbers followed by a search for triples. Thus we can form the list

$1^2 = 1$	$6^2 = 36$	$11^2 = 121$
$2^2 = 4$	$7^2 = 49$	$12^2 = 144$
$3^2 = 9$	$8^2 = 64$	$13^2 = 169$
$4^2 = 16$	$9^2 = 81$	$\vdots$
$5^2 = 25$	$10^2 = 100$	

and then inspect it looking for combinations of two of its terms adding to yield a third. By this method, one will likely first rediscover the solution (3, 4, 5), and then get either (6, 8, 10) or (5, 12, 13), eventually finding others after extending the table of squares. With luck, one will notice at the beginning, or early on at least, that (6, 8, 10) has a special relation to (3, 4, 5). Namely, each number in the first triple is just the double of the corresponding number in the second. From this it is not unreasonable to try (9, 12, 15) and (12, 16, 20)—and they work. (This is the good idea that would have made the exercise easier.) More generally, we have the following fact.

THEOREM 3.1
  If (a, b, c) is a Pythagorean triple and k is a natural number, then (ka, kb, kc) is also a Pythagorean triple.

Proof
  We must show that if $a^2 + b^2 = c^2$, and k is any natural number, then $(ka)^2 + (kb)^2 = (kc)^2$. To do this, multiply both sides of the first equation by k^2, obtaining $k^2(a^2 + b^2) = k^2(c^2)$. From this, we get successively

$$k^2a^2 + k^2b^2 = k^2c^2$$

$$(ka)^2 + (kb)^2 = (kc)^2,$$

as was to be proved. □

We now have a way of getting many Pythagorean triples, just by beginning with one, say (3, 4, 5), and multiplying its members by as many natural numbers as we like to produce new ones. Still, this is not satisfactory as an answer to our most general question. For instance, (5, 12, 13) does not arise from (3, 4, 5) by multiplication by some common term. Although (3, 4, 5) and (6, 8, 10) are closely related, (3, 4, 5) and

(5, 12, 13) are somehow basically different. One fact to be noticed about (3, 4, 5) is that its individual terms have no common factor; the same is true of (5, 12, 13). We call such triples fundamental, in the following sense: a Pythagorean triple (a, b, c) is said to be *fundamental* if no natural number other than 1 is a factor of each of a, b, and c. So (6, 8, 10) is not fundamental because 2 is a factor of 6, 8, and 10. Because we can obtain a fundamental triple from any other triple just by removing the greatest common factor from each of its terms, these fundamental triples are the ones we need to be able to get if we are to get all the Pythagorean triples. Figure 3.1 shows in each column the triples arising

(3, 4, 5)	(5, 12, 13)	(8, 15, 17)	. . .
(6, 8, 10)	(10, 24, 26)	(16, 30, 34)	. . .
(9, 12, 15)	(15, 36, 39)	(24, 45, 51)	. . .
(12, 16, 20)	(20, 48, 52)	(32, 60, 68)	. . .
⋮	⋮	⋮	

Figure 3.1

from a common fundamental one, the fundamental triples (including a new one, (8, 15, 17)) heading different columns. The goal, then, is to find all possible column-heading triples, for it is then obvious how to get all other triples. In fact, there are infinitely many fundamental triples, and Plimpton 322 shows that the Babylonians knew how to go about finding many of them. The following theorem gives a method for producing Pythagorean triples.

THEOREM 3.2
   If m and n are any two natural numbers, with m greater than n, and if

$$a = m^2 - n^2$$
$$b = 2mn$$
$$c = m^2 + n^2,$$

then (a, b, c) is a Pythagorean triple.

Proof
   Using elementary algebra, and assuming a, b, and c as stated, we simply write

$$a^2 + b^2 = (m^2 - n^2)^2 + (2mn)^2$$
$$= m^4 - 2m^2n^2 + n^4 + 4m^2n^2$$
$$= m^4 + 2m^2n^2 + n^4$$
$$= (m^2 + n^2)^2$$
$$= c^2. \quad \square$$

ILLUSTRATION

$m = 2$	and	$n = 1$	give	(3, 4, 5).
$m = 3$	and	$n = 1$	give	(8, 6, 10).
$m = 3$	and	$n = 2$	give	(5, 12, 13).
$m = 5$	and	$n = 4$	give	(9, 40, 41).

The proof of Theorem 3.2 holds no mystery for anyone with a reasonable knowledge of high school algebra. How one would discover the theorem is a completely different matter; Problem 3.7 suggests how this might happen.

Theorem 3.2 allows us to construct Pythagorean triples at will. In fact, it accounts for all of them. For we have already observed that if we can get all of the fundamental triples, then we can get the others, and Theorem 3.2 does yield all fundamental triples. Specifically, the following can be proved.

THEOREM 3.3

If (a, b, c) is any fundamental Pythagorean triple, with b even, then there are natural numbers m and n such that

$$a = m^2 - n^2$$
$$b = 2mn$$
$$c = m^2 + n^2.$$

The assumption here that b is even is not as restrictive as it might appear. It happens that if (a, b, c) is a fundamental triple then either a or b (but not both) must be even (Problem 4.4). Since we have already agreed to consider (a, b, c) and (b, a, c) as essentially the same, we might as well let b denote the even one above. The recipe given also produces some nonfundamental triples, but the important point is that it produces all of the fundamental ones. The proof of Theorem 3.3 would require several technical side trips for which we do not want to take time; it requires some refinement of the procedure outlined in Problem 3.7 indicating how the theorem might be discovered.

The early Greeks apparently did not know how to get all Pythagorean triples. The Pythagoreans themselves were aware that if m is any odd natural number, then $(m, \frac{1}{2}(m^2 - 1), \frac{1}{2}(m^2 + 1))$ is a Pythagorean triple, and Plato is often given credit for realizing that if m is any natural number, then $(2m, (m^2 - 1), (m^2 + 1))$ is a Pythagorean triple. Diophantus of Alexandria, who lived approximately A.D. 250, knew the full solution to this problem.

Problems having to do with natural numbers, as the one we have been considering, belong to the branch of mathematics known as number theory. It is one of the oldest branches of mathematics. One of the interesting features of number theory is that its problems are often easy to state but extremely difficult to solve. For instance, if we free our minds from the geometry behind the equation $a^2 + b^2 = c^2$, and consider its solution strictly as a problem about natural numbers, then it is just as reasonable to consider the equation $a^3 + b^3 = c^3$, or $a^4 + b^4 = c^4$, or for that matter any equation $a^n + b^n = c^n$, where n is a natural number. The Frenchman Pierre de Fermat (1601–1665), probably the greatest amateur mathematician ever, did in fact seek solutions to these equations, and wrote, in the margin of a book, that he had a proof of what has become known as Fermat's Last Theorem: if n is a natural number greater than two, then there are no natural numbers x, y, and z such that $x^n + y^n = z^n$. Fermat did not record a proof of this, and despite the efforts of large numbers of both amateur and professional mathematicians it has been neither proved nor disproved to this day (and so it really should be called a conjecture rather than a theorem); it seems likely that Fermat's proof contained a flaw. It has been proved that there are no solutions if $n < 25000$, and inductive reasoning would lead us to doubt that there are solutions for higher n, but of course what we require is a deductive proof. In any case, we have here a striking example of a difficult, easy to state problem. We shall say more about number theory in Section 48.

Although working on Fermat's Last Theorem may appear to be a frivolous pastime, entire branches of mathematics, often useful for solving seemingly unrelated problems, have been developed in attempts to settle just such questions as this. And to return to a point mentioned near the beginning of this section, the amount of interest mathematicians show in a problem is often determined more by the intrinsic challenge offered than by any practical uses a solution might have. G. H. Hardy discusses this eloquently in *A Mathematician's Apology* [8]. The point is not that mathematicians are always impractical, it is simply that they are often drawn to problems for reasons that have nothing to do with practicality or impracticality. This disposition toward problems is not unique to mathematicians; it is shared by many others, and it has often been the motivation behind basic discoveries that later proved to have very practical consequences. We shall see another product of this attitude in the next section, as we look at another example of Greek mathematics.

PROBLEM SET 3

PROBLEM 3.1. Which of the following triples of numbers are Pythagorean triples? Why?

(a) (18, 24, 30)	(b) (9, 40, 41)
(c) (7, 23, 26)	(d) (3, 5, 4)
(e) (24, 70, 74)	(f) (3/2, 4/2, 5/2)
(g) (−3, −4, −5)	(h) (50, 120, 130)

PROBLEM 3.2. (a) Verify that if m is any natural number, at least 2, then $(2m, m^2 - 1, m^2 + 1)$ is a Pythagorean triple.

(b) Verify that if m is any odd natural number, at least 3, then $(m, \frac{1}{2}(m^2 - 1), \frac{1}{2}(m^2 + 1))$ is a Pythagorean triple. Why must m be odd?

PROBLEM 3.3 (a) Use Theorem 3.2 to find four different Pythagorean triples of the form $(a, 48, c)$. (Suggestion: Use all pairs m, n such that $48 = 2mn$.)

(b) Extend the first column in Figure 3.1 to find a Pythagorean triple of the form $(a, 48, c)$ different from any of those found in part (a) above. Why does this not contradict Theorem 3.3?

(c) Find all fundamental Pythagorean triples of the form $(a, 60, c)$. (Assume Theorem 3.3 to be true.)

PROBLEM 3.4. Prove that the only Pythagorean triple of consecutive natural numbers is $(3, 4, 5)$. (Suggestion: A Pythagorean triple of consecutive natural numbers will have the form $(n, n + 1, n + 2)$. What does this imply about n?)

PROBLEM 3.5. Let (a, b, c) and (x, y, z) denote Pythagorean triples. Making use of Figure 3.1, state a condition under which the two triples will represent lengths of sides of similar triangles. (Suggestion: If the triples represent lengths of sides of similar triangles, then there is a number t such that $a = tx$, $b = ty$, and $c = tz$.)

PROBLEM 3.6. In Problem 1.17 we saw that if w is the length of a diagonal of a rectangular box having sides of lengths x, y, and z, then $x^2 + y^2 + z^2 = w^2$. If (x, y, z, w) is a quadruple of natural numbers satisfying this condition, call it a *Pythagorean quadruple*. An example is $(3, 4, 12, 13)$.

(a) Show that if (x, y, a) and (a, z, w) are both Pythagorean triples, then (x, y, z, w) is a Pythagorean quadruple.

(b) Find four examples of Pythagorean quadruples (other than $(3, 4, 12, 13)$), at least one of which is fundamental (that is, with x, y, z, w having no common factor other than 1). (Suggestion: Use (a) and Figure 3.1.)

(c) Is there a Pythagorean quadruple of consecutive natural numbers? Why? (See Problem 3.4.)

(d) The room in Problem 1.17(c) had its length, width, height, and diagonal each of length a natural number, when measured in feet. Are there likely to be many rooms having this property? Why?

PROBLEM 3.7. Fill in the details in the following sketch of how one might discover Theorem 3.2. Assume $a^2 + b^2 = c^2$. By Problem 4.4, at least one of a or b must be even; assume b even.

(a) Show $b^2 = (c + a)(c - a)$.

(b) Show $c + a$ and $c - a$ must both be even. Then let $c + a = 2u$ and $c - a = 2v$.

(c) Show $c = u + v$ and $a = u - v$.

(d) Show using parts (a) and (b) that $b^2 = 4uv$, that is, $b = 2\sqrt{uv}$.

(e) Show b will be a natural number if u and v are perfect squares, that is, if $u = m^2$ and $v = n^2$ for some natural numbers m and n.

(f) Show that a, b, c, m, n, are related as in Theorem 3.2.

§4. Irrational Numbers

We now return to the subtlety involved in the use of numbers to measure line segments, something we mentioned in Section 1.

We have considered Pythagorean triples and have seen that a great deal of care is needed if one is to pick natural numbers so that they will form such triples. In particular, we cannot pick two of the numbers arbitrarily. For example, there is no Pythagorean triple of the form $(1, 1, c)$ because there is no natural number c such that $1^2 + 1^2 = c^2$. Still there must be *some* number c such that $c^2 = 2$ (that is, $c = \sqrt{2}$) if it is to be possible to use numbers to measure line segments, for this would represent the length of the hypotenuse of a right triangle having each leg of length 1. We know that the Babylonians considered the question of what this $c = \sqrt{2}$ would be, because they computed fractions that would approximate it. Here is an illustration to make clear what we mean by such approximation.

ILLUSTRATION. We can see that 3/2 is larger than $\sqrt{2}$ (in symbols $3/2 > \sqrt{2}$), because $(3/2)^2 = 9/4 > 8/4 = 2$. Similarly, 7/5 is smaller than $\sqrt{2}$, because $(7/5)^2 = 49/25 < 50/25 = 2$. Thus $\sqrt{2}$ is between 7/5 and 3/2, or changing to decimals, $1.4 < \sqrt{2} < 1.5$. So either 1.4 or 1.5 gives an approximation to $\sqrt{2}$, accurate to within 0.1.

Of course what we would like is not just a fraction *near* $\sqrt{2}$ but a fraction *equal* to $\sqrt{2}$. We are not the first to want this. It has already been mentioned that the Babylonians looked for such a fraction, and we know that the Pythagoreans did also. The motivation of the Pythagoreans in this case, as well as what they discovered, is worth our time.

An event having great impact on the Pythagoreans was their discovery of the relation between musical intervals and certain ratios of natural numbers. They possessed (had perhaps even invented) the monochord, which consists of a single string stretched over a sound box, together with a moveable bridge which allows the vibrating length of the string to be varied. The string, if plucked without the bridge, will yield a certain note. If, however, the bridge is placed at the midpoint of the string, the note obtained will be an octave higher; if the bridge is placed at two-thirds the distance from one of the ends to the other, the longer length will yield a note a fifth above the original; if the bridge is placed at three-fourths the distance from one of the ends to the other, the longer length will yield a note a fourth above the original. Thus the ratios 2:1, 3:2, 4:3 correspond to the octave ($c - c'$), the fifth ($c - g$), and the fourth ($c - f$), respectively. This relation between arithmetical ratios and aesthetically satisfying musical intervals is believed to have contributed profoundly to the Pythagorean belief that numbers—

meaning integers* and their ratios—were the key to explaining the universe. The idea that 'number is everything' was basic to the Pythagoreans. And a particular consequence of this belief was the notion that relative to any chosen unit of length, any other length should be measurable by a fraction. Thus we see why, to the Pythagoreans, mere fractional approximation to $\sqrt{2}$ would have been unsatisfying; why they would have wanted a fraction exactly equal to $\sqrt{2}$.

The Pythagoreans discovered that there is no such fraction. This gave the first realization of the problems involved in the use of numbers to measure such things as line segments. We shall prove this important result, but first we introduce some appropriate terminology.

A *rational* number is any number that can be expressed in the form a/b, where a and b denote integers with $b \neq 0$. Thus a rational number is just a number that can be expressed by a fraction, such as $1/2$, $2 = 2/1$, $-17/3$, and so forth. The difference between fraction and rational number is that many fractions will represent the same rational number. For example, $2/1$, $4/2$, $6/3$, and $(-2)/(-1)$ are different fractions representing the same rational number. (We often use incorrect but convenient terms such as 'the rational number 2'.) A number is said to be *irrational* if it is not rational. The question of whether something can be a 'number' if it is not rational is what this and the next section are all about. What we want to prove now is the following theorem.

THEOREM 4.1

$\sqrt{2}$ *is irrational.*

To prove this we employ a useful general method known as *reductio ad absurdum* (reduction to an absurdity). We first look at the strategy behind a proof by *reductio*.

Recall that in the proofs we gave of the Pythagorean Theorem, we began with a statement about a triangle (that it was a right-angled triangle), and then proceeded through a succession of statements, each following logically from those preceding it, until we arrived at the desired conclusion (the relation between the sides of the triangle). Briefly, we relied on the assumption that correct inference from a true statement can lead only to true statements. But what if we begin with a statement, proceed logically through a succession of other statements, and arrive at a statement that is known to be false, or at a set of contradictory statements (or, more colorfully, at an absurdity)? The only conclusion to be drawn in this case is that the statement we began with must have been false. Here is how this is used to prove theorems:

1. Begin with a statement, say S.

---

* The *integers* are the natural numbers together with their negatives and zero: $\ldots, -3, -2, -1, 0, 1, 2, 3, \ldots$.

2. Let C be the contradictory of S (meaning C is true if S is false, and C is false if S is true).
3. Deduce from C a false statement or set of contradictory statements (absurdity).
4. Conclude therefore that C must be false, that is, S must be true.

This method is sometimes called the indirect method, or a combination of indirect and *reductio ad absurdum*. The best way to make the method clear is to use it. This we now do, in proving $\sqrt{2}$ irrational.

Proof of Theorem 4.1

We shall deduce an absurdity from the assumption that $\sqrt{2}$ is not irrational, that is, from the assumption that it is rational. Thus assume that $\sqrt{2} = r/s$, with r and s integers and $s \neq 0$, and choose the fraction r/s reduced to lowest terms (so that r and s have no factor in common). Then $\sqrt{2}s = r$, and so, squaring both sides, $2s^2 = r^2$. Now the left-hand side of this equation is an even integer, being 2 times the integer s^2, and so the right-hand side r^2 must also be even. But if r^2 is even then r must be even, and so $r = 2k$ for some integer k. Then we have $2s^2 = r^2 = (2k)^2 = 4k^2$, so $s^2 = 2k^2$. But $2k^2$ being even implies that s^2 is even and therefore that s must be even. Now we have arrived at the contradictory situation (absurdity) that r and s are even integers having no common factor. This contradiction tells us that $\sqrt{2}$ is not rational, and so we conclude that it must be irrational. $\square$

This theorem shows that it is hopeless to try to find a fraction representing, exactly, the length of the hypotenuse of a right triangle having each of its legs of unit length. As we have indicated, one can, however, approximate $\sqrt{2}$ with rational numbers. One way of doing this is simply to proceed experimentally, either by geometric construction (that is, construct a right triangle having each leg one unit long and then measure the hypotenuse with the best available measuring device), or by trial and error computation (begin with fractions near $\sqrt{2}$, as 7/5 and 3/2 from the earlier illustration, and adjust them to get fractions having their squares still nearer 2). We have already said that the Babylonians had a scheme for approximating $\sqrt{2}$. So did the Pythagoreans, who knew that the terms of the following sequence get successively closer to it: 1, 3/2, 7/5, 17/12, 41/29, ..., where each denominator is the sum of the previous numerator and denominator, and each numerator is the previous numerator plus twice the previous denominator. Problem 4.8 indicates how to develop faith that this sequence approaches $\sqrt{2}$, and Problem 4.9 indicates how to prove that it does.

The discovery that $\sqrt{2}$ is irrational must have had a sobering effect on the Pythagoreans. This was partly because of the central role of the natural numbers in their view of the world. But more importantly, from a mathematical point of view, because their foundations for geometry were built around a theory of proportions that applied only to what they called commensurables, the geometric equivalent of what we call rational numbers. To get a taste of what this means, consider our algebraic-geometric proof of the Pythagorean Theorem in Section 1. In it we assumed that the sides of a triangle could be measured by numbers, and then proceeded confidently, using the usual rules of algebra, to operate on these numbers. But how does this make sense if $a = b = 1$, so that c is the elusive $\sqrt{2}$? How can we multiply and add things if they are not numbers to begin with? For example, is $\sqrt{2}\,\sqrt{3} = \sqrt{6}$? This was the problem the Pythagoreans faced: their theorems were not reliable if they were operating with quantities that were meaningless to them.

These questions were not ignored by the Greeks, and by the time of the appearance of the *Elements* they had developed a theory of incommensurables (irrationals) that was satisfactory for their purposes. This theory of incommensurables appears in Book V of the *Elements*. It was largely the work of the mathematician Eudoxus and represents one of the supreme achievements of Greek mathematics. We should mention that this was done mostly in geometric terms, and not exactly in the terms we are using to discuss it here; for instance, they did not have a symbol for $\sqrt{2}$—it was not even a number to them.

It is reasonable to ask: Is $\sqrt{2}$ an unusual case? Are there any other 'irrationals'? If so what are they, or at least what are some of them? The Greeks asked these questions and were able to determine by Plato's time that each of $\sqrt{3}$, $\sqrt{5}$, $\sqrt{7}$, $\sqrt{11}$, $\sqrt{13}$, and $\sqrt{17}$ is irrational. A modification of the proof we gave for the $\sqrt{2}$ case will handle each of these, as well as many others (see Problem 4.6).

Another irrational quantity is π, the ratio of the circumference of a circle to its diameter. The Ancients used various approximations for π, probably not realizing many times that their approximations were not exact. The Rhind papyrus used a value near $3\frac{1}{6}$, the Babylonians used both 3 and $3\frac{1}{8}$, and the Bible (I Kings 7:23 and II Chronicles 4:2) seems also to have used 3. Proving that π is irrational is more difficult than proving that $\sqrt{2}$ is irrational, and was not accomplished until 1761, by the Swiss-German mathematician Lambert.

In fact, there are many irrational numbers; in Section 5, and in a different way in Chapter IV, we shall see how many.

PROBLEM SET 4

PROBLEM 4.1. Use the method of *reductio ad absurdum* to prove that $\sqrt{5} \neq 2$.

PROBLEM 4.2. (a) Prove: If x is a rational number and y is an irrational number, then xy is an irrational number ($x \neq 0$). (Suggestion: Assume x rational, y irrational, and xy rational, and deduce a contradiction.)

(b) Prove: If x is a rational number and y is an irrational number, then $x + y$ is an irrational number.

PROBLEM 4.3. If a general statement is alleged to be true, but an example is discovered to show it false, then the example is called a *counterexample*. For instance, $\sqrt{2}$ is a counterexample to the statement: 'Every number is rational.' Find counterexamples to show that the following equations are not identities, that is, to show they are not true for all a, b, and c. (These are occasionally used by beginning algebra students as if they were identities.)

(a) $(a + b)^2 = a^2 + b^2$ (b) $(a - b)^2 = a^2 - b^2$

(c) $1/a + 1/b = 1/(a + b)$ (d) $\sqrt{a + b} = \sqrt{a} + \sqrt{b}$

(e) $(a/b)/c = a/(b/c)$ (f) $(a^b)^c = a^{(b^c)}$

PROBLEM 4.4. An integer is even if it is twice some other integer: n is even if $n = 2k$ for some integer k. An integer is odd if it is not even: n is odd if $n = 2k + 1$ for some integer k. (Examples: $-18 = 2(-9)$ is even, $13 = 2(6) + 1$ is odd.)

(a) Prove: A sum of two even integers is even. (Proof: If m and n are even, then $m = 2r$ and $n = 2s$ for some integers r and s. Therefore $m + n = 2r + 2s = 2(r + s)$, twice an integer. Therefore $m + n$ is even.)

(b) Prove: A sum of two odd integers is even.

(c) Prove: If a^2 is even, then a is even. (Proof: Otherwise $a = 2k + 1$, so $a^2 = (2k + 1)^2 = 2(2k^2 + 2k) + 1$, which is odd.)

(d) State and prove the converse of the statement in (c).

(e) Prove: If (a, b, c) is a fundamental Pythagorean triple, then a and b are not both even. (Use parts (d), (a) and (c) above.)

(f) Prove: If (a, b, c) is a Pythagorean triple, then a and b are not both odd. (Assume both a and b are odd. Then $a = 2r + 1$ and $b = 2s + 1$ for integers r and s. Therefore $a^2 + b^2 = (2r + 1)^2 + (2s + 1)^2 = 4(r^2 + r + s^2 + s) + 2 = c^2$. Thus c^2 is even, so c is even. Continue, and then complete the proof by *reductio*.)

PROBLEM 4.5. Prove: There are infinitely many prime numbers. (Prime numbers were defined in Problem 2.8.) (Assume there are only finitely many primes, say $p_1, p_2, \ldots, p_n$. Consider the integer $p = (p_1 p_2, \ldots p_n) + 1$. Then p is larger than all primes (why?), so p is not a prime. But p must be divisible by some prime (why?). It is not divisible by any prime (why?). This finishes the proof, by *reductio* (why?).)

PROBLEM 4.6. Prove: If p is a prime number, then $\sqrt{p}$ is irrational. (Prime numbers were defined in Problem 2.8.) (Suggestion: Proceed here as in Theorem 4.1, noting that to say an integer is even means that 2 is a factor of it, and using that if p is a prime and p divides r^2, then p divides r.)

PROBLEM 4.7. Consider the question: For which natural numbers n is $\sqrt{n}$ irrational? Problem 4.6 gives a partial answer—$\sqrt{n}$ is irrational if n is a prime. And for some n it is clear that $\sqrt{n}$ is rational—4, 9, and 100, for example.

(a) For which natural numbers n less than 30 is $\sqrt{n}$ irrational. (Suggestion: Use the fact, which can be proved, that if n is a natural number and $\sqrt{n}$ is rational, then $\sqrt{n}$ is actually a natural number.)

(b) Answer the original question completely. (Suggestion: It may be helpful to use what is known as the Fundamental Theorem of Arithmetic: each natural number greater than 1 can be written as a product of primes in one and only one way; for example, $6 = 2 \cdot 3$, $18 = 2 \cdot 3 \cdot 3$, $100 = 2 \cdot 2 \cdot 5 \cdot 5$, $101 = 101$. Also, if a prime is a factor of a product of terms then it is a factor of one of the terms; for example, the only prime factors of $14 \cdot 30$ are 2, 3, 5, and 7, being those of 14 (2 and 7) together with those of 30 (2, 3, and 5).)

PROBLEM 4.8. The text states that the terms of the following sequence get successively nearer $\sqrt{2}$: 1, 3/2, 7/5, 17/12, 41/29, ... Verify this for the first six terms by carrying out the steps below.

(a) Verify that the sixth term is 99/70.

(b) Show that the first, third, and fifth terms get successively larger, by converting them to a common denominator. Verify also that $41/29 < \sqrt{2}$.

(c) Show that the second, fourth, and sixth terms get successively smaller. Verify that $\sqrt{2} < 99/70$.

(d) Compute the difference between 2 and the square of each term, and conclude that the sequence, through six terms at least, is alternating below and above $\sqrt{2}$, getting nearer each step.

(e) Compare the decimal representations of the six terms.

PROBLEM 4.9. (Continuation of Problem 4.8.) Prove that the sequence 1, 3/2, 7/5, 17/12, 41/29, . . . , given in the text, approaches $\sqrt{2}$, by verifying the following steps.

(a) If x, y are any integers, then $(2x + y)^2 - 2(x + y)^2 = 2x^2 - y^2$.

(b) Choose $n_1 = 1$ and $d_1 = 1$ (n for numerator, d for denominator, subscripts 1 for first approximation).

(c) Verify that $2d_1^2 - n_1^2 = 1$.

(d) Let $n_2 = n_1 + 2d_1$ and $d_2 = n_1 + d_1$ (to get second numerator and denominator).

(e) Verify that $2d_2^2 - n_2^2 = -1$.

(f) Use (a) to show that if $n' = n + 2d$ and $d' = n + d$, then $2(d')^2 - (n')^2 = 1$ when $2d^2 - n^2 = -1$, and $2(d')^2 - (n')^2 = -1$ when $2d^2 - n^2 = 1$.

(g) Part (f) shows that the values $2d^2 - n^2$ alternate between $+1$ and -1 for the successive fractions in the sequence we are given (n denotes numerator, d denominator). But the d values get larger, and $2d^2 - n^2 = \pm 1$ implies $2 - (n/d)^2 = \pm(1/d^2)$, so $2 - (n/d)^2$ approaches 0. Thus n/d approaches $\sqrt{2}$.

PROBLEM 4.10.

(a) Verify that $(\sqrt{2} - 1)(\sqrt{2} + 1) = 1$.

(b) Use (a) to show that $\sqrt{2} = 1 + \dfrac{1}{1 + \sqrt{2}}$.

(c) Use (b) to show that $\sqrt{2} = 1 + \cfrac{1}{2 + \cfrac{1}{1 + \sqrt{2}}}$.

(d) Use (b) and (c) to show that $\sqrt{2} = 1 + \cfrac{1}{2 + \cfrac{1}{2 + \cfrac{1}{1 + \sqrt{2}}}}$.

(e) Verify that if we continue this process, then we get (by ignoring the last $\cfrac{1}{1 + \sqrt{2}}$ in each case) the sequence

$$1, 1 + \tfrac{1}{2}, 1 + \cfrac{1}{2 + \tfrac{1}{2}}, \quad 1 + \cfrac{1}{2 + \cfrac{1}{2 + \tfrac{1}{2}}}, \ldots$$

Verify that these numbers are 1, 3/2, 7/5, 17/12, . . . , so that we get the same sequence as in Problem 4.9. For this reason the 'infinite continued fraction' obtained by continuing this process *ad infinitum* is said to equal $\sqrt{2}$, in the same sense in which $0.\overline{3}$ equals 1/3 (page 32). It can be proved that any irrational number is equal to some infinite continued fraction.

PROBLEM 4.11. The number π can be approximated by using only persistence and the Pythagorean Theorem. Because the circumference of a circle with radius r is $2\pi r$, it suffices to approximate the circumference of such a circle, then divide by $2r$. The circumference will be approximated by a regular (all sides equal) polygon (triangle, square, pentagon, . . .) inscribed in the circle; Figure 4.1 shows this for a square and a regular

Figure 4.1

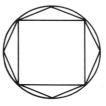

octagon. The Pythagorean Theorem can be used to compute the distance around an inscribed polygon with $2n$ sides if the distance around an inscribed polygon with n sides is known. Thus, by beginning with a square and continually doubling the number of sides, successively better approximations for π can be obtained.

(a) Show that if a circle has radius 1, an inscribed square will have side $\sqrt{2}$. Using 1.414 as an approximation for $\sqrt{2}$, what approximation of π does this give?

(b) Assume AB is a side of an inscribed polygon of n sides (Figure 4.2), and assume AB has length s, with the circle of radius r. Show that OD has length $\sqrt{r^2 - (s/2)^2}$. (Suggestion: Angle ODB is a right angle.)

Figure 4.2

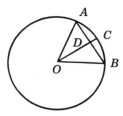

(c) What is the length of CD?

(d) Show that the square of the length of CB is $2r^2 - r\sqrt{4r^2 - s^2}$

(e) Take $r = 1$ and use parts (a) and (d) to compute the approximation of π given by an inscribed octagon. (Approximate any square roots that arise by trial and error.)

(f) An approximate value of π, accurate to five decimal places, is 3.14159. Is the answer in (e) nearer to this than the answer in (a)? It should be.

§5. Real Numbers

We have seen that the collection of all rational numbers is incomplete, in the sense that there are not sufficiently many to describe the length of every line segment in terms of a given unit of length. Thus, if two points are chosen on a straight line and labelled 0 and 1, as in Figure 5.1, and if other points are made to correspond to the rational

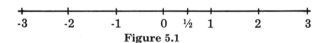

Figure 5.1

numbers in the obvious way (as shown for -3, -2, -1, 2, 3, and 1/2), then there will still be points remaining with no numbers corresponding to them. The point '$\sqrt{2}$ units' to the right of 0 is such a point, as are any of the points determined by the irrational quantities discussed in the previous section. If we are to have a system of numbers that will account for all points on a line, we must extend the system of rational numbers to some larger system. The development of such a system began with Eudoxus' geometric theory of incommensurables, and was concluded only in the latter half of the nineteenth century by the German mathematicians Weierstrass, Dedekind, and Cantor. We now turn to a description of this extension, known as the system of real numbers.

The notion of real number is an abstract one, and what we shall actually describe is one way of representing these numbers; a way that will be familiar. This is analogous to the situation in the previous section, where a distinction was made between rational numbers and the various fractions that could represent them. Explicitly then: a *real number* is any number that can be represented in the decimal system, that is, any number that can be written as $\pm a_n \cdots a_1 a_0 . b_1 b_2 b_3 \cdots$, where each subscripted a and each subscripted b is one of the digits $0, 1, 2, \ldots, 9$, and the sequence of b's may or may not terminate. Here, as usual, a_0 denotes the 'units' digit, a_1 the 'tens' digit, a_2 the 'hundreds' digit, and so on, while b_1 denotes the 'tenths' digit, b_2 the 'hundredths' digit, and so on.

ILLUSTRATION. Each of the following represents a real number:

$$0.0 \qquad 0.333 \cdots \text{ (3 repeated } ad\ infinitum\text{)}$$
$$-1.5 \qquad 76.1984$$

In particular, each rational number is a real number; its decimal representation is obtained by choosing any fraction representing it and dividing its denominator into its numerator. For some rationals, the decimal representation terminates (that is, becomes all 0's from some place on). This is the case with $1/2 = 0.5$ and $-17/4 = -4.25$. For other rationals, the decimal representation does not terminate, but eventually becomes periodic (that is, repeats from some place on). Thus $1/3 = 0.333 \cdots = 0.\overline{3}$ and $9/7 = 1.\overline{285714} \cdots$, where the lines over 3 and 285714 mean that they repeat without end. But there are many decimal numbers that do not terminate or become periodic—for example $0.1010010001 \cdots$, where the number of 0's between the 1's increases one each time. It can be proved, however, that there is no rational number equal to such a nonterminating nonperiodic decimal number. In fact, the following can be proved (and Problems 5.1 and 5.2 suggest how):

The decimal numbers representing rational numbers are precisely those that either terminate or become periodic.*

Thus all other decimal numbers represent irrational numbers.

It is natural to ask how one can get the decimal representation of a number such as $\sqrt{2}$, known to be irrational. In the case of $\sqrt{2}$, the sequence of fractions $1/1, 3/2, 7/5, 17/12, 41/29, \ldots$, previously mentioned as approaching $\sqrt{2}$, can be used (Problem 4.8). In this way (or in any of various other ways that we shall not discuss), the decimal representation can be determined to a degree of accuracy limited only by one's patience or the size of the computer available. The decimal value of $\sqrt{2}$, accurate to twenty decimal places, is 1.41421356237309504880. While it might be useful to know this for some purposes, it is important to realize that the value given is still just an approximation and not equal to $\sqrt{2}$, for, as stated, no terminating decimal number can equal $\sqrt{2}$.

---

* Terminating decimals can also be represented as decimals with 9 repeating on the end. For example, $1.0 = 0.\overline{9}$ (see Problem 5.2 or Example 45.1). This leads to difficulties in some proofs that can usually be overcome by always choosing the representation ending in zeros.

The reason given for enlarging the system of rational numbers to the system of real numbers was the inadequacy of the rationals for describing completely the set of points on a straight line. How do we know that the system of real numbers is sufficient for this purpose? We do not know it—we only assume it. This is far from being an arbitrary assumption, however. As has been pointed out, the concept of real number as now used by mathematicians evolved very slowly over a period of several thousand years. The need was for a system adequate to describe such quantities as length, area, weight, and time, and sufficient to satisfy some very strict demands created by advances in mathematics itself, such as the development of the calculus. The crucial property for all of these requirements is what is known as continuity, and this is built into the system of real numbers.

The idea of continuity, as used in this sense, is not a superficial one; otherwise it would have been easier to identify and define. In the familiar case of a straight line, continuity means intuitively that a line is smooth, that it is unbroken, that it has no holes, that there really are points corresponding to things like $\sqrt{2}$ and π. Similar interpretations hold with regard to time. But a more careful formulation of continuity is necessary if one is to use the notion in mathematical proofs, and this is what it took mathematicians until the last century to see the need for and accomplish. When we use the real numbers to describe a straight line, we are relying on twin assumptions: the first about the continuity of the line, the second about the continuity of the real numbers. The first is derived from our sense perceptions and intuition about the line, the second is a translation of this into a form applicable to numbers. We now state both of these in the form given originally by Richard Dedekind (1831–1916).

We observe, as Dedekind did before stating this fundamental assumption about lines, that every point of a straight line separates the line into two parts, such that every point of one part lies to the left of every point of the other part (Figure 5.2). Dedekind singled out the converse of this observation as the key to the principle of the continuity of the line.

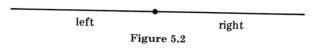

left   right

Figure 5.2

DEDEKIND'S POSTULATE

'If all points of the straight line fall into two classes such that every point of the first class lies to the left of every point of the second class, then there exists one and only one point which produces this division of all points into two classes, this severing of the straight line into two portions.' [5]

This unique point is either an extreme right member of the left part or an extreme left member of the right part (see Problem 5.5).

Shortly after stating this principle in his *Continuity and Irrational Numbers*, Dedekind writes: 'The majority of my readers will be very much disappointed in learning that by this commonplace remark the secret of continuity is to be revealed.' That may be, but as Dedekind knew, and made clear, the consequences of the remark are many. We shall use it at only one place (in Chapter II), but Dedekind's Postulate, or some equivalent statement, is indispensable for much of contemporary mathematics.

The translation of Dedekind's Postulate from geometry into arithmetic is suggested by Figure 5.1. The details are somewhat technical, and we shall not take time to discuss them (they can be found in [5]). Briefly, though, one first enlarges the system of rational numbers to the system of real numbers, and one of the axioms (fundamental assumptions) about this latter system is the following: if the set of real numbers is divided into two parts, such that every number in the first part is smaller than every number in the second, then there is a unique number determining this division; it will be either a largest member of the first part or a smallest member of the second. (Problem 5.4 gives an example to show that the system of rational numbers does not have this property.)

We now give an 'angular' form of Dedekind's Postulate; it is the version we shall need in Chapter II. (Problem 5.6 indicates how to prove this from Dedekind's Postulate.)

Dedekind's Postulate (Angular Form)

Let PA and PB be two lines through point P, and assume that angle BPA is less than two right angles. Assume further that all of the lines through P and lying in angle BPA can be separated into two classes, such that every line PQ of the first class makes a smaller angle with PB than every line PR of the second class. Then there exists one and only one line which brings about this division into two classes (Figure 5.3).

Figure 5.3

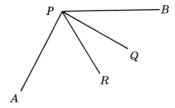

Let us summarize briefly what we have done thus far. We have seen that by the third century B.C. mathematics had evolved from an unorganized collection of facts into a rational deductive science. We have made a first attempt at distinguishing between two different but complementary ways of obtaining knowledge: inductive reasoning, the art of making informed guesses, in which one tries to discover general laws from observing special cases; and deductive reasoning, where guesswork is not allowed, in which one proves statements from other statements previously assumed to be true. And we have introduced some of the mechanics of the deductive method: several illustrative proofs, converse statements, and *reductio ad absurdum.*

We have seen that the study of such simple objects as right triangles can lead naturally to nontrivial mathematical problems and ideas, some with profound scientific applicability (as the real number system), some of interest primarily for their own sake (as Fermat's Last Theorem). At the same time, we have had our first glimpse of two forces that make mathematics what it is: problems from outside mathematics, such as questions raised by attempts to use numbers to explain the universe, and an attitude toward these problems that leads to further questions of intrinsic interest.

Finally, as we shall see, we have made a running start at some once revolutionary mathematics to be presented in Chapter II.

PROBLEM SET 5

PROBLEM 5.1. Find the decimal representation of each of the following rational numbers.

(a) $1/11$ (b) $1/6$
(c) $1/7$ (d) $2/13$
(e) $8/5$ (f) $1/14$

(Solution for $1/11$: $1/11 = 0.\overline{09}$, where the line over 09 indicates that it is the repeating part.)

These computations suggest why the decimal representation of a rational number terminates or becomes periodic. In computing the decimal representation of a fraction r/s, the remainders in the division process will be either $0, 1, 2, \ldots$, or $s - 1$. If we can get 0, the decimal terminates. If not, one of the numbers $1, 2, \ldots$, or $s - 1$ must repeat as a remainder (in fewer than s steps after we start bringing down zeros); then the decimal starts repeating.

PROBLEM 5.2. Find fractions equal to each of the following decimal numbers.

(a) $0.\overline{1}$ (b) $0.\overline{12}$
(c) $0.\overline{9}$ (d) $1.8\overline{3}$
(e) $0.\overline{384615}$ (f) $0.27\overline{351}$

(Solution for $0.\overline{1}$: Let $x = 0.\overline{1}$. Then $10x = 1.\overline{1}$. Therefore, $10x - x = 1.\overline{1} - 0.\overline{1}$, that is, $9x = 1$ so $x = 1/9$.)

These computations suggest why all repeating decimals represent rational numbers.

PROBLEM 5.3. State whether each of the following is true or false. Give a reason in each case.

(a) There is a smallest natural number.

(b) There is a smallest integer.

(c) There is a largest real number.

(d) There is a smallest positive rational number.

(e) There is a shortest length.

(f) Between any two different rational numbers there is a third rational number.

(g) Between any two different real numbers there is a rational number.

PROBLEM 5.4. Show that the set of all rational numbers does not satisfy Dedekind's Postulate. (Suggestion: Let L denote the negative rationals together with the set of positive rationals with squares less than 2, and R the set of positive rationals with squares greater than 2.)

PROBLEM 5.5. (a) Describe a division of the set of all real numbers, as in Dedekind's Postulate, with 1 in L and 2 in R. What is the number determining the division? Is it in L or in R?

(b) Can (a) be done if it is required instead to put 1 in R and 2 in L? Why?

PROBLEM 5.6. Deduce the angular form of Dedekind's Postulate by drawing segment AB in Figure 5.3 and applying Dedekind's Postulate (for lines) to the points where lines such as PR and PQ intersect AB.

REFERENCES

1. BOYER, C. B., *History of the Calculus*, Columbia University Press, New York, 1939; paperback edition, Dover, New York, 1959.

2. BOYER, C. B., *A History of Mathematics*, John Wiley & Sons, New York, 1968.

3. COHEN, M. R., and I. E. DRABKIN, *A Source Book in Greek Science*, Harvard University Press, Cambridge, Mass., 1958.

4. COURANT, R., and H. ROBBINS, *What is Mathematics?*, Oxford University Press, London, 1941.

5. DEDEKIND, R., *Essays on the Theory of Numbers*, trans. by W. W. Beman, Open Court, Chicago, 1901.

6. *Encyclopedia Britannica*, Chicago, 1969.

7. EVES, HOWARD, *An Introduction to the History of Mathematics*, rev. ed. Holt, Rinehart and Winston, New York, 1964.

8. HARDY, G. H., *A Mathematician's Apology*, Cambridge University Press, New York, 1969.

9. HEATH, T. L., *Manual of Greek Mathematics*, Oxford University Press, London, 1931; paperback edition, Dover, New York, 1963.

10. HEATH, T. L., ed., *The Thirteen Books of Euclid's Elements*, 3 vols., Cambridge University Press, Cambridge, 1908; paperback edition, Dover, New York, 1956.

11. MENNINGER, K., *Number Words and Number Symbols*, A Cultural History of Numbers, trans. by P. Broneer, The MIT Press, Cambridge, Mass., 1969.

12. NEUGEBAUER, O., *The Exact Sciences in Antiquity*, Brown University Press, Providence, R. I., 1957; paperback edition, Harper Torchbook, New York.

13. VAN DER WAERDEN, B. L., *Science Awakening*, trans. by Arnold Dresden, Oxford University Press, New York, 1961; paperback edition, John Wiley & Sons, New York, 1963.

CHAPTER II

Non-Euclidean Geometry

§6. The *Elements*

Non-Euclidean geometry, meaning a kind of geometry different from that in Euclid's *Elements*, is a product of the nineteenth century, when mathematicians became aware that attempts to improve the *Elements* had actually led to a revolutionary alternative to it. We can learn a great deal from a study of this geometry, especially if we look at its history and its role in attempts to describe the universe. The content is such that one's prejudices about geometry are continually challenged; only the most careful thought allows logic to overcome these prejudices. And no topic is better suited for showing what mathematics is and what it is not.

A general view of non-Euclidean geometry can be obtained from Sections 6, 7, and 14, and reading these sections first should help motivate the more technical material in the remainder of the chapter.

In order to trace the history of non-Euclidean geometry, we must first take a closer look at the method and content of Book I of the *Elements*. Because Book I ends with proofs of the Pythagorean Theorem and its converse, it is convenient to return once more to those results.

The Pythagorean Theorem is not obvious. We believe it because we can deduce it logically from more elementary geometric statements. But some of these may not be obvious either. For instance, in the geometric proof in Section 1, we made use of several such statements about triangles, such as that the sum of the angles of a triangle is two right angles. Thus, one tries to deduce these from statements that are still more elementary. It is clear that this process cannot continue indefinitely—not everything can be proved, some things must be assumed. And the central idea behind the *Elements* is that the things assumed should be as self-evident as possible and as few as possible, while sufficient in number so that an accurate description of the geometry of the plane and of space can be built up from them. If we can believe these basic assumptions, then we can believe everything that follows from them.

In the *Elements* these basic assumptions are of two kinds: postulates and common notions. Book I contains five of each. It is more customary now to refer to all such assumptions as axioms, but the Greeks appear to have made a distinction between principles common to all branches of mathematics (the common notions), and those relating to a particular subject (as the postulates for geometry).

In addition to the postulates and common notions, Book I begins with twenty-three definitions. The role of definitions in a deductive system requires some explanation, and will be of more concern later. We point out now, though, that just as one cannot prove every fact, one cannot define every word: Euclid's definitions of point and line, given below, are useless from a logical point of view.

We now list the definitions, postulates, common notions, and propositions from Book I of the *Elements*. These will not be of equal importance for us, but we state them all, omitting only the proofs of the propositions. What is given is based on Heath's edition of the *Elements* [8], an excellent source for information concerning the history and content of the *Elements*. Modern geometry books normally use a different but essentially equivalent set of axioms (postulates and common notions), but for our purposes Euclid is more appropriate: we may lose logical precision, but we gain a sense of history.

A remark about the translation may be helpful: statements involving 'to draw', 'to produce', 'to bisect', ... may be restated in a form using 'can be drawn', 'can be produced (extended)', 'can be bisected', ... Thus Postulate 1 may be restated: 'A straight line can be drawn from any point to any point.' Proposition 1 may be restated: 'On a given finite straight line an equilateral triangle can be constructed.'

Finally, it is certainly not essential that the reader know all of these results for what follows in later sections; it is suggested that they be skimmed now and then referred to as needed.

SUMMARY OF EUCLID'S *ELEMENTS*, BOOK I*

DEFINITIONS

1. A *point* is that which has no part.
2. A *line* is breadthless length.
3. The extremities of a line are points.
4. A *straight line* is a line which lies evenly with the points on itself.
5. A *surface* is that which has length and breadth only.
6. The extremities of a surface are lines.
7. A *plane surface* is a surface which lies evenly with the straight lines on itself.
8. A *plane angle* is the inclination to one another of two lines in a plane which meet one another and do not lie in a straight line.
9. And when the lines containing the angle are straight, the angle is called *rectilineal*.
10. When a straight line set up on a straight line makes the adjacent angles equal to one another, each of the equal angles is *right*, and the straight line standing on the other is called a *perpendicular* to that on which it stands.
11. An *obtuse angle* is an angle greater than a right angle.
12. An *acute angle* is an angle less than a right angle.
13. A *boundary* is that which is an extremity of anything.
14. A *figure* is that which is contained by a boundary or boundaries.
15. A *circle* is a plane figure contained by one line such that all the straight lines falling upon it from one point among those lying within the figure are equal to one another;
16. And the point is called the *centre* of the circle.
17. A *diameter* of the circle is any straight line drawn through the center and terminated in both directions by the circumference of the circle, and such a straight line also bisects the circle.
18. A *semicircle* is the figure contained by the diameter and the circumference cut off by it. And the centre of the semicircle is the same as that of the circle.
19. *Rectilineal figures* are those which are contained by straight lines, *trilateral* figures being those contained by three, *quadrilateral* those contained by four, and *multilateral* those contained by more than four straight lines.
20. Of trilateral figures, an *equilateral triangle* is that which has its three sides equal, an *isosceles triangle* that which has two of its sides alone equal, and a *scalene triangle* that which has its three sides unequal.
21. Further, of trilateral figures, a *right-angled triangle* is that which has a right angle, an *obtuse-angled triangle* that which has an obtuse angle, and an *acute-angled triangle* that which has its three angles acute.
22. Of quadrilateral figures, a *square* is that which is both equilateral and right-angled; an *oblong* that which is right-angled but not equilateral; a *rhombus* that which is equilateral but not right-angled; and a *rhomboid* that which has its opposite sides and angles equal to one another but is

---

* Based on Heath's edition of the *Elements* [8], with permission of Cambridge University Press.

neither equilateral nor right-angled. And let quadrilaterals other than these be called *trapezia*.

23. *Parallel* straight lines are straight lines which, being in the same plane and being produced indefinitely in both directions, do not meet one another in either direction.

POSTULATES

Let the following be postulated:

1. To draw a straight line from any point to any point.
2. To produce a finite straight line continuously in a straight line.
3. To describe a circle with any centre and distance.
4. That all right angles are equal to one another.
5. That, if a straight line falling on two straight lines make the interior angles on the same side less than two right angles, the two straight lines, if produced indefinitely, meet on that side on which are the angles less than two right angles.

COMMON NOTIONS

1. Things which are equal to the same thing are also equal to one another.
2. If equals be added to equals, the wholes are equal.
3. If equals be subtracted from equals, the remainders are equal.
4. Things which coincide with one another are equal to one another.
5. The whole is greater than the part.

PROPOSITIONS

1. On a given finite straight line to construct an equilateral triangle.
2. To place at a given point (as an extremity) a straight line equal to a given straight line.
3. Given two unequal straight lines, to cut off from the greater a straight line equal to the less.
4. If two triangles have the two sides equal to two sides respectively, and have the angles contained by the equal straight lines equal, they will also have the base equal to the base, the triangle will be equal to the triangle, and the remaining angles will be equal to the remaining angles respectively, namely those which the equal sides subtend.
5. In isosceles triangles the angles at the base are equal to one another, and, if the equal straight lines be produced further, the angles under the base will be equal to one another.
6. If in a triangle two angles be equal to one another, the sides which subtend the equal angles will also be equal to one another.
7. Given two straight lines constructed on a straight line (from its extremities) and meeting in a point, there cannot be constructed on the same straight line (from its extremities), and on the same side of it, two other straight lines meeting in another point and equal to the former two respectively, namely each to that which has the same extremity with it.
8. If two triangles have the two sides equal to two sides respectively, and have also the base equal to the base, they will also have the angles equal which are contained by the equal straight lines.
9. To bisect a given rectilineal angle.

10. To bisect a given finite straight line.

11. To draw a straight line at right angles to a given straight line from a given point on it.

12. To a given infinite straight line, from a given point which is not on it, to draw a perpendicular straight line.

13. If a straight line set up on a straight line make angles, it will make either two right angles or angles equal to two right angles.

14. If with any straight line, and at a point on it, two straight lines not lying on the same side make the adjacent angles equal to two right angles, the two straight lines will be in a straight line with one another.

15. If two straight lines cut one another, they make the vertical angles equal to one another.

16. In any triangle, if one of the sides be produced, the exterior angle is greater than either of the interior and opposite angles.

17. In any triangle two angles taken together in any manner are less than two right angles.

18. In any triangle the greater side subtends the greater angle.

19. In any triangle the greater angle is subtended by the greater side.

20. In any triangle two sides taken together in any manner are greater than the remaining one.

21. If on one of the sides of a triangle, from its extremities, there be constructed two straight lines meeting within the triangle, the straight lines so constructed will be less than the remaining two sides of the triangle, but will contain a greater angle.

22. Out of three straight lines, which are equal to three given straight lines, to construct a triangle: thus it is necessary that two of the straight lines taken together in any manner should be greater than the remaining one.

23. On a given straight line and at a point on it to construct a rectilineal angle equal to a given rectilineal angle.

24. If two triangles have the two sides equal to two sides respectively, but have the one of the angles contained by the equal straight lines greater than the other, they will also have the base greater than the base.

25. If two triangles have the two sides equal to two sides respectively, but have the base greater than the base, they will also have the one of the angles contained by the equal straight lines greater than the other.

26. If two triangles have the two angles equal to two angles respectively, and one side equal to one side, namely, either the side adjoining the equal angles, or that subtending one of the equal angles, they will also have the remaining sides equal to the remaining sides and the remaining angle to the remaining angle.

27. If a straight line falling on two straight lines make the alternate angles equal to one another, the straight lines will be parallel to one another.

28. If a straight line falling on two straight lines make the exterior angle equal to the interior and opposite angle on the same side, or the interior angles on the same side equal to two right angles, the straight lines will be parallel to one another.

29. A straight line falling on parallel straight lines makes the alternate angles equal to one another, the exterior angle equal to the interior and opposite angle, and the interior angles on the same side equal to two right angles.

30. Straight lines parallel to the same straight line are also parallel to one another.

31. Through a given point to draw a straight line parallel to a given straight line.

32. In any triangle, if one of the sides be produced, the exterior angle is equal to the two interior and opposite angles, and the three interior angles of the triangle are equal to two right angles.

33. The straight lines joining equal and parallel straight lines (at the extremities which are) in the same directions (respectively) are themselves also equal and parallel.

34. In parallelogrammic areas the opposite sides and angles are equal to one another, and the diameter bisects the areas.

35. Parallelograms which are on the same base and in the same parallels are equal to one another.

36. Parallelograms which are on equal bases and in the same parallels are equal to one another.

37. Triangles which are on the same base and in the same parallels are equal to one another.

38. Triangles which are on equal bases and in the same parallels are equal to one another.

39. Equal triangles which are on the same base and on the same side are also in the same parallels.

40. Equal triangles which are on equal bases and on the same side are also in the same parallels.

41. If a parallelogram have the same base with a triangle and be in the same parallels, the parallelogram is double of the triangle.

42. To construct, in a given rectilineal angle, a parallelogram equal to a given triangle.

43. In any parallelogram the complements of the parallelograms about the diameter are equal to one another.

44. To a given straight line to apply, in a given rectilineal angle, a parallelogram equal to a given triangle.

45. To construct, in a given rectilineal angle, a parallelogram equal to a given rectilineal figure.

46. On a given straight line to describe a square.

47. In right-angled triangles the square on the side subtending the right angle is equal to the squares on the sides containing the right angle.

48. If in a triangle the square on one of the sides be equal to the squares on the remaining two sides of the triangle, the angle contained by the remaining two sides of the triangle is right.

PROBLEM SET 6*

PROBLEM 6.1 (Converse of Pythagorean Theorem).   Here is a sketch of Euclid's proof of Proposition 48 of his Book I. Fill in the missing details. (Suggestion: Use Propositions 3, 8, 11, and 47, together with postulates and common notions, at the appropriate places.)

---

* These problems relate to, but are not restricted to, mathematics in the first five books of the *Elements*; only Book I is referred to in later sections.

(a) Assume given triangle ABC with the square on the side BC equal to the sum of the squares on sides BA and AC (Figure 6.1). We shall prove that angle BAC is a right angle.

Figure 6.1

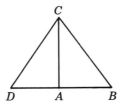

$$C$$
$$D \quad A \quad B$$

(b) Draw AD perpendicular to AC and equal to AB. (Why can this be done?)

(c) The sum of the squares on DA and AC is equal to the sum of the squares on BA and AC. (Why?)

(d) The square on DC is equal to sum of the squares on DA and AC. (Why?)

(e) Therefore $DC = BC$. (Why?)

(f) Therefore angle DAC = angle BAC. (Why?)

(g) Therefore angle BAC is right. (Why?)

PROBLEM 6.2 (Golden Section.) Book II of the *Elements* is devoted largely to geometric algebra, the Greek equivalent of our algebra; there are examples in Problem 1.19. Proposition 11 of Book II shows how to divide a line segment AB with a point C such that $AB:AC = AC:CB$. Denoting the lengths AB, AC, CB by z, x, y, respectively, we have $z = x + y$ and $z/x = x/y$ (Figure 6.2).

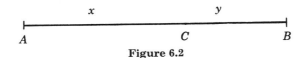

$$x \qquad\qquad y$$
$$A \qquad\qquad C \qquad\qquad B$$

Figure 6.2

(a) Replace y by $z - x$ in $z/x = x/y$ and show that $z^2 - zx - x^2 = 0$.

(b) Divide the last equation through by x^2, and show that

$$(z/x)^2 - (z/x) - 1 = 0.$$

(c) This is a quadratic equation with unknown z/x; solve it for z/x, using the quadratic formula (Problem 46.7).

(d) There are two values for z/x; show that the positive one is $(1 + \sqrt{5})/2$.

(e) Using 2.2361 as an approximation for $\sqrt{5}$, what is the value in part (d)?

(f) The sequence 1, 1, 2, 3, 5, 8, 13, 21, ..., where each term after the first two is the sum of the two immediately preceding it, is called a *Fibonacci sequence*. Find the next two terms of the sequence. Now compute decimal approximations for the ratios of successive terms: 3/2, 5/3, 8/5, ..., up through the two new ones, and compare the values with that determined for $(1 + \sqrt{5})/2$ in part (e). (Compare Problem 4.9.)

(g) Let $w = (1 + \sqrt{5})/2$. Then $w^2 - w - 1 = 0$, by part (d). Show that $w = 1 + \dfrac{1}{w}$. Deduce that $w = 1 + \dfrac{1}{1 + \dfrac{1}{w}}$. Continue, to get an infinite con-

tinued fraction for $(1 + \sqrt{5})/2$. (See Problem 4.10.) (A segment divided in this way is said to be divided in *Golden Section* or *divine section*. This ratio has been of interest in aesthetics and phyllotaxis. For example, rectangles having this ratio between length and height have been claimed to have the most pleasing proportions; the Parthenon is an example. Such explanations of beauty in terms of mathematics are not taken as seriously as they once were. See under 'Golden Section' in [5].)

PROBLEM 6.3 (Angles inscribed in circles.) Book III is on the geometry of the circle (Figure 6.3). Proposition 20 states that if ACB is a central angle of

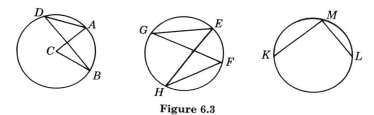

Figure 6.3

a circle determined by arc AB (C is the center of the circle) and ADB is an inscribed angle determined by the same arc AB (D is on the circumference), then angle ACB is double angle ADB. Proposition 21 states that any two inscribed angles determined by the same arc are equal (as EGF and EHF).

(a) Prove Proposition 21 using Proposition 20.

(b) In Proposition 31 it is shown that if the arc KL is a semicircle, then the inscribed angle KML is a right angle. Prove this using Proposition 20.

Here is a diversionary application of Proposition 21. If a picture is hung at eye level in a rectangular gallery, and an observer moves around the gallery from A_1 to A_2 to A_3 to A_4 (see Figure 6.4(a)), staying against the wall, then the angle subtended at the observer by the picture will be maximum at A (directly across from the picture), increasing from A_1 to A,

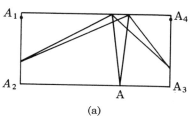

(a)

(b)

Figure 6.4

decreasing from A to A_4. If the gallery is circular and the observer moves from B_1 to B_2 to B_3 (Figure 6.4(b)), staying against the wall, then the subtended angle will be the same at every position around the room.

PROBLEM 6.4 (Pentagon construction.) Proposition 10 of Book IV shows how to construct an isosceles triangle having each of the angles at the base double the remaining angle.

(a) Determine, in degrees, the size of each of the angles in such a triangle. (Angle B = angle C, each is twice angle A, and the sum of the three angles is $180°$ (Figure 6.5).)

Figure 6.5

The Pythagoreans had evidently used such triangles as part of the construction of regular pentagons, by making use of stars, like that shown in Figure 6.6, in which the pentagon in the middle has its five angles equal.

(b) What is the sum of the interior angles of a pentagon? (Suggestion: Divide into triangles.) What is each of the interior angles of a regular pentagon?

Figure 6.6

(c) Using (b), deduce that each of the outside triangles on the star shown has the property of the triangle in part (a).

PROBLEM 6.5 (Proportions, means.) Book V presents the theory of proportions, a significant achievement of the Greeks. The last proposition in the book, Proposition 25, states, in algebraic terms, that if $w/x = y/z$, and w is the greatest of the four numbers appearing (so that z is the least), then $w + z > x + y$. (The numbers are real and positive, and $w > x$.)

(a) Prove this proposition by justifying the following steps.

   (i) $wz = xy$.

   (ii) $wx - wz = wx - xy$.

   (iii) $w/x = (w - y)/(x - z)$.

   (iv) $w - y > x - z$. (Recall $w > x$.)

   (v) $w + z > x + y$.

(b) Rewrite Proposition 25 of Book V in the special case $x = y$.

(c) The *arithmetic mean* of numbers w and z is $(w + z)/2$ ('ordinary' average); their *geometric mean* is $\sqrt{w \cdot z}$. Verify that if $w/x = x/z$, then x is the geometric mean of w and z.

(d) Find the arithmetic mean and the geometric mean of each of the pairs $(1, 4)$, $(2, 8)$, and $(2, 50)$.

(e) Note that for each pair in (d), the arithmetic mean exceeds the geometric mean. Use (b) above to prove that the arithmetic mean of a pair of (unequal) numbers will always exceed their geometric mean.

(f) If a rectangle has dimensions w by z, how does its area compare with the area of a square $(w + z)/2$ units on each side? How is this related to part (e)?

§7. Alternatives

One of the most difficult problems faced by Euclid was that of choosing postulates and common notions that would fulfill the requirements we have mentioned: they should be self-evident, few in number, and complete enough so that an accurate description of the geometry of the plane and of space can be built up from them. We now look at how well he succeeded with each of these.

First consider the question of completeness: Can all of the forty-eight propositions in Book I be proved from the five postulates and five common notions? The answer is 'No'. The proofs in Book I make use of a number of assumptions not explicitly stated by Euclid. We need not pursue these extensively, but will give three of the most important ones.

The first is the principle of continuity, or as stated in Section 5, Dedekind's Postulate. Some form of this is required, among other places, in the proof of I1, the first proposition, where we encounter the situation shown in Figure 7.1. Here A and B are the centers of the

Figure 7.1

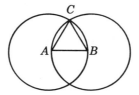

circles shown, and Euclid makes use of point C, a point of intersection of the circles. But might not one or both of the circles have a 'hole' where C is claimed to be? The answer is that they might, unless it is assumed otherwise, that is, unless a form of Dedekind's Postulate for circles is assumed. This Euclid failed to do.

In addition to using the principle of continuity, Euclid used the assumption that straight lines are infinite. Euclid's Postulate 2, stating that a finite straight line can be produced continuously in a straight line, does not imply that straight lines are infinite. We shall see an illustration of this when we consider the geometry of the earth's surface, later in this section. (The use of 'continuously' in Postulate 2 is not related to the concept discussed in the previous paragraph. As Euclid uses Postulate 2, 'produced continuously' simply means 'extended'.)

The other hidden assumption of Euclid that we want to record is known as Pasch's Axiom; we shall need it in Sections 8, 9, and 10.

PASCH'S AXIOM

Let A, B, and C be three points, not lying in a straight line, and let l be a straight line lying in the plane ABC, and not passing through any one of the points A, B, or C. Then, if l passes through a point of the segment AB, it must pass through a point of the segment BC, or a point of the segment AC (Figure 7.2).

Figure 7.2

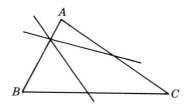

It can be proved from Pasch's Axiom that if a line enters a triangle at a vertex, then it must cut the opposite side (see Problem 7.1). (When we state that something follows from Pasch's Axiom, we shall sometimes mean that it follows from this latter statement.) Pasch's Axiom is used in the proof of I21.

We stress that if something is used in a proof, it must have been either previously proved or explicitly stated as an assumption. Thus the 'obviousness' of Pasch's Axiom should not exempt it from the list of explicitly stated assumptions. We shall always assume the things used but not explicitly stated by Euclid.

Now consider the other two questions concerning Euclid's postulates and common notions: Are they self-evident? Can any of them be omitted? These questions are related, in that if one of these assumptions is not self-evident, it is natural to try to prove it from the others, thereby reducing the number of postulates or common notions. This is precisely what happened with the Fifth Postulate. It was never accepted as being as self-evident as the other postulates and common notions, and there were constant attempts to prove it as a proposition. The doubt surrounding the Fifth Postulate is of such importance for us that we restate both it and the definition of parallel with which it is concerned.

DEFINITION 23

Parallel *straight lines are straight lines which, being in the same plane and being produced indefinitely in both directions, do not meet one another in either direction.*

FIFTH POSTULATE

That, if a straight line falling on two straight lines make the interior angles on the same side less than two right angles, the two straight lines, if produced indefinitely, meet on that side on which are the angles less than two right angles (Figure 7.3).

Figure 7.3

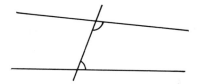

Euclid evidently felt reluctant to use the Fifth Postulate, for it is not used in the proofs of any of his first twenty-eight propositions. And Proposition I27 is the converse of the Fifth Postulate. Why assume one and not the other? The answer is that Euclid was able to prove I27, but not the Fifth Postulate, from the other assumptions. We know from Proclus (A.D. 410–485), whose commentary on Book I is our richest source for information concerning the history of the *Elements*, that the Fifth Postulate was considered controversial well before his own time. The attempts to prove it from the common notions and other postulates led to many statements equivalent with it. One of the best known of these, and the one that will be most useful for us, is known as Playfair's Axiom; named for Playfair (Scottish, 1748–1819), but stated already by Proclus.

PLAYFAIR'S AXIOM
Through a given point, not on a given line, (one and) only one parallel to the given line can be drawn.

To say that Playfair's Axiom is equivalent with the Fifth Postulate means: Playfair's Axiom can be proved assuming Euclid's five postulates and five common notions; and Euclid's Fifth Postulate can be proved assuming Euclid's first four postulates and five common notions together with Playfair's Axiom. Schematically:

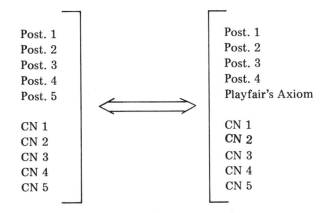

If Playfair's Axiom were to be substituted for the Fifth Postulate, one could deduce exactly the same propositions that can be deduced from Euclid's original ten assumptions.

We now prove this equivalence, recalling that Euclid does not use the Fifth Postulate in proving his first twenty-eight propositions. Thus we are free to use any of these propositions whenever we have assumed his first four postulates and five common notions. And we are free to use any of the forty-eight propositions whenever we have assumed all five postulates and the five common notions.

THEOREM 7.1

Euclid's Fifth Postulate implies Playfair's Axiom (given Postulates 1–4 and Common Notions 1–5).

Proof

We must prove that if P is any point not on a line l, then there is precisely one parallel to l through point P (Figure 7.4). In proving this, we may use Postulates 1–5, Common Notions 1–5, and Propositions 1–48.

Figure 7.4

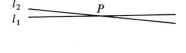

By I31, there is at least one parallel to l through P, say l_1.

Assume there is a second parallel to l through P, say l_2. Then l_1 is parallel to l_2 by I30. But since l_1 and l_2 have point P in common, this contradicts Definition 23 if $l_1 \neq l_2$. Therefore (by *reductio*) there can be only one parallel to l through P.   □

THEOREM 7.2

Playfair's Axiom implies Euclid's Fifth Postulate (given Postulates 1–4 and Common Notions 1–5).

Proof

We must prove that if l_1 is any line through point P, with P not on line l, and if $APQ + PQB <$ two right angles (see Figure 7.5), then l_1

Figure 7.5

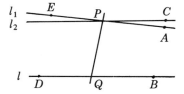

intersects l on the side of A and B. In proving this, we may use Postulates 1–4, Common Notions 1–5, and Propositions 1–28 (*not* 29–48).

Construct PC (l_2) so that angle $CPQ = $ angle DQP. Then l_2 is parallel to l by I27. But $l_1 \neq l_2$ because angle $CPQ + $ angle $PQB = $

angle DQP + angle PQB = two right angles, and therefore l_1 is not parallel to l because of Playfair's Axiom. Therefore l_1 intersects l. We must prove the intersection is on the side of A and B.

Since $EPQ + APQ$ and $DQP + PQB$ are both straight angles, $EPQ + APQ + DQP + PQB$ = four right angles. But $APQ + PQB$ < two right angles, so $EPQ + DQP$ > two right angles. Therefore l_1 cannot intersect l on the side of D and E because of I17. So l_1 must intersect l on the side of A and B, as was to be proved. □

(We shall be going through a number of proofs, such as the preceding one, where the use of a diagram is helpful and suggestive. It must be remembered that these diagrams are only a guide, and we must not use conclusions based on them that cannot be proved from our axioms. Still, we shall not hesitate to use the diagrams to simplify the statements of proofs where possible; for example, letters, lines, and numbers are occasionally introduced by means of a diagram (as A and B in Figure 7.5), and in such cases they will have whatever obvious meaning the diagram gives them.)

An advantage of having statements that are equivalent with the Fifth Postulate, such as Playfair's Axiom, is that if one can prove (disprove) one of these statements from the first four postulates and five common notions, it will follow that the Fifth Postulate can be proved (disproved) from them. There were efforts to prove the Fifth Postulate in this way for two thousand years after Euclid. All failed. One of these unsuccessful attempts is especially worthy of mention, however.

The Italian Gerolamo Saccheri (1667–1733) attempted to prove the Fifth Postulate by *reductio ad absurdum*. That is, he attempted to prove that the first four postulates and five common notions imply the Fifth Postulate by showing that he could obtain an absurdity if he assumed otherwise. Let us consider the options one has when trying for a *reductio* proof in this case.

Because of the equivalence of Playfair's Axiom and the Fifth Postulate, the Fifth Postulate could be proved by showing that neither of the two possible alternatives to Playfair's Axiom is true if the first four postulates and five common notions are true. These two alternatives are:

ALTERNATIVE A. Through a given point, not on a given line, *no* parallel to the given line can be drawn.

ALTERNATIVE B. Through a given point, not on a given line, *more than one* parallel to the given line can be drawn.

Saccheri used an equivalent of the Fifth Postulate different from Playfair's Axiom, and in terms of it he proved (correctly) that Alternative A could not hold. His failure came in trying to dispose of Alternative B. Saccheri proved a large number of propositions based on (his version of) Alternative B, hoping to find an absurdity. He concluded, incorrectly, that he had found one. In a narrow sense, his effort must be considered a failure. This failure was due not to lack of ability or persistence, however, but rather to his inability to overcome the prejudice that what he was trying to prove was true. He evidently believed it so strongly that he convinced himself that he had proved it when in fact he had not. In the end he was relying on faith rather than logic.

The basic idea of attempting a *reductio* proof was used more successfully by others, early in the nineteenth century. They were no more successful than Saccheri in obtaining a valid proof of the Fifth Postulate, but they were more accurate in their interpretations of what they had and had not proved. We shall discuss their work. But first, lest it be thought that A and B are too foolish even to bother with, we give an example to show that in a certain sense Alternative A should seem more reasonable to us than Playfair's Axiom.

On the surface of the earth, considered as a sphere, the shortest distance between two points is not a straight line segment, but rather an arc of a great circle. This is the curve formed by the intersection of the earth's surface with the plane determined by the center of the earth and the two given points (Figure 7.6); it is the path followed by an efficient

Figure 7.6

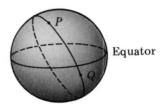

Equator

navigator. If we interpret 'point' to have its usual meaning, and 'straight line' to mean great circle, then the resultant geometry on the earth's surface satisfies Alternative A rather than Playfair's Axiom; every two 'straight lines' intersect in this geometry, so there can be no parallels. With 'distance' interpreted to mean shortest distance measured along the earth's surface, and 'angle' interpreted in a natural way, the first four postulates are satisfied also. (The 'angle' formed by the intersection of two great circles is taken to mean the angle formed by the straight lines one gets by straightening out the two great circles at the point of their intersection. Thus any great circle through the North and South poles intersects the equator at right angles. See Problem 7.7, also.)

Notice that in this geometry 'straight lines' are finite, each having length equal to the circumference of the earth. Thus it is important to point out that in disposing of Alternative A, Saccheri had to make use of Euclid's unstated assumption that straight lines are infinite. Had he been able to deduce an absurdity on the basis of (his version of) Alternative A without using this assumption, the absurdity would manifest itself in the geometry of the earth's surface. But as the physical world possesses no such absurdities (contradictory situations) this would be impossible.* Thus Saccheri could not have disproved Alternative A without assuming straight lines to be infinite.

With an example behind us to show that alternatives to Playfair's Axiom (and therefore the Fifth Postulate) may be practicable, we examine the method of *reductio* as it would apply to Alternative B. Notice that *reductio* is inconclusive until one has actually obtained an absurdity. If we prove propositions on the basis of the first four postulates, five common notions, and Alternative B to Playfair's Axiom, and do not succeed in obtaining an absurdity, then *reductio* tells us nothing. It could be that we have not been persistent enough. Or it could be that obtaining an absurdity is impossible in this case. That is, it could be that, logically, Alternative B is a perfectly legitimate substitute for Playfair's axiom. This is the possibility Saccheri and others before the nineteenth century refused to take seriously.

The role of the Fifth Postulate was finally clarified by three men, working independently: C. F. Gauss (German, 1777–1855), N. I. Lobachevsky (Russian, 1793–1856), and J. Bolyai (Hungarian, 1802–1860). They were the first to recognize that it might be impossible to prove the Fifth Postulate from Euclid's other axioms. Gauss, perhaps the best mathematician ever, was probably the first to realize this. He did not publish his results on this topic, however, fearing adverse reactions from other mathematicians. Lobachevsky and Bolyai made their discoveries public in 1829 and 1832, respectively, neither aware at the time of the work of the other.

The view taken by Gauss, Lobachevsky, and Bolyai was that the replacement of Playfair's Axiom by Alternative B would lead not to an absurdity, but to a system of propositions fully as consistent as those in Book I of the *Elements*. The key word here is 'consistent'. There is an important distinction that must be made between two possible meanings of this word as it applies to the axioms for geometry. It is a distinction that Saccheri and others had been unable to make, or at least fully appreciate, but one that we must make if we are to understand what Gauss, Lobachevsky, and Bolyai accomplished.

One meaning of 'consistent' is implicit in the third requirement for axioms stated at the beginning of this section: the axioms must be complete enough so that an accurate description of the geometry of the plane and of space can be built up from them. Here it is implied that the system of axioms and the propositions provable from them must be consistent with something external, the physical world as we perceive it. The other meaning of 'consistent' refers to an internal property: the axioms are required to be consistent in the sense that no absurdity (inconsistency) can be deduced from them. More precisely, there must

---

* Strictly speaking, what we are assuming here is the consistency of Euclidean geometry. See Section 14.

be no logically contradictory statements that are deducible from the axioms. With this meaning, there is no reference to the physical world or anything else outside of the system of axioms and postulates provable from them.

What Gauss, Lobachevsky, and Bolyai came to recognize is that either Playfair's Axiom or Alternative B, used in conjunction with Euclid's first four postulates and five common notions, will lead to a geometry that is consistent in the sense of the second meaning of the word. Furthermore, the question of consistency in the sense of this second meaning is the only one mathematics can properly answer, the question of consistency with the physical world being outside the province of mathematics. From a mathematical point of view, Playfair's Axiom and Alternative B (and Alternative A if we permit 'straight lines' to be finite) each lead to valid geometric systems. The question of which of these, if any, accurately describes the physical world is of fundamental importance in cosmology—it is not a simple question. We shall discuss this in Section 14.

In summary, Saccheri did not succeed with a *reductio* proof of the Fifth Postulate simply because there was no absurdity (contradiction, inconsistency) to be had. Gauss, Lobachevsky, and Bolyai finally understood this, and furnished us with a logically consistent geometry based on an alternative to Euclid's Fifth Postulate. We shall examine this non-Euclidean geometry in some detail.

PROBLEM SET 7

PROBLEM 7.1. Assume Euclid's first four postulates and five common notions as axioms. Relying on remarks in the text, decide which of the following statements, when added as a tenth axiom, would lead to a logically consistent geometry, and which would lead to a logically inconsistent geometry.
(a) Euclid's Fifth Postulate.
(b) Playfair's Axiom.
(c) Alternative A to Playfair's Axiom.
(d) Alternative B to Playfair's Axiom.
(e) The contradictory of Alternative A.
(f) The contradictory of Alternative B.
(g) Pasch's Axiom.
(h) The contradictory of one of the five common notions.
(i) The contradictory of one of the first twenty-eight propositions of Book I.
(j) The angle sum of a triangle is two right angles (I 32).

PROBLEM 7.2. (a) through (j). Assume Euclid's five postulates and five common notions as axioms. Relying on remarks in the text, decide which of the statements (a) through (j) in Problem 7.1, when added as another axiom, would lead to a logically consistent geometry, and which would lead to a logically inconsistent geometry.

PROBLEM 7.3. (a) through (j). Consider the geometry obtained by assuming as axioms Euclid's first four postulates and five common notions, together with the following:

Through a given point, not on a given line, *at least* one parallel to the given line can be drawn.

Relying on remarks in the text, place each of the statements (a) through (j) in Problem 7.1 in one of the following three categories.

I. The statement can be proved as a proposition in the geometry.

II. The statement is logically consistent with the ten axioms for the geometry, but it cannot be proved as a proposition in the geometry.

III. The statement is logically inconsistent with the ten axioms for the geometry.

PROBLEM 7.4. (a) through (j). Same as Problem 7.3 with *at least* replaced by *at most* in the tenth axiom.

PROBLEM 7.5. Use Pasch's Axiom to prove the statement that follows it in the text.

PROBLEM 7.6. Let m and n denote natural numbers. The following two statements are logically inconsistent:

m *is greater than* n.

n *is greater than* m.

Write three statements such that each pair is logically consistent but the three taken together are logically inconsistent.

PROBLEM 7.7. The following questions pertain to the geometry discussed accompanying Figure 7.6.

(a) How many 'lines' are determined by N and S, the North and South poles? (Note that the answer contradicts Postulate 1. We avoid this difficulty by treating N and S, and more generally any two antipodal points, as a single point. Postulate 1 does not say explicitly that two points determine only one line, but this is implied by the way Euclid uses it. This more precise meaning of Postulate 1 is in effect another hidden assumption.)

(b) If the 'lines' through N are 'perpendicular' to each other, what is the sum of the angles in the triangle shown?

Figure 7.7

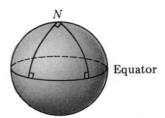

(c) If one of the sides of a triangle is along the equator, and N is a vertex, state upper and lower limits for the possible angle sum of the triangle. (Assume the angle at N to be less than two right angles.)

§8 Lobachevsky's Postulate

We now begin a systematic study of the non-Euclidean geometry of Gauss, Lobachevsky, and Bolyai, which we shall pursue until we get a clear idea of how this geometry differs from that of Euclid. It will be essential that our proofs not depend on any results other than those we know to follow logically from our axioms. In particular, we must not inadvertently use a fact from Euclidean geometry unless it can be proved from our axioms. We summarize what those axioms are.

We assume the same postulates and common notions as Euclid, *except* that Euclid's Fifth Postulate is replaced by what we have called Alternative B to Playfair's Axiom. Because the word 'parallel' will take on a more refined meaning in what follows, we now restate Alternative B in a form that avoids its use.

LOBACHEVSKY'S POSTULATE
Through a given point, not on a given line, more than one line not intersecting the given line can be drawn.

We also assume the hidden assumptions of Euclid discussed at the beginning of the previous section. And, once more, we may use the first twenty-eight propositions of Book I since the Fifth Postulate is not used in their proof.

With these basic assumptions made explicit, we now occupy ourselves with deducing consequences of them. The first few theorems are the most formidable. We call our results theorems rather than propositions, simply as a matter of choice. For a less detailed look at non-Euclidean geometry, the proofs of any of the theorems in Sections 8 through 12 may be omitted; the smaller print has been used to emphasize this. The development will mean more, however, if at least some of these proofs are studied; the highest priority should go to the proof of Theorem 8.1, to see how things get started, and the next highest to the proofs in Section 12, to see how they finish.

Once we assume at least two lines through a given point and not intersecting a given line, we can conclude there are infinitely many different lines through the point and not intersecting the given line (Problem 8.4). For instance, if l_1 and l_2 contain P, and l_1 and l_2 do not intersect l, then any line through P and lying between l_1 and l_2 (such as l_3 in Figure 8.1) will have the same property. We show next that among all these lines there are two of particular importance.

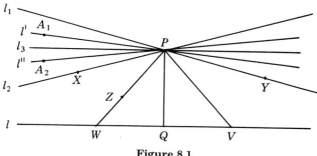

Figure 8.1

THEOREM 8.1

Let l be any line and P any point not on l. Then there are two lines l_1 and l_2 through P such that:

(a) l_1 and l_2 do not intersect l,

(b) l_1 and l_2 make equal acute angles with the perpendicular from P to l,

(c) every line through P lying within the angle containing that perpendicular intersects l, and

(d) every other line through P does not intersect l.

Proof

(i) Let PQ be the perpendicular from P to l.

(ii) Claim: If l' and l'' are two lines through P not intersecting l, with A_1 on l' and A_2 on l'' as shown, and l_3 is any line through P lying within angle A_1PA_2 (the angle not containing PQ), then l_3 does not intersect l. Proof of claim: If l_3 were to intersect l to the right of Q, then l' would also have to intersect l, by Pasch's Axiom. But l' does not intersect l, so, by *reductio*, l_3 cannot intersect l to the right of Q. Similarly l_3 cannot intersect l to the left of Q.

(iii) Now consider the lines between PQ and l'. Some of these (like PQ) will intersect l, and some (like l') will not. Applying the angular form of Dedekind's Postulate, we see there is a line l_1 which divides these lines into two classes, those which do intersect l and those which do not.

(iv) Claim: The line l_1 does not intersect l. Proof of claim: Assume l_1 intersects l, say at point C. Let D be any point on l to the right of C. Then angle $QPD >$ angle QPC, contradicting the way l_1 was chosen using Dedekind's Postulate. Thus l_1 cannot intersect l, by *reductio*.

(v) Now consider the lines between PQ and l'' to get a line l_2 which is to the left as l_1 is to the right. Then l_1 and l_2 satisfy conditions (a), (c), and (d) of Theorem 8.1, so it only remains to verify (b). Choose X and Y on l_2 and l_1 as shown in Figure 8.1.

(vi) Claim: angle $XPQ =$ angle YPQ. Proof of claim: Assume the angles are not equal, say $XPQ > YPQ$. Construct PZ so that $ZPQ = YPQ$. Then PZ will cut l, say at W. Measure QV on l to the right of Q so that $QV = QW$. Draw PV. Then triangle PWQ is congruent* to triangle PVQ by I4, so angle $WPQ =$ angle VPQ. But angle

---

* When we say that two triangles are congruent, we mean that they are related as in I4. This can be taken to mean that by moving one of the triangles it can be made to coincide with the other. This involves another of Euclid's unstated assumptions.

WPQ = angle ZPQ, so angle VPQ = angle YPQ. Thus PY lies along PV, contradicting the fact that PY does not intersect l. Therefore angle XPQ = angle YPQ. Now it only remains to show that these angles are acute.

(vii) Claim: angles XPQ and YPQ are acute.

Proof of claim: If angles XPQ and YPQ were right angles then PX and PY would lie on the same straight line, namely the perpendicular to PQ through P. But by I28 this line does not intersect l. There must then be some other line through P not intersecting l, by Lobachevsky's Postulate, and such a line would have to fall within angle XPY, a contradiction. Therefore angles XPQ and YPQ are acute. $\square$

The lines l_1 and l_2 of Theorem 8.1 will be called the *parallels* to l through P, and the other lines through P not intersecting l will be called *nonintersecting* with respect to l. We shall refer to l_2 as the *left-hand* parallel to l, and to l_1 as the *right-hand* parallel to l. Many of the theorems to be proved have both a left and right version, but we shall often state only one of these explicitly.

PROBLEM SET 8

PROBLEM 8.1. (a) through (j). Consider the non-Euclidean geometry discussed beginning with this section, that is, the geometry obtained by assuming Euclid's first four postulates and five common notions together with Lobachevsky's Postulate. Relying on remarks in the text, place each of the statements (a) through (j) in Problem 7.1 in one of the following categories.

I. The statement can be proved as a proposition in the geometry.

II. The statement is logically consistent with the ten axioms for the geometry, but it cannot be proved as a proposition in the geometry.

III. The statement is logically inconsistent with the ten axioms for the geometry.

PROBLEM 8.2. Let l be any line and P any point not on l.

(a) How many lines through P are parallel to l, in the sense of the definitions in this section?

(b) How many lines through P are nonintersecting with respect to l, in the sense of the definitions in this section?

PROBLEM 8.3. Assume that l_1 is the right-hand parallel to l through P, with the straight line APQ perpendicular to l. Is angle APB acute? right? obtuse? (Figure 8.2.)

Figure 8.2

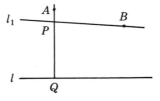

PROBLEM 8.4. Prove this statement from the text: Once we assume at least two lines through a given point and not intersecting a given line, we can conclude there are infinitely many different lines through the point and not intersecting the given line. (Use I9, part (ii) of the proof of Theorem 8.1, and *reductio*.)

PROBLEM 8.5. Consider step (i) in the proof of Theorem 8.1. How do we know there is a perpendicular from P to l in the geometry being considered here?

PROBLEM 8.6. Choose a point U on l_1 to the left of P in Figure 8.1. Prove that the bisector of angle UPX is perpendicular to PQ. (Suggestion: Use Theorem 8.1 and Definition 10 of Book I.)

PROBLEM 8.7. If l_1 and l_2 have a common perpendicular, PQ, then one of the following is true. Which one?
(a) l_1 intersects l_2.
(b) l_1 is a parallel to l_2 through P.
(c) l_1 and l_2 are nonintersecting.

§9. Parallels

In this section we prove three important properties of the parallels we introduced in Section 8. Notice that Theorems 9.1 and 9.2 have analogues in Euclidean geometry, but they are essentially trivial because of the Euclidean definition of parallel. Theorem 9.3 should be compared with the Euclidean Proposition I30.

THEOREM 9.1
If l_1 is the right-hand parallel to l through P, and Q is any other point on l_1, then l_1 is also the right-hand parallel to l through Q. Similarly for left-hand parallels.

Proof
Case I. (Q to the right of P.) Let PA and QB be the perpendiculars from P and Q to l, as shown in Figure 9.1. Let R be any point on l_1 to the right of

Figure 9.1

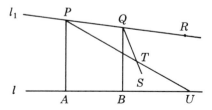

Q and let S be any point such that QS is within angle RQB. We must prove that QS intersects l.
Choose T to be any point on QS and draw PT. Since PR is the right-hand parallel to l through P, PT produced must intersect l, say at U. Therefore by Pasch's Axiom (applied to triangle PAU), QS must intersect l.

Case II. (Q to the left of P.) Let PA and QB be the perpendiculars from P and Q to l, as shown in Figure 9.2. Let S be any point such that QS is within angle PQB. We must prove that QS intersects l.

Figure 9.2

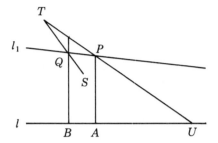

Choose a point T on QS produced through Q, and draw TP. Since QP is the right-hand parallel to l through P, TP produced must intersect l, say at U. Therefore, by Pasch's Axiom, QS must intersect l. $\square$

THEOREM 9.2

If l_1 is parallel to l_2, then l_2 is parallel to l_1.

Proof

Let l_1 be the right-hand parallel to l_2 through P (Figure 9.3). Then we want to prove that l_2 is the left-hand parallel to l_1 through each of the points on l_2. By Theorem 9.1 it does not matter which point we choose on l_2, so we use Q where PQ is perpendicular to l_2 through P. Let QR be the perpendicular from Q to l_1.

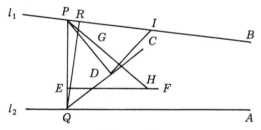

Figure 9.3

Claim: R is to the right of P.

Proof of Claim: R cannot coincide with P because angle BRQ is a right angle while angle BPQ must be an acute angle by Theorem 8.1(b). For the same reason, R cannot be to the left of P, for if it were then triangle PQR would have an interior (obtuse) angle at P greater than the exterior (right) angle at R, which is impossible by I16.

We must prove that every line through Q and lying within angle RQA intersects l_1. Let QC be such a line.

Construct PD perpendicular to QC. Then D must lie in the direction of C from Q, because of I16 applied to triangle PDQ. Measure PE equal to PD on PQ. Since PD is the perpendicular to QC, PE will be shorter than PQ.

Draw EF perpendicular to PQ, as shown in Figure 9.3. Construct angle QPG equal to angle BPD. PG must cut l_2, because l_1 is the right-hand parallel to l_2. Hence PG must cut EF, say, at H, by Pasch's Axiom.

Measure PI equal to PH along PB, and join D and I. Then triangles EPH and DPI are congruent ($PE = PD$, $PH = PI$, angle $EPH =$ angle DPI, and Proposition I4).

Therefore angle PDI is a right angle. Therefore DI and DC coincide. Therefore QC intersects l_1 at I. $\square$

THEOREM 9.3

If l_1 and l_2 are parallel to l_3 in the same direction, then l_1 is parallel to l_2.

Proof

Case I. (l_3 between l_1 and l_2) (Figure 9.4). Choose A on l_1, B on l_2. Then the segment AB intersects l_3 (that is, what it means to say, l_3 is 'between' l_1 and l_2). Let C be the point of intersection.

Figure 9.4

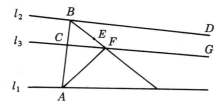

Let D be on l_2 in the direction of parallelism from B. Choose any line BE within angle DBA. We must show that BE (produced) intersects l_1.

We know BE (produced) intersects l_3 (say at F) because l_2 is the right-hand parallel to l_3 at B. Then BE (produced) must also intersect l_1 because it lies within GFA and l_3 is the right-hand parallel to l_1 at F.

Case II. (l_1 and l_2 on the same side of l_3) (Figure 9.5). Assume l_2 between l_1 and l_3. Let A be any point on l_1, and let l be the parallel to l_2 through A.

Figure 9.5

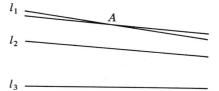

Then l is also parallel to l_3, by case I above. But by Theorem 8.1, there is only one parallel (in the given direction) to l_3 through A. Therefore l and l_1 must coincide, that is, l_1 is parallel to l_2. $\square$

PROBLEM SET 9

PROBLEM 9.1. Assume that l_1 is the right-hand parallel to l through P, and that AR and PQ are both perpendicular to l (Figure 9.6).

(a) Is angle APQ right? acute? obtuse? Why?

Figure 9.6

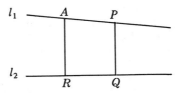

(b) Is angle PAR right? acute? obtuse? Why?

(c) Which one of the following is true? Why?

   (i) AR (produced) is the right-hand parallel to PQ (produced) through R.

   (ii) AR (produced) is the left-hand parallel to PQ (produced) through R.

   (iii) AR (produced) and PQ (produced) are nonintersecting.

   (iv) Not enough information given to say.

PROBLEM 9.2. Prove: Two lines that are perpendicular to a third line are nonintersecting.

PROBLEM 9.3. Consider the situation shown in Figure 9.7, with l_1 the right-hand parallel to l_2 through P and l_2 the left-hand parallel to l_3 through Q.

Figure 9.7

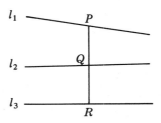

(a) Is l_1 the right-hand parallel to l_3 through P? Why?

(b) Is l_1 the left-hand parallel to l_3 through P? Why?

§10. Triangles

Although parallel lines do not intersect, it is convenient and suggestive to introduce a new notion, that of a *point at infinity,* and to speak of parallel lines as intersecting at such a point. Thus each line l has two points at infinity associated with it, a right and a left, and to say that l_1 intersects l at infinity is just another way of saying that l_1 is parallel to l. We shall denote these new points by either Ω or Ω' (omega or omega prime). We stress that points at infinity are not points in the ordinary sense, such as in Postulate 1, but simply furnish a convenience when working with parallel lines.

It is useful to consider properties of the figure formed by the line segment between two given points together with parallel lines through the two points (actually, we only use 'half' of each of the two parallel lines, or what are sometimes called *rays*). (Figure 10.1.)

Figure 10.1

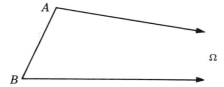

We shall refer to the 'triangle' $AB\Omega$ with 'sides' AB, $A\Omega$, and $B\Omega$, but stress that these must not be confused with ordinary triangles; the context will always make clear which is meant. Notice that these triangles have three sides (two infinite, one finite), but only two vertices and only two angles. We first prove that a form of Pasch's Axiom holds for these new triangles.

THEOREM 10.1

If a line passes through A, B, or Ω, as well as a point within $AB\Omega$, then it will intersect the opposite side.

Proof

Let P be a point within $AB\Omega$, as shown in Figure 10.2. Then AP will intersect $B\Omega$ because $A\Omega$ is parallel to $B\Omega$. Similarly BP will intersect $A\Omega$. Therefore it only remains to prove that $P\Omega$ (produced) intersects AB.

Figure 10.2

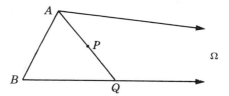

Let AP intersect $B\Omega$ at Q. Then $P\Omega$ must intersect either AB or BQ by Pasch's Axiom for ordinary triangles. But $P\Omega$ does not intersect BQ because $P\Omega$ is parallel to $B\Omega$. Therefore $P\Omega$ must intersect AB. $\square$

THEOREM 10.2

If a straight line intersects one side of $AB\Omega$, but does not pass through a vertex, then it will intersect one and only one of the other two sides.

Proof

Case I. If the given line intersects AB, say at P, then we can construct $P\Omega$. Then because $P\Omega$ is parallel to $A\Omega$ and $B\Omega$, by Theorem 10.1 the given line must intersect either $A\Omega$ or $B\Omega$ ($A\Omega$ if the line passes through C between $A\Omega$ and $P\Omega$, as in the case shown in Figure 10.3).

Figure 10.3

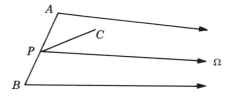

Case II. If the line passes through Q on $A\Omega$, then draw BQ. If the given line passes within ABQ, then it will intersect AB by Pasch's Axiom, and if the given line passes within $BQ\Omega$, then it will intersect $B\Omega$ by Theorem 10.1 (applied to $BQ\Omega$). (Figure 10.4.)

Figure 10.4

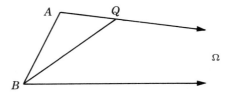

Case III. The case where the given line intersects $B\Omega$ is like Case II. □

THEOREM 10.3

The exterior angle at A or B is greater than the opposite interior angle. (Compare I16.)

Proof

Referring to Figure 10.5, we want to prove, for instance, that angle $CA\Omega$ is greater than angle $CB\Omega$, where BC is BA produced.

Figure 10.5

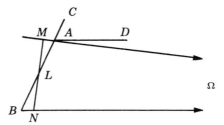

Construct angle CAD equal to angle $CB\Omega$. AD (produced) cannot intersect $B\Omega$ because if it did, say at E, then triangle ABE would contradict I16 (the exterior angle CAD would equal the interior opposite angle CBE).
Claim: AD (produced) does not coincide with $A\Omega$.
Proof of claim: Let L be the midpoint of AB, and construct LM perpendicular to $A\Omega$. Measure off on $B\Omega$ a distance BN equal to AM, with N on the side of AB opposite M. Draw LN. Assume AD (produced) does coincide with $A\Omega$. (This will give us a contradiction.)
Triangles MAL and NBL are congruent ($AL = LB$, $AM = BN$, angle MAL = angle CAD = angle LBN, and I4). Therefore angle ALM = angle BLN, so that MLN is a straight line. But then MN is perpendicular to both $A\Omega$ and $B\Omega$, contradicting Theorem 8.1(b). This proves the claim.
We now have that AD lies within angle $CA\Omega$, and therefore angle CAD < angle $CA\Omega$, and so angle $CB\Omega$ < angle $CA\Omega$, as was to be proved. □

THEOREM 10.4

In triangles $AB\Omega$ and $A'B'\Omega'$ (Figure 10.6), if $AB = A'B'$ and angle $BA\Omega$ = angle $B'A'\Omega'$, then angle $AB\Omega$ = angle $A'B'\Omega'$. (One side and one angle of a triangle $AB\Omega$ determine the other angle.)

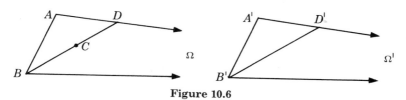

Figure 10.6

Proof

Assume angle $AB\Omega \neq$ angle $A'B'\Omega'$, say angle $AB\Omega >$ angle $A'B'\Omega'$. Construct angle $ABC =$ angle $A'B'\Omega'$. Then BC (produced) must intersect $A\Omega$, say, at D (because $A\Omega$ is parallel to $B\Omega$). Measure $A'D'$ on $A'\Omega'$ so that $A'D' = AD$. Then triangles ABD and $A'B'D'$ are congruent ($AD = A'D'$, $AB = A'B'$, angle $BAD =$ angle $B'A'D'$, and I4). Therefore angle $ABD =$ angle $A'B'D'$ and so angle $A'B'\Omega' =$ angle $A'B'D'$. This is a contradiction (because $B'\Omega'$ does not intersect $A'\Omega'$). Thus, by *reductio*, angle $AB\Omega =$ angle $A'B'\Omega'$. $\square$

Theorem 10.5

In triangles $AB\Omega$ and $A'B'\Omega'$ (Figure 10.7), if $AB = A'B'$, angle $BA\Omega = $ angle $AB\Omega$, and angle $B'A'\Omega' = $ angle $A'B'\Omega'$, then all four of these angles are equal.

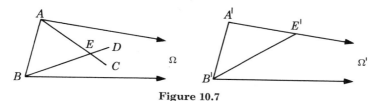

Figure 10.7

Proof

It suffices to prove that angle $BA\Omega =$ angle $B'A'\Omega'$. To do this, assume otherwise, say angle $BA\Omega >$ angle $B'A'\Omega'$. Take AC such that angle $BAC =$ angle $B'A'\Omega'$, and take BD such that angle $ABD =$ angle $A'B'\Omega'$. Then AC and BD must intersect, say at E (by Pasch's Axiom). Measure $A'E'$ along $A'\Omega'$ with $A'E' = AE$. Then triangles ABE and $A'B'E'$ are congruent ($AB = A'B'$, angle $BAE =$ angle $B'A'E'$, $AE = A'E'$, and I4). Therefore angle $A'B'E' =$ angle $ABE =$ angle $A'B'\Omega'$, so that we have have reached a contradiction. $\square$

Theorem 10.6

In triangles $AB\Omega$ and $A'B'\Omega'$ (Figure 10.8), if angle $BA\Omega = $ angle $B'A'\Omega'$ and angle $AB\Omega = $ angle $A'B'\Omega'$, then $AB = A'B'$. (If the

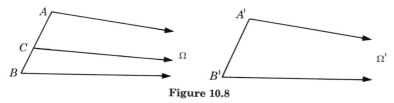

Figure 10.8

angles of two triangles are respectively equal, then the finite sides are equal.)

Proof

If $AB \neq A'B'$, then one is greater, say $AB > A'B'$. Measure $AC = A'B'$ along AB, and draw $C\Omega$ (necessarily parallel to $A\Omega$ and $B\Omega$). By Theorem 10.4, angle $AC\Omega$ = angle $A'B'\Omega'$, so angle $AC\Omega$ = angle $AB\Omega$. But by Theorem 10.3, angle $AC\Omega$ > angle $AB\Omega$. Thus we have a contradiction, and so $AB = A'B'$. $\square$

Let P be a point not on a line l, and let l_1 be the right-hand parallel to l through P (Figure 10.9). If PQ is the perpendicular to l from P, then

Figure 10.9

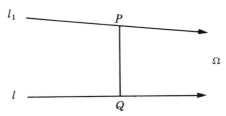

we know by Theorem 8.1(b) that angle $QP\Omega$ is acute. Furthermore, the angle $QP\Omega$ is uniquely determined by the distance PQ (this can be seen by taking angles $AB\Omega$ and $A'B'\Omega'$ to be right angles in Theorem 10.4). This angle is called the *angle of parallelism* corresponding to the distance PQ. If the distance PQ is d, we shall denote the angle of parallelism by $\Pi(d)$.

Now suppose we have two points P_1 and P_2 at different distances d_1 and d_2 from l. How do $\Pi(d_1)$ and $\Pi(d_2)$ compare? Because $\Pi(d_1)$ and $\Pi(d_2)$ depend only on the distance of P_1 and P_2 from l, we may assume P_1 and P_2 to be on the same perpendicular PQ to l, as shown in Figure 10.10.

Figure 10.10

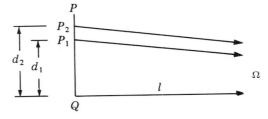

By Theorem 10.3, the exterior angle $QP_1\Omega$ of triangle $P_1P_2\Omega$ is greater than the opposite interior angle $QP_2\Omega$: angle $QP_2\Omega$ < angle $QP_1\Omega$. Thus we have proved that

$$d_2 > d_1 \text{ implies } \Pi(d_2) < \Pi(d_1).$$

It can be shown that as d approaches 0, $\Pi(d)$ approaches a right angle. And as d becomes infinite (that is, gets larger without bound),

$\Pi(d)$ approaches 0. (These statements assume that a way of measuring angles and line segments with real numbers has been introduced. See [4] or [13] for details.)

PROBLEM SET 10

PROBLEM 10.1. Prove: In triangle $AB\Omega$ (Figure 10.11), the sum of angles $AB\Omega$ and $BA\Omega$ is less than two right angles. (Produce BA to P. Use Theorem 10.3.)

Figure 10.11

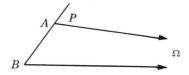

PROBLEM 10.2. Prove: If $\Pi(d_1)$ and $\Pi(d_2)$ are the angles of parallelism corresponding to d_1 and d_2, and $\Pi(d_1) > \Pi(d_2)$, then $d_1 < d_2$. (*Reductio.*)

PROBLEM 10.3. Prove: If the perpendicular bisector of AB is parallel to both $A\Omega$ and $B\Omega$ in triangle $AB\Omega$, then angle $BA\Omega$ = angle $AB\Omega$.

PROBLEM 10.4. Prove: If angle $BA\Omega$ = angle $AB\Omega$ in triangle $AB\Omega$, then the perpendicular bisector of AB is parallel to both $A\Omega$ and $B\Omega$.

PROBLEM 10.5. Prove: If l_1 and l_2 are nonintersecting, angle CAB = angle DBA, and l is the perpendicular bisector of AB, then l is nonintersecting with respect to both l_1 and l_2 (Figure 10.12).

Figure 10.12

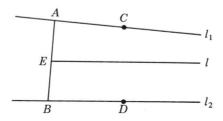

§11. Saccheri Quadrilaterals

A quadrilateral $ABDC$ with the angles at A and B both right angles, and sides AC and BD equal, will be called a *Saccheri* quadrilateral (Figure 11.1). The side AB adjacent to the two given right angles is called the *base*, the side opposite the *summit*, and the angles adjacent to the summit the *summit angles*. Saccheri studied such quadrilaterals in his attempt to obtain a *reductio* proof of the Fifth Postulate. They will be useful to us in obtaining information about the sum of the angles of a triangle.

THEOREM 11.1

The line joining the midpoints of the base and summit of a Saccheri quadrilateral is perpendicular to both of them, and the summit angles are equal and acute.

Proof

Referring to Figure 11.1, we are given that the angles at A and B are right angles, that $AC = BD$, that E bisects AB, and that F bisects CD. We must prove that EF is perpendicular to AB and CD and that angles ACF and BDF are equal and acute.

Figure 11.1

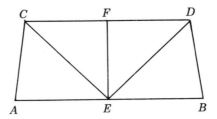

Draw CE and DE. Triangles ACE and BDE are congruent ($AC = BD$, $AE = BE$, angle $CAE =$ angle DBE, and I4). Therefore $CE = DE$. Therefore triangles CFE and DFE are congruent ($CF = DF$, $FE = FE$, $CE = DE$, and I8).

It follows that angle $ACF =$ angle $ACE +$ angle $ECF =$ angle $BDE +$ angle $EDF =$ angle BDF, and that EF is perpendicular to CD (because angle $EFC =$ angle EFD). Also, angle $AEF =$ angle BEF, and so EF is perpendicular to AB.

Finally, to show angles ACF and BDF are acute, we draw $C\Omega$ and $D\Omega$ parallel to AB (Figure 11.2), and produce CD, say, to E. By Theorem

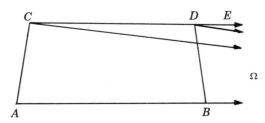

Figure 11.2

10.3, angle $ED\Omega >$ angle $DC\Omega$, while by Theorem 10.4 angle $\Omega DB =$ angle ΩCA. Therefore angle $EDB =$ angle $ED\Omega +$ angle $\Omega DB >$ angle $DC\Omega +$ angle $\Omega CA =$ angle DCA. Since angle $BDC =$ angle DCA, it follows that angle $EDB >$ angle BDC, and so angle BDC (= angle BDF) is acute. Thus both summit angles are acute, since we have already proved angle $ACF =$ angle BDF. □

THEOREM 11.2

If, in the quadrilateral $ABDC$, the angles at A and B are right angles, *and side AC is greater than side BD, then the angle at C is less than the angle at D.*

Proof

Measure AE equal to BD along AC, and draw DE (Figure 11.3). By Theorem 11.1, angle AED = angle BDE. But angle AED > angle ACD by I16, and

Figure 11.3

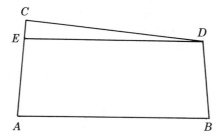

angle BDC > angle BDE. Therefore angle BDC > angle ACD, as was to be proved. □

THEOREM 11.3

If ABDC is a quadrilateral in which the angles at A, B, and C are right angles, then the angle at D must be acute.

Proof

Produce BA through A to B', so that $AB' = AB$. Construct $B'D'$ perpendicular to AB', with $B'D' = BD$, and draw $D'C$, AD', and AD (Figure 11.4). Then triangles $AB'D'$ and ABD are congruent ($AB' = AB$, $BD =$

Figure 11.4

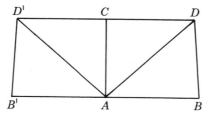

$B'D'$, angle ABD = angle $AB'D'$, and I4). Therefore angle $B'AD'$ = angle BAD, and so angle $D'AC$ = angle DAC, as well as $AD = AD'$. This yields triangles $AD'C$ and ADC congruent (angle $D'AC$ = angle DAC, $AC = AC$, $AD = AD'$, and I4). Thus angle ACD' = angle ACD and so angle ACD' + angle ACD = two right angles. Therefore DCD' is a straight line (by I14). Now we may apply Theorem 11.1 to quadrilateral $B'BDD'$, and thereby conclude that angle BDC is acute. □

Theorem 11.3 reveals that in our non-Euclidean geometry the sum of the interior angles of a quadrilateral is less than four right angles, if three of the angles of the quadrilateral are right angles. In fact, the sum of the interior angles of any quadrilateral is less than four right angles in this geometry, as we shall see from the corollary following Theorem 12.2. This is in contrast with Euclidean geometry, where the sum of the angles of a quadrilateral is always equal to four right angles (Problem 12.4). In seeking a proof of Playfair's Axiom by *reductio*, Saccheri began with the various possibilities for the angle sum of (what we now call) Saccheri quadrilaterals, rather than the possibilities for the number of parallels through a point not on a given line. Playfair's Axiom corresponds to angle sum four right angles, our Alternative A corresponds to angle sum greater than four right angles (this can be proved), and our Alternative B (equivalently, Lobachevsky's Postulate) corresponds to angle sum less than four right angles (Corollary to Theorem 12.2).

PROBLEM SET 11

PROBLEM 11.1 (Converse of Theorem 11.2.) Prove: If, in quadrilateral *ABDC* (Figure 11.5), the angles at *A* and *B* are right angles, and the angle

Figure 11.5

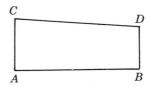

at *C* is less than the angle at *D*, then side *AC* is greater than side *BD*. (Use Theorems 11.1 and 11.2, and *reductio*.)

PROBLEM 11.2. Assume that *A*Ω is the right-hand parallel to *R*Ω through *P*, that *Q* is on *R*Ω, and that *AR* and *PQ* are both perpendicular to *R*Ω (see Figure 11.6). Use Problem 11.1 to prove that *AR > PQ*. (Conclusion:

Figure 11.6

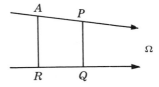

The (perpendicular) distance from one of two parallel lines to the other gets smaller as one moves in the direction of parallelism, and larger as one moves in the opposite direction.)

PROBLEM 11.3. If three of the angles of a quadrilateral are right angles, then each of the sides adjacent to the fourth angle is greater than the side opposite it. (Suggestion: Use Problem 11.1.)

PROBLEM 11.4. Assume given a quadrilateral *ABDC* with right angles at *A* and *D* and with *AC = BD* (Figure 11.7). Prove that neither the angle at *B* nor the angle at *C* is a right angle. (Suggestion: Use Problem 11.3.)

Figure 11.7

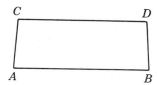

PROBLEM 11.5. Assume that $ABDC$ is a Saccheri quadrilateral with base AB, and assume that E bisects AB and that F bisects CD. Which of the following is true? $AC > EF$, $AC = EF$, $AC < EF$ (Figure 11.8). Why? (Suggestion: Use Problem 11.3.)

Figure 11.8

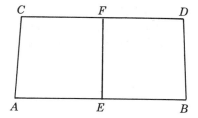

PROBLEM 11.6. Prove: The summit of a Saccheri quadrilateral is greater than the base. (Suggestion: Use Figure 11.8, and first compare AE with CF, and EB with FD, using Problem 11.3.)

§12. The Angle Sum of a Triangle

We are now in a position to prove that in the non-Euclidean geometry based on Lobachevsky's Postulate, the sum of the angles of any triangle is less than two right angles. We first prove this for triangles containing a right angle.

THEOREM 12.1

The sum of the angles of any right triangle is less than two right angles.

Proof

Let ABC be a triangle with a right angle at C (Figure 12.1). The other two angles of the triangle must be acute by I17.

Figure 12.1

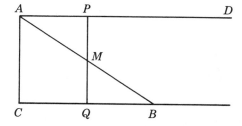

Construct AD so that angle BAD = angle ABC. Let M be the midpoint of AB, and draw MP perpendicular to AD and MQ perpendicular to

CB. Triangles *APM* and *BQM* are congruent (*AM* = *BM*, angle *PAM* = angle *QBM*, angle *APM* = angle *BQM*, and I26). Therefore angle *AMP* = angle *BMQ* and so *PMQ* is a straight line (using I14).

Quadrilateral *CQPA* now fulfills the conditions of Theorem 11.3 (angles at *C*, *Q*, and *P* being right angles). Thus angle *CAP* is an acute angle. But angle *CAP* = angle *CAB* + angle *ABC*, and so angle *BCA* + angle *CAB* + angle *ABC* is less than two right angles. $\square$

THEOREM 12.2

The sum of the angles of any triangle is less than two right angles.

Proof

Let *ABC* be a triangle. At least two of the angles of the triangle are acute (by I17), say *B* and *C*. This insures that if *AD* is the perpendicular from *A* to side *BC*, then *D* will fall between *B* and *C*, as shown in Figure 12.2.

Figure 12.2

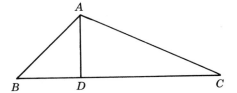

Applying Theorem 12.1 to each of the two right triangles *ADB* and *ADC*, we get that angle *DBA* + angle *BAD* < one right angle and angle *DAC* + angle *ACD* < one right angle, and so angle *CBA* + angle *BAC* + angle *ACB* < two right angles, as was to be proved. $\square$

COROLLARY

The sum of the angles of any quadrilateral is less than four right angles. (Compare Problem 12.4.)

Proof

Given *ABDC*, draw *AD*, use Theorem 12.2 on each of the two triangles, and add (Figure 12.3). $\square$

Figure 12.3

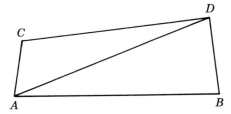

We conclude our deductions from Lobachevsky's Postulate with the following remarkable result: similar triangles are necessarily congruent.

THEOREM 12.3

If the three angles of one triangle are equal, respectively, to the three angles of a second triangle, then the triangles are congruent.

Proof

Assume triangles ABC and $A'B'C'$ having corresponding angles equal (Figure 12.4). If any side of ABC equals the corresponding side of $A'B'C'$, then the two triangles are congruent by I26, and we are finished. Therefore assume $A'B'$ smaller than AB.

Figure 12.4

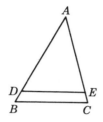
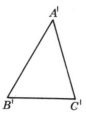

Lay off AD equal to $A'B'$ along AB. Also lay off AE equal to $A'C'$ along AC (produced, if necessary). Then triangles ADE and $A'B'C'$ are congruent.

Claim: E falls between A and C.

Proof of Claim: If AE were greater than AC (Figure 12.5(a)), then there would result a triangle FEC with angle FCA = angle FEC, contradicting I16. If AE were equal to AC (Figure 12.5(b)), then we would get a contradiction of the fact that angle BCA = angle DCA. This proves the claim.

Figure 12.5

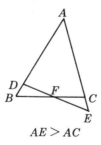

$$AE > AC \qquad\qquad AE = AC$$

We now have a quadrilateral $BCED$ with angle CBD + angle BDE + angle DEC + angle ECB = (angle EDA + angle BDE) + (angle DEC + angle AED), which equals four right angles, contradicting the Corollary of Theorem 12.2.

Therefore $AB = A'B'$, and so triangles ABC and $A'B'C'$ are congruent. ☐

PROBLEM SET 12

PROBLEM 12.1 Consider triangle ADE, with B on AD, C on AE, $AB < AD$, and $AC < AE$ (as shown in Figure 12.6). If angle ABC = angle ADE, then which of the following is true? Why?

(a) Angle $ACB <$ angle AED.

Figure 12.6

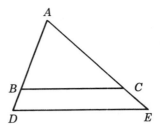

(b) Angle ACB > angle AED.
(c) Angle ACB = angle AED.
(d) Not enough information given to say.

PROBLEM 12.2. Given triangles ABC and DEF (Figure 12.7), with angle A = angle D, angle B = angle E, and $AC \neq DF$. Which one of the following is correct? Why?
(a) Angle C = angle F.
(b) Angle $C \neq$ angle F.
(c) Not enough information given to say.

Figure 12.7

PROBLEM 12.3. Consider the triangles shown in Figure 12.8, with a right angle at A, and D on AB with $AD < AB$. The angle sum of triangle ACD is:
(a) Less than the angle sum of triangle ACB.
(b) Greater than the angle sum of triangle ACB.
(c) Equal to the angle sum of triangle ACB.
(d) Not enough information given to say.
    Why?

Figure 12.8

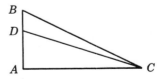

PROBLEM 12.4. Prove that in Euclidean geometry the sum of the angles of a quadrilateral is always equal to four right angles. (Use Problem 1.12.)

§13. Further Results

The proofs we have given on the basis of Lobachevsky's Postulate should be adequate to illustrate the methods of geometry as a deductive science, and the care required when proving theorems from axioms that may conflict with one's intuition and previously acquired knowledge. We shall now state, without proof, some further results in this geometry.

We know from Theorem 8.1 that two parallel lines cannot have a common perpendicular: a line perpendicular to one of two parallel lines will necessarily make an acute angle (on the side of parallelism) with the other. In contrast with this, two nonintersecting lines in a plane will have a perpendicular in common; more surprising, perhaps, they will have only one such common perpendicular (Problem 13.3).

In Euclidean geometry, the perpendicular distance from a point on one of two parallel lines to the other of the two lines does not depend on the point chosen: two parallel lines are everywhere equidistant (I33). In the geometry based on Lobachevsky's Postulate, this perpendicular distance does depend on the point chosen, getting smaller as the point moves in the direction of parallelism (see Problem 11.2). Furthermore, the perpendicular distance can be made arbitrarily small or great by moving sufficiently far to the right or left (Problem 13.1).

It is possible to associate real numbers with line segments in this geometry, and thereby give meaning to length as a real number. But when this has been done, we cannot develop a concept of area in terms of square units as we did in Euclidean geometry, because 'unit squares' do not exist: there are *no* squares in this geometry (Problem 13.2). Still, the idea of area as a real number can be given a meaning, and when this is done, the area of a triangle is completely determined by the sum of its interior angles, the area of the triangle becoming larger as this angle sum becomes smaller.

References [4], [6], and [13] contain proofs of all of these facts, as well as much more concerning this geometry.

PROBLEM SET 13

PROBLEM 13.1. In Problem 11.2 it was shown that the distance from one of two parallel lines to the other gets smaller as one moves in the direction of parallelism, and larger as one moves in the opposite direction. Prove that a point can be chosen on one of the lines so that the (perpendicular) distance from it to the other line is equal to any preassigned magnitude. (Outline of proof: Given l_1 the right-hand parallel to l through P, and PQ perpendicular to l (Figure 13.1), if PQ is equal to the given distance, we are through. (1) If PQ is larger than the given distance, choose A on PQ such that AQ is equal to the given distance. Let l_2 be the left-hand parallel to l through A. Then l_2 intersects l_1 (why?), say at R. Measure $RB = AR$ as shown. Let RS be perpendicular to l and measure $ST = QS$ as shown. Now show BT perpendicular to l and $BT = AQ$. (2) If PQ is smaller than the given distance, proceed similarly, using Figure 13.1(b).)

PROBLEM 13.2. Why are there no squares in this geometry? (Use Section 11.)

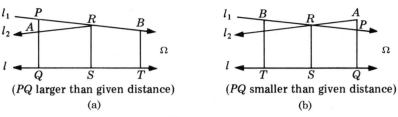

(*PQ* larger than given distance)	(*PQ* smaller than given distance)
(a)	(b)

Figure 13.1

PROBLEM 13.3. Prove that two nonintersecting lines can have at most one common perpendicular. (Use Section 11.)

§14. Alternatives Again

Our discussion of non-Euclidean geometry began with a critical look at Euclid's *Elements*. We then considered possible alternatives to it. Now, having studied one of these alternatives, we shall examine in broad terms some of the meaning and significance of this part of mathematics.

We should first point out that logically-valid geometries have been developed that satisfy Alternative A to Playfair's Axiom (Section 7), just as the geometry of Gauss, Lobachevsky, and Bolyai satisfies Alternative B. For reasons that need not concern us, geometries based on Alternative A are said to be *elliptic*, and those based on Alternative B are said to be *hyperbolic*.

Now consider the question: Which of these geometries, if any, accurately describes the physical space we live in? We have already said that this is not a simple question; it takes an unusually open mind even to take it seriously. And with few exceptions other than Gauss, Lobachevsky, and Bolyai, the question was not taken seriously until the latter half of the nineteenth century, more than thirty years after logically-valid alternatives to Euclidean geometry had been seen to exist. The prevailing belief was that Euclidean geometry was necessarily 'true'. And in this regard non-Euclidean geometry—even to be considered as a legitimate alternative—had to overcome the authority of such men as the philosopher Immanuel Kant, who had argued that the concept of space did not arise from experience, but rather from intuition. And this space of intuition was Euclidean; and that was that.

To those who did take alternatives to Euclidean geometry seriously, however, there was an obvious method for attempting to answer the question we have raised. The disparities between the possible values for the angle sum of a triangle suggest an experiment for determining which of Euclidean or hyperbolic or elliptic geometry, if any, describes physical space: in Euclidean geometry this angle sum is equal to two right angles (I32), in hyperbolic geometry it is less than two right angles

(Theorem 12.2), and in elliptic geometry it is more than two right angles (as in Problem 7.7). By simply measuring the angles of a triangle one could perhaps decide between the three possibilities. As mentioned in the previous section, in hyperbolic geometry the angle sum of a triangle varies with the size of the triangle: the smaller the triangle the larger the sum. The angle sum also varies in elliptic geometry: in this case the smaller the triangle the smaller the sum. For small triangles, either kind of non-Euclidean geometry will give an angle sum near two right angles, with the meaning of 'small' here depending on the particular hyperbolic or elliptic geometry. Thus an experiment with a physical triangle would more likely be decisive if the triangle were large. Lobachevsky carried out such a computation, using angle measurements for a triangle formed by a star and two different positions of the earth. Although he did not obtain an angle sum of exactly two right angles, the sum was not sufficiently different from two right angles to be conclusive. (A similar experiment, based on angle measurements for a triangle formed by the peaks of three mountains, has often been attributed to Gauss. It seems doubtful that his measurements were carried out for this purpose, however.)

Notice that although it might seem possible to decide in favor of either hyperbolic or elliptic geometry by the method of angle measurement, it is not possible to decide in favor of Euclidean geometry on the basis of it. The method cannot furnish a decisive answer in favor of Euclidean geometry because one cannot guarantee that any measurement is exact. Experimental errors (not to be confused with mistakes or blunders) are unavoidable due to the imperfection of even the best of measuring instruments, and so if measurement were to show the angle sum of a triangle to be exactly two right angles, it is still possible that the true sum differs from that by some small amount, thereby allowing for a sum consistent with either hyperbolic or elliptic geometry. On the other hand, if we were to measure a triangle and obtain a sum differing from two right angles by more than what we knew to be our greatest possible error, then we might decide that Euclidean geometry does not accurately describe physical triangles: Lobachevsky obtained an angle sum closer to two right angles than the possible errors due to measurement.

If we rely on information available from experiments on or near the earth, we are left in the position of not knowing whether the geometry of physical space is Euclidean or non-Euclidean. This does not, of course, prevent us from functioning satisfactorily under the assumption that the space immediately around us is Euclidean. Any variation is too small to be of consequence, and our day-to-day technology has been safely based on the use of Euclidean geometry.

In fact, however, the question of whether physical space is Euclidean is more complicated than the discussion above may have made it appear. The French mathematician Poincaré (1854–1912) pointed out that in experiments such as those mentioned, we are involved not only with assumptions about geometry, but also with assumptions about physical laws. And in any description of physical space these two apparently different kinds of assumptions are in fact inseparably connected. For example, in working with physical triangles some decision must be made about what to regard as straight lines. In the experiments described above, this decision was that the straight line connecting two points would be the path followed by a light ray between them. But once we introduce any such kind of physical phenomenon, we are involved with the whole variety of assumptions about such physical phenomena and their behavior. For example, we are involved with the idea of various kinds of forces, such as gravity. This bears on our original question in the following way. Suppose we were to measure the angles of a triangle and arrive at an angle sum greater than two right angles; sufficiently greater so that it could not be due to experimental error alone. Then we could, if we chose, say that this was due not to the fact that geometry is elliptic, but rather to the fact that there were forces acting on the light rays in such a way as to make them bend. And this, we would say, is why we did not get an angle sum of exactly two right angles. In other words, when we pass from mathematical geometry to physical geometry we are involved with basic assumptions in addition to those concerning geometry; we are also involved with the assumptions of physics. What we have said is that we can simply *insist* that the geometry be Euclidean and let the assumptions explaining the physics pay the consequences. If this means that we must make the assumptions about physics more complicated—by assuming the existence of forces that make light rays bend, for instance—then so be it.

In spite of Poincaré's claim that it is impossible to divorce mathematical geometry from physics when describing physical space, he did believe that one would not be led to complications in the assumptions about physical laws from an insistence that geometry be Euclidean. For he believed that regardless of how much we learned from observation, the necessary adjustment in the total set of assumptions, geometrical plus physical, would be such that the simplest way out would be to assume, whatever else, that the geometry was Euclidean. In this he was wrong.

Indeed, much of the interest in non-Euclidean geometry during this century was stimulated by Einstein's use of a form of non-Euclidean geometry in his general theory of relativity developed in 1915. The geometry he used was a sophisticated form of elliptic geometry that was first introduced in 1854 by the German Bernhard Riemann (1826–1866). This Riemannian geometry is thus the appropriate one for describing a number of physical phenomena studied by modern physicists: it is appropriate in the sense that the total collection of assumptions (geometrical plus physical) required to describe these phenomena is simplest when the geometry is taken to be Riemannian. The description of this geometry is considerably more complicated than that of the hyperbolic geometry we have considered, and we shall not pursue it. Cosmological theories have been developed using both Euclidean and non-Euclidean geometries; all such theories agree with Euclidean geometry for distances on the order of magnitude of the earth's dimensions. It is important to realize that without the break from traditional Euclidean geometry in the nineteenth century, motivated by purely mathematical considerations, much of this work done by twentieth-century physicists would not have been possible, or would at least have been more difficult.

This discussion of the complications involved in matching mathematical geometry with physical geometry can be summarized by quoting Einstein:

> As far as the laws of mathematics refer to reality, they are not certain; and as far as they are certain, they do not refer to reality.

We turn now to the question of the logical consistency of the hyperbolic geometry of Gauss, Lobachevsky, and Bolyai. We implied in Section 7 that their geometry is logically consistent, but we have not proved it. In fact, they did not prove it either. The first such proof was not given until 1868, by Eugenio Beltrami, an Italian, and it was dependent on the consistency of Euclidean geometry: if Euclidean geometry is consistent, then the hyperbolic geometry of Gauss, Lobachevsky, and Bolyai is consistent. Rather than describe Beltrami's proof, we shall sketch a simpler one given in 1870 by the German mathematician Felix Klein, using ideas of the English geometer Cayley (1821–1895); this proof is also dependent on the consistency of Euclidean geometry.

Before discussing the Cayley-Klein consistency proof, it will be helpful to make some comments about the role of definitions in a deductive system, something promised in Section 6. The crucial point here is that deductive arguments are true because of their form, without regard to the meaning of certain of the words involved. For example, consider the argument (technically a syllogism):

> *All men are mortal.*
> *Socrates is a man.*
> *Therefore, Socrates is mortal.*

This argument is true independently of the meaning of 'men', 'mortal', or 'Socrates'. Thus, replacing men by A, mortal by B, and Socrates by x, we get the equally true argument:

> *All A's are B's.*
> *x is an A.*
> *Therefore, x is a B.*

Geometry, as a deductive science, consists of arguments of this kind, with things like x, A, and B replaced by points, lines, and so forth. The kinds of theorems one can prove in the geometry are determined by the relationships between the terms used as specified by the axioms (postulates, common notions), and not by the definitions of these terms. For instance, in the example above, we would know that x is a B *if* the axioms (or theorems previously proved from the axioms) told us that all A's are B's and that x is an A, and this would have nothing to do with any interpretation we might try to give to x, A, and B. Of course, in using words such as 'point' and 'line' when writing axioms for geometry, one sets up relationships among them that correspond with the world one is trying to describe (such as: one and only one straight line can be drawn through two given points). But once this has been done, if we replace 'point' and 'line' by any other words related as the axioms specify, then the theorems we deduce will give true descriptions relative to these other words. David Hilbert (German, 1862–1943) summed up the irrelevance of definitions in deductive systems as follows: 'It must be possible to replace in all geometric statements the words *point*, *line*, *plane* by *table*, *chair*, *mug*' [12]. Summarizing, the words used in the axioms are defined implicitly by the axioms.

We now outline the Cayley-Klein consistency proof. Choose a circle C in a Euclidean plane, and interpret the points in its interior as the 'points' of the hyperbolic 'plane'. Given two 'points' P and Q, interpret the portion of the (Euclidean) line through P and Q, and within C, as the 'line' through P and Q. Here are interpretations of some of the things we assumed or proved earlier*: Figure 14.1 shows the 'line' through P and Q. Figure 14.2 shows two different 'lines' through P that are non-intersecting with respect to l. Figure 14.3 shows the right-hand (l_1) and

Figure 14.1

Figure 14.2

Figure 14.3

left-hand (l_2) parallels to l through P (they have no 'point' in common with l because our 'plane' contains only the points interior to C, not points on the circumference). With suitable definitions for 'distance' and 'angle', this yields a model in which all of the axioms of the hyperbolic geometry are satisfied. Postulate 1 and Alternative B are easily seen to be true here. Postulate 2 would not be satisfied if we used the

---

* Nonintersecting lines and right- and left-hand parallels were introduced in Section 8.

ordinary Euclidean notion of distance. For example, PQ produced in the direction of P by an amount equal to PQ would take us outside of our 'plane' (the interior of circle C). The notion of 'distance' is defined in a way that removes this problem; it is chosen so that if one of two points remains fixed and the other moves toward the boundary, the 'distance' between them increases without limit. The technical details are reasonably complicated, and we shall not present them. (See Problem 36.12.) But, again, 'distance' and 'angle' can be defined so that Postulate 2 and Postulates 3 and 4 are satisfied. Once this has been verified, we can conclude that the hyperbolic geometry of Gauss, Lobachevsky, and Bolyai is consistent if Euclidean geometry is consistent: for any contradictory theorems that could be proved in this geometry (that is, on the basis of Postulates 1–4, Alternative B, and the Common Notions) would translate into contradictory theorems in Euclidean geometry (as it applied to the interior of circle C)—if there is no inconsistency in the latter geometry, there can be none in the former.

Logic now demands an answer to the question: How do we know that Euclidean geometry is consistent? It is true that mathematicians have been proving theorems on the basis of Euclid's axioms for more than 2,000 years and have yet to find an inconsistency, but this does not insure that they could never find one.

The significant step with regard to this question was taken by Hilbert. In 1899 he published *Grundlagen der Geometrie* (*Foundations of Geometry* [9]), a book ranking with Euclid's *Elements* as a classic in geometry. In this, Hilbert established geometry as a purely deductive discipline, freeing it from the hidden assumptions and logical inadequacies that had been present in the works of Euclid and others. It was a brilliant piece of axiomatics, and furnished a valuable example for twentieth-century mathematics. It also contained his contribution to the question of consistency. It was, as those of Beltrami, Cayley, Klein, and others, a relative one: if the real number system is consistent, then Euclidean geometry is consistent (and therefore the known non-Euclidean geometries are consistent). Thus, with Hilbert, the problem of consistency of known geometries was replaced by a corresponding problem about number systems.

The question of the logical consistency of mathematical systems is one whose delicacy was not fully appreciated until the appearance, in 1931, of a far-reaching paper by Kurt Gödel (1906–   ), an Austrian who became a member of the Institute for Advanced Study at Princeton in 1938. In this paper Gödel proved that it is impossible to establish the logical consistency of any complex deductive system by operating only within that system: essentially, all consistency proofs must be relative.

With that disconcerting chord we end our discussion of non-Euclidean geometry. But we shall receive another surprise from Gödel in Chapter IV.

REFERENCES

1. BARKER, S. F., *Philosophy of Mathematics*, Prentice-Hall, Englewood Cliffs, N. J., 1964.

2. BELL, E. T., *Men of Mathematics*, Simon and Schuster, New York, 1937.

3. BONOLA, R., *Non-Euclidean Geometry*, trans. by H. S. Carslaw, Dover reprint, New York, 1955.

4. CARSLAW, H. S., *The Elements of Non-Euclidean Geometry and Trigonometry*, Longmans, Green & Co., London, 1916. Reprinted in *String Figures and Other Monographs*, Chelsea Publishing Co., New York, 1960.

5. *Encyclopedia Britannica*, Chicago, 1969.

6. EVES, HOWARD, *A Survey of Geometry*, 2 vols., Allyn and Bacon, Boston, 1963.

7. GÖDEL, KURT, *On Formally Undecidable Propositions of Principia Mathematica and Related Systems*, trans. by B. Melzer, introduction by R. B. Braithwaite, Oliver and Boyd, Edinburgh and London, 1962.

8. HEATH, T. L., ed., *The Thirteen Books of Euclid's Elements*, 3 vols., Cambridge University Press, Cambridge, 1908; paperback edition, Dover, New York, 1956.

9. HILBERT, D., *Foundations of Geometry*, trans. by E. J. Townsend, Open Court, Chicago, 1910.

10. *Mathematics in the Modern World*, readings from Scientific American with introductions by M. Kline, W. H. Freeman, San Francisco, 1968.

11. NAGEL, E., and J. R. NEWMAN, *Gödel's Proof*, New York University Press, New York, 1958. Reprinted in part in [10].

12. REID, C., *Hilbert*, Springer-Verlag, New York, 1970.

13. WOLFE, H. E., *Introduction to Non-Euclidean Geometry*, Holt, Rinehart and Winston, New York, 1945.

CHAPTER III

Probability

§15. Probability Defined

The theory of probability, now a respectable branch of mathematics with broad practical application, originated from questions about gambling. The subject was first developed extensively in the mid-seventeenth century, by the French mathematicians Pascal (1623–1662) and Fermat (1601–1665), and the Dutch mathematician and scientist Christiaan Huygens (1629–1695); some of their work had been anticipated in the sixteenth century, however, primarily by the Italian Jerome Cardan (1501–1576).

Whereas non-Euclidean geometry arose from a question concerning the internal logical structure of mathematics, and only later proved useful for applications outside mathematics, the theory of probability has from the beginning been influenced by questions from the outside. In order to stress this aspect of probability, one it shares with many other branches of mathematics, we shall concentrate on three specific problems and the ideas used in their solution. In doing this, we shall be able to see on a small scale something that is typical of mathematics and applications. For in solving the three original problems we shall be forced to develop some systematic techniques and understand some fundamental ideas; once this has been done, it will become apparent that these techniques and ideas can be used to solve other problems as well. The theory of probability, and indeed a great deal of mathematics, has continually expanded in this way: the solution of problems leads to the development of theory, which is then refined and generalized; this in turn opens up new applications, which lead to new problems; and the cycle is repeated. It is by this process that probability has grown into a subject which on the one hand is of interest in its own right, and on the other is of use in analyzing random events in the natural sciences, social sciences, medicine, technology, engineering, business, production processes, environmental control, or wherever they may occur.

Here, then, are the problems that will guide us.

PROBLEM 15A. Which is more probable: obtaining at least one 6 in four throws of a single die, or at least one (6, 6) (pair of 6's) in twenty-four throws of a pair of dice?

PROBLEM 15B. If a coin is tossed 10,000 times and 5,200 heads are obtained, is it reasonable to assume that the coin is not a fair one?

PROBLEM 15C. Suppose that the normal rate of death from a certain disease is 25 percent. If 10 victims of the disease are given injections of a new vaccine, and all of them recover, is it reasonable to assume that the vaccine is effective? What if 25 victims are given the vaccine and 23 recover? Which of these two sets of data would be the more convincing?

Problem 15A was one of the first ever settled by using significant ideas of mathematical probability. A French gambler, Chevalier de Méré, posed the problem, and it was discussed, with its solution, in an exchange of letters between Pascal and Fermat in 1654.

Applying a rule of thumb used by gamblers at that time, de Méré reasoned as follows about the two events in Problem 15A. Of the six ways a single die can fall, one way will yield a 6. And of the thirty-six ways two dice can fall (any number on the first paired with any number on the second), one way will yield a (6, 6). Thus obtaining a 6 in one throw of a single die should be six times more likely than obtaining a (6, 6) in one throw of two dice. Therefore, according to the gamblers' rule, obtaining at least one 6 in four throws of a single die should be just as likely as obtaining at least one (6, 6) in twenty-four throws (six times as many) of a pair of dice. In other words, the two events in Problem 15A should be equally probable.

De Méré knew, however, that four throws of a single die would yield at least one 6 slightly more than half the time, while twenty-four throws of a pair of dice would yield at least one (6, 6) slightly less than half the time. Thus the first of the events in Problem 15A is more probable than the second. De Méré asked Pascal for an explanation of the apparent paradox.

Before we can analyze either this problem or the other two we have stated, we must introduce some basic definitions and examples. In particular, we must say what we shall mean by 'probability'. The word is used in everyday speech in ways that do not fall within our scope. For example, a question such as 'What is the probability there will be peace in our time?', however important, is not one for the subject we are considering. It is perhaps no easier to give a definition of mathematical probability as a discipline than to give a definition of mathematics; the former, just as the latter, ranges from the simplest computations with numbers to the most abstract and general of theories. Mathematical probability, as many other branches of mathematics, arose from attempts to formulate laws that would enable predictions to be made about real events. We shall be concerned here with trying to make numerical statements about events involving random behavior, events that we can imagine to be performed many times, and we shall see that these numerical statements will be related in a natural way to everyday use of 'probability'. Thus, if an event has probability 0.5 of occurring when a certain experiment is performed, then the event can be expected, in the long run, to occur fifty times out of a hundred. Not exactly fifty times out of every hundred, certainly, but the ratio will tend to be this. That is the connection between intuition and mathematical probability.

Let us be more definite. We shall be concerned with (i) *experiments* (such as throwing a die, throwing a pair of dice, tossing a coin 200 times, observing results of vaccinations); (ii) the *possible outcomes* of these experiments; and (iii) certain combinations of these possible outcomes, which we call *events* (such as obtaining 6, (6, 6), at least 90 heads, no deaths).

EXAMPLE 15.1.
Experiment: Toss a coin 3 times. Let H denote head and T denote tail.

Possible outcomes: $H H H$ $H T H$ $T H H$ $T T H$
                    $H H T$ $H T T$ $T H T$ $T T T$

Here are some sample events.

Event (a): Exactly two heads.
Event (b): At least two heads.
Event (c): No heads.
Event (d): All heads.

The possible outcomes corresponding to these events are:

(a) $H H T, H T H, T H H$;
(b) $H H H, H H T, H T H, T H H$;
(c) $T T T$;
(d) $H H H$.

EXAMPLE 15.2.
Experiment: Select a number at random from the list 1, 2, 3, 4, 5, 6, 7, 8, 9.

Possible outcomes: 1, 2, 3, 4, 5, 6, 7, 8, 9.

Here are some sample events.

Event (a): An even number is selected.
Event (b): An odd number is selected.
Event (c): A negative number is selected.
Event (d): A positive number is selected.

The possible outcomes corresponding to these events are:

(a) 2, 4, 6, 8;
(b) 1, 3, 5, 7, 9;
(c) none;
(d) all.

DEFINITION
   The probability *of an event E, in an experiment in which all possible outcomes are equally likely, is defined to be*

$$\Pr(E) = \frac{n(E)}{N},$$

where N denotes the total number of possible outcomes of the experiment and $n(E)$ denotes the number of possible outcomes corresponding to the event E.

   Thus $N = 8$ for each of the events in Example 15.1 because there are eight possible outcomes of that experiment. And if E denotes the event 'exactly two heads' then $n(E) = 3$, because three of the possible outcomes correspond to that event; so $\Pr(E) = 3/8$ in this case.

EXAMPLE 15.3. The probabilities of the events described in the examples above are as follows.

Example 15.1(a): 3/8	Example 15.2(a): 4/9
Example 15.1(b): 4/8 = 1/2	Example 15.2(b): 5/9
Example 15.1(c): 1/8	Example 15.2(c): 0/9 = 0
Example 15.1(d): 1/8	Example 15.2(d): 9/9 = 1

   Our definition of probability applies only to experiments having a finite number N of possible outcomes, and these outcomes must all be equally likely. The definition of probability for such experiments was given by the Frenchman Pierre S. Laplace (1749–1827), whose *Théorie analytique des probabilities,* published in 1812, is one of the classics of probability theory. There are more general definitions, appropriate for different levels of application or abstraction, but the one given is the best for our purposes.

Return to Problem 15A. What we must do is calculate the probability of each of the two events described there, and then compare these two probabilities. There are two different experiments involved in Problem 15A, one consisting of four throws of a single die, the other consisting of twenty-four throws of a pair of dice. In order to compute the relevant probabilities, we must first of all count (or compute) the number of possible outcomes for each of these experiments. Because these computations, as well as those used to get the number of outcomes corresponding to the events in which we are interested, will be easier to carry out once we have a systematic counting technique, we shall wait until Section 16 to complete this problem; it could be carried out now as an exercise, of course. The important point is that in calculating probabilities of the kind we are considering, one must compute two numbers, N and $n(E)$, and if the problem is complicated, this will be virtually impossible unless one has available some basic formulas and procedures. The next three sections are devoted to developing some of these formulas and procedures; they form the basis of what is known as combinatorial analysis. After that, we shall be ready to finish Problem 15A and then look at Problems 15B and 15C.

PROBLEM SET 15

PROBLEM 15.1. A number is formed by arranging the digits 1, 2, 3 in random order. (a) List the possible outcomes. (b) What is the probability that the number selected is greater than 100? greater than 200? greater than 220? greater than 330?

PROBLEM 15.2. A word is selected randomly from the sentence *The sky is blue*. What is the probability that the number of letters in the selected word is:
(a) 2?   (b) 3?
(c) 5?   (d) less than 5?

PROBLEM 15.3. What is the probability of obtaining a vowel (a, e, i, o, u) if one letter is chosen at random from the English alphabet?

PROBLEM 15.4. A three-volume set of books is placed on a shelf in random order. What is the probability that the books are in the proper order (from left to right)?

PROBLEM 15.5. Assume a pair of dice is thrown. List the thirty-six possible outcomes ((1, 1), (1, 2), and so forth), and then compute the probability of each of the following events.
(a) Double 4 is obtained.
(b) Neither die falls 3.
(c) Neither 3 nor 4 appears.
(d) Each die shows more than 3.
(e) At least one die shows more than 3.
(f) Only one die shows more than 3.

(g) The two numbers showing are different.

(h) The sum is greater than 12.

(i) The sum is a prime number.

PROBLEM 15.6. What are the probabilities of obtaining each of the sums 2 through 12 if two dice are thrown? What is the sum of these probabilities?

PROBLEM 15.7. A number is chosen randomly from the set {17, 18, 19, 20, 21, 22}.

(a) What is the probability that it is even?

(b) What is the probability that the sum of the digits is even?

(c) What is the probability that either the number is even or the sum of its digits is even, or both?

(d) The probability in (c) is not the sum of the probabilities in (a) and (b). Why?

PROBLEM 15.8. A card is selected randomly from an ordinary bridge deck. Compute the probability of each of the following events.

(a) The card is a spade.

(b) The card is not a spade.

(c) The card is an ace.

(d) The card is not an ace.

(e) The card is red.

(f) The card is a jack, queen, or king.

PROBLEM 15.9. Assume that in families with three children all of the eight arrangements *GGG, GGB, GBG, . . . , BBB* are equally likely; where, for example, *GGB* denotes that the oldest is a girl, the next is also a girl, and the youngest is a boy. Compute the probability of each of the following events.

(a) There is exactly one boy.

(b) There is at least one boy.

(c) There is at most one boy.

(d) All are girls.

(e) The number of boys is the same as the number of girls.

(f) The oldest is a boy.

(g) There is no boy older than a girl.

(h) There is no boy older than a girl and no girl older than a boy.

PROBLEM 15.10. (a) through (h). Same as Problem 15.9 with three children replaced by four children. There will be sixteen possible arrangements in this case; begin by listing them all.

PROBLEM 15.11. Two events associated with an experiment are said to be *mutually exclusive* if none of the possible outcomes corresponding to one of the events also corresponds to the other event. Thus in selecting a number from {1, 2, 3, 4}, the event 'the number is more than 3' and the event 'the number is less than 3' are mutually exclusive; the event 'the number is at least 3' and the event 'the number is at most 3' are not mutually exclusive.

(a) List all pairs of mutually exclusive events from among the four events in Example 15.1.

(b) List all pairs of mutually exclusive events from among the four events in Example 15.2.

(c) Note that if A and B are mutually exclusive events, then $n(A \text{ or } B) = n(a) + n(b)$. ($A$ or B means A or B or both; we shall always use 'or' in this inclusive sense, as opposed to the exclusive A or B but not both.) Show that if A and B are mutually exclusive events, then $\Pr(A \text{ or } B) = \Pr(A) + \Pr(B)$.

(d) Give an example of events E and F that are not mutually exclusive, and verify that $\Pr(E \text{ or } F) \neq \Pr(E) + \Pr(F)$ (see Problem 15.7, for instance).

PROBLEM 15.12. If E denotes an event associated with an experiment, then the *complementary event* of E is the event determined by all possible outcomes other than those corresponding to E; denote it by E'. Thus if E is the event 'obtain an even number' in the experiment of throwing a die, then E' is the event 'obtain an odd number' in the same experiment.

(a) What are the complements of the events in Example 15.1?

(b) What are the complements of the events in Example 15.2?

(c) What is $n(E')$ in terms of N and $n(E)$?

(d) Show that $\Pr(E) + \Pr(E') = 1$, for every event E.

(e) In the experiment of throwing a die three times, what is the complement of the event 'obtain at least one 6'? What is the probability of this complementary event? What is the probability of obtaining at least one 6?

(f) Are complementary events always mutually exclusive? Are mutually exclusive events always complementary? (See Problem 15.11.)

PROBLEM 15.13. Imagine a game in which a player either wins, in which case he receives a certain prize, or loses, in which case he receives nothing. The player's *mathematical expectation* for such a game is defined to be his probability of winning times the value of the prize. This can be thought of as the reasonable amount to pay for the privilege of playing. For example, in 100 rounds of coin tossing with prize $1 for each tail, a player can reasonably expect to win $50, or, on the average, $0.50 (the mathematical expectation) per round.

(a) If a die is to be thrown once and a prize of $3 is to be awarded if it turns up 6, what is the mathematical expectation?

(b) What is the mathematical expectation in part (a) if every even number wins?

(c) How much should a gambling house charge for each turn at a certain game if the player has probability 1/5 of winning, the prize is $10, and the house wants a profit of $0.50 per turn on the average?

(d) If mortality tables show that of each 1000 males of age sixty, 980 will live more than one year (on the average), what is a reasonable price for a man to pay for a one year term life insurance policy (ignoring interest and insurance company expenses)?

(e) Would you pay $1 for a chance to win $1,000,000 if your chances of winning were only one in five million? Compute the relevant mathematical expectation. (Be honest—lotteries thrive because commercial value can exceed mathematical expectation.)

(f) Would you pay $10,000 for a chance to win $100,000 if your chance of winning were one in five? Compute the relevant mathematical expectation. (The point here is the opposite of that in (e)—mathematical expectation can exceed commercial value. Of course, your answer here may depend on how much $10,000 means to you.)

(The notion of mathematical expectation began with Huygens. It can be generalized beyond the definition given here; see Problem 19.8. After Pascal had given up the worldly for the religious life, he gave a 'practical' application of mathematical expectation in Section 3 of *Pensées*: No matter how small one might think the probability of immortality, the reward is infinite, and thus the expectation is infinite, any small number times infinity being infinity; therefore any sacrifice for the religious life is justified.)

§16. A Counting Principle

As indicated at the end of the previous section, if we are to be able to determine probabilities then we must learn how to count. We begin this process by illustrating a systematic method for counting, which we shall use to obtain a basic counting principle. We shall then finish Problem 15A.

If a coin is tossed twice, the possible outcomes are

$$H\,H$$
$$H\,T$$
$$T\,H$$
$$T\,T,$$

where $H\,H$ indicates two heads, $H\,T$ indicates first a head and then a tail, and so forth. Although it is not necessary in an example as simple as this one, it is often useful to indicate the possible outcomes of such an experiment by means of a 'tree'. Here are several examples to illustrate the idea.

EXAMPLE 16.1. For two tosses of a coin, the relevant tree is shown in Figure 16.1. The H and T in the first column (reading from the left) indicate the

Figure 16.1

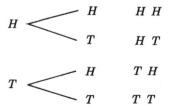

possibilities for the first toss, and the H's and T's in the second column indicate the possibilities for the second toss corresponding to the different possible outcomes on the first toss. By following the different paths through the tree, we get all possible outcomes, as indicated in the right-hand column.

EXAMPLE 16.2. Figure 16.2 shows the tree for the experiment of tossing a coin three times, the eight possible outcomes being listed to the right.

Figure 16.2

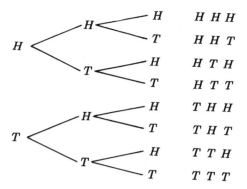

EXAMPLE 16.3. Assume that students in three departments, English, History, and Philosophy, are to be classified according to sex (M, F), year (1, 2, 3, 4), and department (E, H, P). How many different categories are possible?

The complete list of possibilities can be read from the tree in Figure 16.3. For each sex there are 4 possible years, and then 3 possible departments for each of these. Thus altogether there are $2 \cdot 4 \cdot 3 = 24$ different categories.

EXAMPLE 16.4. In how many different ways can three people (A, B, C) be seated in a row?

There are $3 \cdot 2 = 6$ different possible arrangements, as listed to the right of the tree in Figure 16.4.

Thinking about the tree corresponding to an experiment can be helpful even when the size of a problem makes it impractical to write the tree out in full.

EXAMPLE 16.5. In how many different ways can ten persons (A_1, A_2, ..., A_{10}) be seated in a row?

Generalizing from the previous example, we can see that here the relevant tree would have each of A_1 through A_{10} in the first column, and for each of these there would be nine possibilities in the second column, and so on, until altogether there would be $10 \cdot 9 \cdot 8 \cdot 7 \cdot 6 \cdot 5 \cdot 4 \cdot 3 \cdot 2 \cdot 1 = 3,628,800$ different paths through the tree. This then is the number of possible seating arrangements.

These examples lead us to the following counting principle.

BASIC COUNTING PRINCIPLE

If one thing can be done in any of n_1 ways, and after it has been done in any of these ways a second thing can be done in any of n_2 ways, and after any of these a third thing can be done in any of n_3 ways, and so on until we get to a kth thing which can be done in any of n_k ways, then the k things can be done together in $n_1 \cdot n_2 \cdot n_3 \cdots n_k$ different ways.

The relevant tree would have k columns, with n_1 places in the first column, and so forth.

Figure 16.3

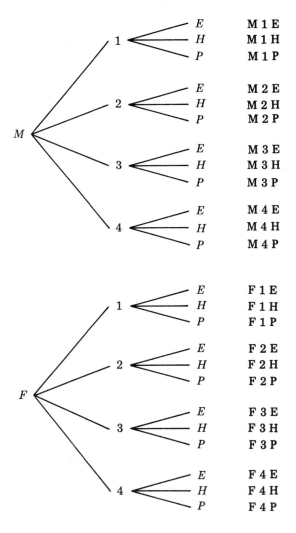

Figure 16.4

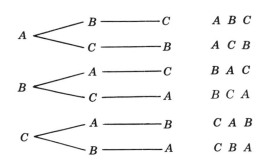

Solution of Problem 15A

We can now complete the solution of Problem 15A. Let N_1 denote the number of possible outcomes for four throws of a single die, and let E_1 denote the event of obtaining at least one 6 in this experiment. There are six different ways the die can fall on each throw, and so the number of possible outcomes for four throws is $6 \cdot 6 \cdot 6 \cdot 6$, by the Basic Counting Principle. That is, $N_1 = 6^4$. These 6^4 different outcomes can be divided into two classes: those involving at least one 6, and those involving no 6's. The number of outcomes involving no 6's is just the number of possible outcomes there would be if only the numbers 1, 2, 3, 4, 5 were available on each throw, that is, 5^4. Therefore $n(E_1) = 6^4 - 5^4$. Thus

$$\Pr(E_1) = \frac{n(E_1)}{N_1} = \frac{6^4 - 5^4}{6^4} = 1 - \left(\tfrac{5}{6}\right)^4.$$

Let N_2 denote the number of possible outcomes for twenty-four throws of a pair of dice, and let E_2 denote the event of obtaining at least one (6, 6). There are thirty-six different possible outcomes on each throw of the pair of dice, and so in twenty-four throws there are 36^{24} different possible outcomes: $N_2 = 36^{24}$. The number of outcomes involving no (6, 6)'s is just the number of possible outcomes there would be if only the thirty-five pairs other than (6, 6) were available on each throw. Therefore $n(E_2) = 36^{24} - 35^{24}$. Thus

$$\Pr(E_2) = \frac{n(E_2)}{N_2} = \frac{36^{24} - 35^{24}}{36^{24}} = 1 - \left(\tfrac{35}{36}\right)^{24}.$$

If these probabilities are converted to decimal form, they become

$$\Pr(E_1) = 0.5177 \quad \text{and} \quad \Pr(E_2) = 0.4913,$$

approximately. The first, which is 671/1296, can be done directly; for the second a computer or logarithms can be used. Thus the first event does have probability slightly greater than 0.5, and the second does have probability slightly less than 0.5, as originally claimed. The gamblers' rule of thumb, which suggested that the two events should be equally probable, was simply not accurate. One last remark: if two dice are thrown twenty-five times, rather than twenty-four, then the probability of obtaining at least one (6, 6) becomes greater than 0.5, namely, approximately 0.5054.

PROBLEM SET 16

PROBLEM 16.1. Draw a tree showing the twelve possible outcomes of the two-part experiment: toss a coin (outcomes H or T), then roll a die (outcomes 1, 2, 3, 4, 5, or 6).

PROBLEM 16.2. Assume a pair of dice is thrown. Draw trees showing the possible outcomes corresponding to each of the following conditions.
(a) Sum of 3.   (b) Sum of 7.
(c) Both numbers even.

PROBLEM 16.3. Assume that three dice are thrown. Compute the probability of each of the following events.
(a) Three 4's are obtained.   (b) No 4's are obtained.
(c) The sum is 3.   (d) The sum is 4.
(e) The sum is 5.   (f) No two dice show the same number.

PROBLEM 16.4. How many different possible outcomes are there if a die is thrown four times? What is the probability of getting all 6's? What is the probability of getting 6 at least once?

PROBLEM 16.5. What is the probability of getting all questions correct on a ten question true-false exam if the questions are answered randomly? What is the probability of getting at least nine of the questions correct?

PROBLEM 16.6. Determine how many of the natural numbers between 9 and 100 (10, 11, 12, ... , 99) satisfy each of the following conditions.
(a) First digit even.   (b) Both digits even.
(c) Sum of digits even.   (d) Product of digits even.
(e) Both sum and product of digits even.

PROBLEM 16.7. (a) Two shoes are chosen randomly from the twelve shoes making up six distinguishable pairs. What is the probability the two shoes belong to a single pair?
(b) A left shoe and a right shoe are chosen randomly from six distinguishable pairs. What is the probability the two shoes belong to a single pair?

PROBLEM 16.8. (a) In how many different ways can six persons be seated in a row?
(b) In how many different ways can six persons be seated in a row if two of the persons insist on occupying adjacent seats?
(c) If the six persons making up three married couples are seated in a row, what is the probability that a particular man and wife will be in adjacent seats?
(d) If the six persons making up three married couples are seated in a row, what is the probability that a particular man and wife will be in seats that are not adjacent?

PROBLEM 16.9. Assume two letters are chosen randomly from the English alphabet, with replacement (that is, the second letter chosen is allowed to be the same as the first).
(a) What is the probability of obtaining no vowels (a, e, i, o, u)? (Suggestion: Think of the relevant tree.)
(b) What is the probability of obtaining at least one vowel?
(c) What is the probability of obtaining two vowels?
(d) Answer (a), (b), and (c) requiring the second letter to be different from the first.

PROBLEM 16.10. (a) In a city with east-west streets numbered 1, 2, 3, ... (in order, with 1 farthest south), and north-south streets lettered A, B, C, ...

(in order, with A farthest west), how many different six block routes are there from 1,A to 4,D?

(b) A route is chosen randomly from among those in part (a). What is the probability that it passes through 4,A?

(c) Same as (b) with 4,A replaced by 3,A.

(d) Same as (b) with 4,A replaced by 2,A.

(e) A route is chosen randomly from among those in part (a). If the route is known to pass through 2,D, what is the probability that it also passes through 1,D?

(f) Same as (e) with 1,D replaced by 3,D.

(g) Same as (e) with 2,D replaced by 2,C.

§17. A Counting Problem

To enable us to introduce and illustrate some notions that will be useful now and in Chapter IV, we shall prove a theorem about sets, Theorem 17.1. We must first make some definitions.

If S and T denote sets (collections) of elements (their members), then S is a *subset* of T if each element of S is an element of T.

EXAMPLE 17.1 (Subsets). (a) The set of even integers is a subset of the set of all integers.

(b) More generally, any set of integers is a subset of the set of all integers.

(c) Any set is a subset of itself.

(d) $\{x, y\}$ is a subset of $\{x, y, z\}$. (Here we have used the standard device of specifying sets by listing their elements in braces.)

It is convenient to introduce a set called the *empty* set, denoted ϕ (Greek letter phi), with the defining property that the statement

'x is an element of ϕ'

is false for every element x. Thus ϕ is a set containing no elements.

EXAMPLE 17.2 (Empty set). (a) The set of all integers that are both positive and negative is ϕ.

(b) ϕ is a subset of every set.

The property of ϕ stated in (b) is perhaps most easily understood by using this (equivalent) definition of subset: S is a subset of T if each element not in T is also not in S.

By the *power set* of a set S we mean the set of all subsets of S. So the elements of a power set are sets.

EXAMPLE 17.3 (Power sets). (a) The power set of the set $\{x\}$ is the set $\{\phi, \{x\}\}$.

(b) The power set of the set $\{x, y\}$ is the set $\{\phi, \{x\}, \{y\}, \{x, y\}\}$.

From Example 17.3 it can be seen that if a set contains 1 element, then its power set contains 2 elements; if a set contains 2 elements, its power set contains 4 elements. Our goal is to prove the following more general fact.

THEOREM 17.1

If a finite set contains n elements, then its power set contains 2^n elements.

To start with, consider a set with 3 elements, say $\{x, y, z\}$. We can list the subsets of this set systematically as follows:

> Row 0: ϕ
> Row 1: $\{x\}$ $\{y\}$ $\{z\}$
> Row 2: $\{x, y\}$ $\{x, z\}$ $\{y, z\}$
> Row 3: $\{x, y, z\}$.

Here Row 0 lists the only subset containing 0 elements, Row 1 all 1-element subsets, Row 2 all 2-element subsets, and Row 3 the only 3-element subset. In order to count the number of elements in the power set of $\{x, y, z\}$, we can simply count the number of subsets in each row, and then add the results. We get $1 + 3 + 3 + 1 = 8 = 2^3$, as claimed. This illustrates the basic plan we shall use in the general case.

Assume then that we are given a set S containing n elements (n being some natural number). We can list the elements in the power set of S systematically by writing Rows 0 through n, putting ϕ in Row 0, all the 1-element subsets of S in Row 1 (there will be n of these), all the 2-element subsets of S in Row 2, and so forth, until we get to Row n, which will contain the only n-element subset of S, namely S itself. Now, as in the special case illustrated above, we could get the number of elements in the power set of S by counting the number of sets in each row and then adding the results. In order to do this we would need a formula for the number of subsets in the various rows of our diagram, and then we would need to add these various numbers. It turns out that we can get the sum of the number of subsets in all the rows without finding explicitly the number of subsets in the different rows, as we now show.

We shall use the symbol $C(n, k)$ to denote the number of subsets in Row k of our diagram. Let us formalize this definition.

DEFINITION

$C(n, k)$ will denote the number of k-element subsets of a set containing n elements. (Here n is a natural number and k is one of the integers $0, 1, \ldots, n$.)

EXAMPLE 17.4. By looking at the special case of a set with 3 elements dissected above, we see that $C(3, 0) = 1$, $C(3, 1) = 3$, $C(3, 2) = 3$, $C(3, 3) = 1$. It is clear that $C(n, 0) = 1$ for each n, $C(n, 1) = n$ for each n, and $C(n, n) = 1$ for each n. Later we shall obtain a formula for $C(n, k)$ in terms of n and k.

The notation $_nC_k$ or C_k^n or $\binom{n}{k}$ is sometimes used for our $C(n, k)$.
The various numbers $C(n, k)$ are called *binomial coefficients*, for reasons
that will become clear shortly.

To return to our problem, we see that what we computed to get the
number of elements in the power set of $\{x, y, z\}$ was

$$C(3, 0) + C(3, 1) + C(3, 2) + C(3, 3).$$

What we need to compute to get the number of elements in the power set
of a set with n elements is

$$C(n, 0) + C(n, 1) + \cdots + C(n, n).$$

Because we have to digress slightly to solve this problem, we set it off for
later reference.

PROBLEM 17A. Compute

$$C(n, 0) + C(n, 1) + \cdots + C(n, n).$$

We now discuss another way of looking at the numbers $C(n, k)$.
First, recall from elementary algebra that if a and b stand for any
numbers, then

$$(a + b)^2 = (a + b)(a + b) = a(a + b) + b(a + b)$$
$$= aa + ab + ba + bb$$
$$= a^2 + 2ab + b^2,$$

and

$$(a + b)^3 = (a + b)(a + b)(a + b)$$
$$= aaa + aab + aba + abb$$
$$+ baa + bab + bba + bbb$$
$$= a^3 + a^2b + a^2b + ab^2$$
$$+ a^2b + ab^2 + ab^2 + b^3$$
$$= a^3 + 3a^2b + 3ab^2 + b^3.$$

The important thing here is that we need all products of a's and b's that
can be obtained by choosing one letter from each of the factors $a + b$;
we then combine products that are equal (such as aab, aba, baa).

More generally, the expansion of $(a + b)^n$ will have the form

$$(a + b)^n = ?a^n + ?a^{n-1}b + ?a^{n-2}b^2 + \cdots + ?ab^{n-1} + ?b^n,$$

where the ?'s are coefficients to be computed. Here each term has the
form $?a^k b^{n-k}$. Notice $k + (n - k) = n$, that is, the sum of the powers on a
and b is n for each term. The term $a^k b^{n-k}$ is obtained by selecting a from k
of the factors, and b from the remaining $n - k$ factors. The number of
different ways of doing this is just the number of ways of selecting the k
factors from which the a's will be taken, that is, the number of k-element
subsets of a set with n elements (the n different factors $(a + b)$). Thus
the coefficient for $a^n b^{n-k}$ is $C(n, k)$.

ILLUSTRATION. To find the coefficient for a^2b^2 in the expansion of $(a + b)^4$, we must determine the number of ways that terms identically equal to a^2b^2 can arise from using one factor from each occurrence of $(a + b)$ in $(a + b)(a + b)(a + b)(a + b)$. There are six ways:

aabb	*baab*
abab	*baba*
abba	*bbaa.*

We have a set with 4 elements (the 4 factors $(a + b)$), and each of the six products corresponds to a different 2-element subset of that set: *aabb* corresponds to the subset consisting of first and second factors, *baab* to the subset consisting of the second and third factors, and so forth. Thus the coefficient for a^2b^2 is 6; but more important conceptually, it is $C(4, 2)$.

We have proved the following theorem.

BINOMIAL THEOREM
If n is a positive integer, then

$$(a + b)^n = C(n, n)a^n + C(n, n - 1)a^{n-1}b + C(n, n - 2)a^{n-2}b^2 + \cdots + C(n, k)a^kb^{n-k} + \cdots + C(n, 2)a^2b^{n-2} + C(n, 1)ab^{n-1} + C(n, 0)b^n.$$

EXAMPLE 17.5. In the case $n = 4$, the Binomial Theorem becomes

$$(a + b)^4 = C(4, 4)a^4 + C(4, 3)a^3b + C(4, 2)a^2b^2 + C(4, 1)ab^3 + C(4, 0)b^4.$$

Problem 17.6 suggests how to determine the binomial coefficients appearing here.

Now return to Problem 17A. To solve it without an appropriate tool can be a chore—with the Binomial Theorem at our disposal it becomes a triviality. We simply notice that the numbers we want to sum are the coefficients on the right-hand side of the equality sign in the Binomial Theorem. If we let $a = 1$ and $b = 1$ (recall the theorem is true for all numbers a and b), then the terms a^kb^{n-k} become $1^k1^{n-k} = 1 \cdot 1 = 1$ for each k. We then get

$$(1 + 1)^n = C(n, n) \cdot 1 + C(n, n - 1) \cdot 1 + \cdots + C(n, 0) \cdot 1,$$

or, reversing the order on the right-hand side,

$$2^n = C(n, 0) + C(n, 1) + \cdots + C(n, n).$$

We have therefore solved Problem 17A and proved Theorem 17.1.
We close this section by using this Basic Counting Principle to give a different proof of Theorem 17.1. Recall that the proof given above was chosen for the ideas it brought together, and not for its brevity.

EXAMPLE 17.6. To count the number of different subsets of the set {1, 2, 3, ..., n}, we can think of the elements as being lined up in the order given, and realize that in forming a subset we must make n decisions:

include 1 in the subset, or not
include 2 in the subset, or not

· · ·

include n in the subset, or not.

By the Basic Counting Principle, the total number of different ways we can make these n decisions, having 2 choices for each one, is

$$2 \cdot 2 \cdot 2 \cdot 2 \cdot \cdots 2 \ (n \text{ factors}),$$

that is, 2^n.

We can make a tree for the case $n = 3$ by using Y for Yes and N for No (Figure 17.1). Thus Y in the first column indicates that 1 will go in the subset, and N in the first column indicates that 1 will not go in the subset, and so forth. The subsets corresponding to the different paths are shown at the right. Notice the similarity with Example 16.2.

Figure 17.1

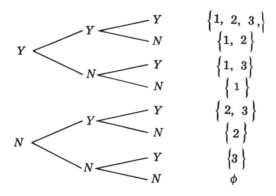

PROBLEM SET 17

PROBLEM 17.1. (a) Write out the power set of {A, B}.
(b) Write out the power set of the power set of {A, B}.

PROBLEM 17.2. (a) If a set S consists of 5 elements, how many elements are in the power set of S?
(b) With S as in part (a), how many elements are in the power set of the power set of S?

PROBLEM 17.3. An element is chosen randomly from the power set of {x, y, z}.
(a) What is the probability it is ϕ?
(b) What is the probability it contains x?
(c) What is the probability it contains x and y?
(d) What is the probability it contains only x and y?
(e) What is the probability it contains at least two elements?
(f) What is the probability it contains exactly two elements?

PROBLEM 17.4.   A set is chosen randomly from among those subsets of $\{x, y, z\}$ that contain x.
(a) What is the probability it is $\{x, y\}$?
(b) What is the probability it contains y?
(c) What is the probability it contains at least two elements?

PROBLEM 17.5.   Which of the following are subsets of the power set of $\{x, y, z\}$? (Note that if w is an element of a set S, then $\{w\}$ is a subset of S, $\{w\}$ is an element of the power set of S, and $\{\{w\}\}$ is a subset of the power set of S.)

(a) x (b) $\{x\}$ (c) $\{\{x\}\}$
(d) ϕ (e) $\{\{x\}, y\}$ (f) $\{\{x\}, \{y\}\}$
(g) $\{x, y, z\}$ (h) $\{\phi\}$ (i) $\{\{x, y, z\}\}$

PROBLEM 17.6.   Write the elements of the power set of $\{x, y, z, w\}$, and then find $C(4, k)$ for each of $k = 0, 1, 2, 3,$ and 4.

PROBLEM 17.7.   Use the results of Problem 17.6 to write $(a + b)^4$. (See Example 17.5.)

PROBLEM 17.8.   (a) List all 2-element subsets of $\{v, w, x, y, z\}$. What is $C(5, 2)$?
(b) List all 3-element subsets of $\{v, w, x, y, z\}$. What is $C(5, 3)$?

PROBLEM 17.9.   If n and k are integers with $n \geq k \geq 0$, then $C(n, k) = C(n, n - k)$. Why?

PROBLEM 17.10.   (a) Write the Binomial Theorem in the special case $n = 6$.
(b) Write the Binomial Theorem in the special case $n = 7$.

PROBLEM 17.11   (a) How many terms are in the expansion of $(a + b)^{50}$?
(b) What is the sum of the coefficients in the expansion of $(a + b)^{50}$?

PROBLEM 17.12.   (a) Show that $C(2, 2) - C(2, 1) + C(2, 0) = 0$.
(b) Show that $C(3, 3) - C(3, 2) + C(3, 1) - C(3, 0) = 0$.
(c) What is $C(n, n) - C(n, n - 1) + C(n, n - 2) - + \cdots \pm C(n, 0)$? Why? (Suggestion: Compute $(1 + (-1))^n$.)
(d) What is $C(10, 10)2^{10} + C(10, 9)2^9 + C(10, 8)2^8 + \cdots + C(10, k)2^k + \cdots + C(10, 0)$?

§18. Combinations and Permutations

To answer Problems 15B and 15C, and others like them, we shall need more information about the binomial coefficients $C(n, k)$ and some related numbers $P(n, k)$, to be defined below.   Before presenting this information we look at two critical questions related to counting problems:
1.   Does the order in which elements are chosen (or things are arranged, or events happen) matter?
2.   Is repetition allowed?   That is, can a given element be chosen or used more than once?

EXAMPLE 18.1.   To emphasize the importance of order and repetition, consider the possible ways of selecting 2 letters from A, B, and C.

(a) Order matters and repetition allowed:

$$AA, \; AB, \; AC, \; BA, \; BB, \; BC, \; CA, \; CB, \; CC.$$

(Here we list *AA*, *BB*, and *CC* because repetition is allowed. And we list both *AB* and *BA*, for instance, because they give *A* and *B* in different orders, and order matters.)

(b) Order matters and repetition not allowed:

$$AB, \; AC, \; BA, \; BC, \; CA, \; CB.$$

(c) Order does not matter and repetition allowed:

$$AA, \; AB, \; AC, \; BB, \; BC, \; CC.$$

(d) Order does not matter and repetition not allowed:

$$AB, \; AC, \; BC.$$

EXAMPLE 18.2.
(a) How many different hands of 13 cards can be selected from a bridge deck of 52 cards?
(b) In how many ways can 5 people be seated in a row?
(c) How many different sets of initials can be formed if it is assumed that each person has a family name and two given names?

Parts (b) and (c) here can be answered fairly easily by looking at the appropriate trees; (a) is trickier conceptually as well as computationally. But at the moment we are interested only in determining when order and repetition make a difference. In (a) the order in which the cards are chosen does not matter; in (b) the order in which the people are arranged is the only thing that does matter; in (c) the order in which the three initials are arranged does matter. In (a) repetition is not allowed (a card cannot occur twice in the same hand); in (b) repetition is not allowed (each person occupies only one seat); in (c) repetition is allowed (*DCD* is a permissible set of initials). (The answers are: (a) $C(52, 13)$; (b) $5 \cdot 4 \cdot 3 \cdot 2 \cdot 1 = 120$; (c) 26^3.)

EXAMPLE 18.3.
(a) In how many ways can 3 officers, President, Vice-President, and Secretary, be selected from a club with 10 members?
(b) In how many ways can a 3-member committee be selected from a club with 10 members? (In other words, what is $C(10, 3)$?)

We shall analyze these two questions in detail, and then use the same counting arguments to obtain two general formulas. First notice that order matters in (a) but not in (b). (Having Smith as President, Jones as Vice-President, and Doe as Secretary, is not the same as having Doe as President, Jones as Vice-President, and Smith as Secretary, for example. But the committee {Smith, Jones, Doe} is the same as the committee {Doe, Jones, Smith}.) Repetition is not allowed in either (a) or (b).

For (a), we can first elect a President, and there are 10 possible choices for this. We can then elect a Vice-President, and there are 9 possible choices for this after the President has been chosen. Finally, there remain 8 possible choices for Secretary. Therefore there are $10 \cdot 9 \cdot 8$ ($= 720$) different ways of filling the 3 offices.

To solve (b), we make use of a very useful counting device: we count one thing in two different ways, and get something else as a by-product. In the present case, we shall solve (a) in two different ways, and get the answer to (b) as a by-product.

We have already solved (a) by one method; here is a second. Instead of electing the 3 officers directly, suppose we elect a slate of 3, not specifying who will be President, and so on, but simply agreeing that the persons on the slate will be the officers, in a way to be agreed on among themselves. This method still allows for the same number of possibilities as the first method, but is conceptually different for counting purposes. (We ignore the fact that it also may be different politically.) To compute the number of possibilities by the second method, use the Basic Counting Principle with two steps: first count the number of ways of selecting 3 members from 10 (this is $C(10, 3)$), then count the number of ways the 3 chosen members can be given the 3 different offices, then multiply. The number of ways 3 members can be given the 3 different offices is $3 \cdot 2 \cdot 1$ ($= 6$) (any of 3 for President, then any of the remaining 2 for Vice-President, then the remaining 1 for Secretary). Thus this second method gives the answer to (a) as $C(10, 3) \cdot 3 \cdot 2 \cdot 1$.

Again, the two methods must give the same number, that is, we must have

$$C(10, 3) \cdot 3 \cdot 2 \cdot 1 = 10 \cdot 9 \cdot 8.$$

Therefore

$$C(10, 3) = \frac{10 \cdot 9 \cdot 8}{3 \cdot 2 \cdot 1} = 120$$

and (b) has been answered.

We now generalize the two parts of Example 18.3 to obtain the two formulas promised. First we make two definitions.

DEFINITION

An arrangement of k different elements, selected from a set of n elements, is called a permutation *of n objects taken k at a time. We denote the number of such permutations by P(n, k).*

DEFINITION

A selection of k different elements from a set of n elements, without regard to order, is called a combination *of n objects taken k at a time. The number of such combinations is the number C(n, k).*

In Example 18.3(a) we computed $P(10, 3)$, and in Example 18.3(b) we computed $C(10, 3)$. Now we apply the same ideas to compute $P(n, k)$ and $C(n, k)$ for general n and k (k not larger than n).

To obtain $P(n, k)$, we want to count the ways of selecting k different things from n things, taking order into account. There are n possibilities for the first choice, then $n - 1$ for the second, then $n - 2$

for the third, and so on until we have made k choices. There will be $n - k + 1$ possibilities for the kth choice, and therefore we have

$$P(n, k) = n(n - 1)(n - 2) \cdots (n - k + 1).$$

To obtain $C(n, k)$, we compute $P(n, k)$ by another method, just as we did in the special case of Example 18.3(b). Thus in order to get $P(n, k)$ we can think first of selecting k elements from n without regard to order (this can be done in $C(n, k)$ different ways), and then realize that the elements in each of these k-element subsets can be arranged in $k(k - 1)(k - 2) \cdots 1$ different ways (arguing just as in Example 18.3(b)). Thus

$$C(n, k) \cdot k(k - 1)(k - 2) \cdots 1 = P(n, k),$$

and so

$$C(n, k) = \frac{P(n, k)}{k(k - 1)(k - 2) \cdots 1}$$

or

$$C(n, k) = \frac{n(n - 1)(n - 2) \cdots (n - k + 1)}{k(k - 1)(k - 2) \cdots 1}.$$

EXAMPLE 18.4.

$$P(5, 2) = 5 \cdot 4 = 20$$

$$P(20, 3) = 20 \cdot 19 \cdot 18 = 6840$$

$$C(5, 2) = \frac{5 \cdot 4}{2 \cdot 1} = 10$$

$$C(20, 3) = \frac{20 \cdot 19 \cdot 18}{3 \cdot 2 \cdot 1} = 1140$$

$$P(100, 22) = 100 \cdot 99 \cdot 98 \cdot \cdots 79.$$

In order to be able to write these formulas in a more compact form, we make another definition.

DEFINITION

If n is a positive integer, we define $n!$ (read n factorial) to be

$$n(n - 1)(n - 2) \cdots 1.$$

EXAMPLE 18.5.

$$1! = 1$$
$$2! = 2 \cdot 1 = 2$$
$$3! = 3 \cdot 2 \cdot 1 = 6$$
$$4! = 4 \cdot 3 \cdot 2 \cdot 1 = 24$$
$$5! = 5 \cdot 4 \cdot 3 \cdot 2 \cdot 1 = 120$$
$$10! = 3,628,800$$
$$20! = 2,432,902,008,176,640,000$$

Notice that if n is an integer greater than 1, then $n! = n \cdot (n-1)!$. In order to make this true for n = 1 (and to make some formulas simpler), we *define* 0! by 0! = 1.

Returning now to $P(n, k)$ and $C(n, k)$, we can write

$$P(n, k) = n(n-1) \cdots (n-k+1)$$

$$= \frac{n(n-1) \cdots (n-k+1)(n-k)(n-k-1) \cdots 1}{(n-k)(n-k-1) \cdots 1}$$

$$= \frac{n!}{(n-k)!}$$

and

$$C(n, k) = \frac{n(n-1) \cdots (n-k+1)}{k!}$$

$$= \frac{n(n-1) \cdots (n-k+1)(n-k)(n-k-1) \cdots 1}{k! \, (n-k)(n-k-1) \cdots 1}$$

$$= \frac{n!}{k! \, (n-k)!}$$

Formulas for Permutations and Combinations

$$P(n, k) = \frac{n!}{(n-k)!} \qquad C(n, k) = \frac{n!}{k! \, (n-k)!}$$

We can use this formula for the $C(n, k)$ to obtain several interesting and frequently useful facts about these numbers.

EXAMPLE 18.6. $C(n, n-k) = C(n, k)$, for $0 \le k \le n$.

Proof

Using $n - k$ in place of k in the formula for $C(n, k)$ gives

$$C(n, n-k) = \frac{n!}{(n-k)! \, (n-(n-k))!}$$

$$= \frac{n!}{(n-k)! \, k!}$$

$$= \frac{n!}{k! \, (n-k)!}$$

$$= C(n, k). \quad \square$$

For example, $C(5, 3) = C(5, 2)$ and $C(100, 73) = C(100, 27)$.

We can get another proof here just by remembering that $C(n, k)$ denotes the number of k-element subsets of an n-element set, and there is the same number of $(n - k)$-element subsets as k-element subsets (for the set of elements omitted from an $(n - k)$-element subset forms a k-element subset).

EXAMPLE 18.7. Expand $(a + b)^5$.

We use the Binomial Theorem (Section 17), and need $C(5, 0)$, $C(5, 1)$, ..., $C(5, 5)$. But by Example 18.6, $C(5, 5) = C(5, 0)$, $C(5, 4) = C(5, 1)$, and $C(5, 3) = C(5, 2)$, and so it suffices to compute $C(5, 0)$, $C(5, 1)$, and $C(5, 2)$. We already know that $C(5, 0) = 1$ and $C(5, 1) = 5$ (see Example 17.4), and we get $C(5, 2) = \dfrac{5!}{2! \, 3!} = 10$. Therefore

$$(a + b)^5 = a^5 + 5a^4b + 10a^3b^2 + 10a^2b^3 + 5ab^4 + b^5.$$

EXAMPLE 18.8. $C(n + 1, k) = C(n, k - 1) + C(n, k)$, for $0 \leq k \leq n$.

First Proof

Let S be a set with $n + 1$ elements $x_1, \ldots, x_{n+1}$. $C(n + 1, k)$ is the number of k-element subsets of S, and these can be divided into two classes, those which do contain x_1, and those which do not. There are $C(n, k - 1)$ of the first kind (the number of ways we can choose $k - 1$ elements from $x_2, \ldots, x_n$), and $C(n, k)$ of the second kind (the number of ways we can choose k elements from $x_2, \ldots, x_n$). Adding these we get what we set out to prove. $\square$

Second Proof

$C(n, k - 1) + C(n, k)$

$$= \frac{n!}{(k - 1)! \, (n - (k - 1))!} + \frac{n!}{k! \, (n - k)!}$$

$$= \frac{k(n!)}{k(k - 1)! \, (n - k + 1)!} + \frac{(n!)(n - k + 1)}{k! \, (n - k)! \, (n - k + 1)}$$

$$= \frac{k(n!) + (n - k + 1)(n!)}{k! \, (n - k + 1)!}$$

$$= \frac{(n + 1)(n!)}{k! \, (n - k + 1)!}$$

$$= \frac{(n + 1)!}{k! \, (n + 1 - k)!}$$

$$= C(n + 1, k). \quad \square$$

This formula provides a convenient scheme for computing binomial coefficients $C(n, k)$ for reasonably small n. This is given by the following triangle (Figure 18.1), named for Pascal but known to the Chinese at least three hundred years before his time.

Here $C(n, k)$ stands at the intersection of the nth row and the kth diagonal, and Example 18.8 tells us that each entry can be obtained by adding the numbers immediately to the left and right in the row above it. Notice that for the rows shown the sum of the numbers in the nth row is 2^n, in agreement with the result obtained in Section 17.

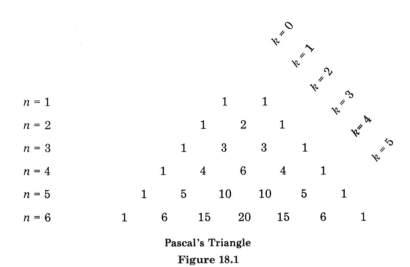

Pascal's Triangle

Figure 18.1

PROBLEM SET 18

PROBLEM 18.1. Compute each of the following.

(a) 6!   (b) 7!
(c) $P(7, 2)$ (d) $P(6, 3)$
(e) $P(5, 4)$ (f) $P(100, 2)$
(g) $C(7, 2)$ (h) $C(6, 3)$
(i) $C(52, 1)$ (j) $C(100, 2)$
(k) $P(100, 5)/C(100, 5)$ (l) $P(n, k)/C(n, k)$

PROBLEM 18.2. (a) What is the coefficient of $a^6 b^2$ in $(a + b)^8$?
(b) What is the coefficient of $a^7 b^{43}$ in $(a + b)^{50}$?
(c) What is the coefficient of $a^7 b^3$ in $(a + 2b)^{10}$?
(d) What is the coefficient of $x^7 y^3$ in $(x - 2y)^{10}$?
(e) What is the coefficient of $x^{10} y^6$ in $(x^2 + 2y^2)^8$?

PROBLEM 18.3. Write rows 7 and 8 of Pascal's triangle.

PROBLEM 18.4. (a) An organization contains 5 men and 5 women. In how many different ways can a 3-member committee be formed from the members of the organization?
(b) Do part (a), requiring at least one of each sex on the committee.

PROBLEM 18.5. How many ways are there of answering a ten question true-false examination if it is required that there be five true responses and five false responses?

PROBLEM 18.6. (a) How many different hands of 13 cards can be selected from a bridge deck of 52 cards?
(b) How many different hands of 13 cards, none of which is a spade, can be selected from a bridge deck of 52 cards?

(c) How many different hands of 13 cards, none of which is an ace, can be selected from a bridge deck of 52 cards?

(d) How many different hands of 13 cards, containing all four aces, can be selected from a bridge deck of 52 cards?

PROBLEM 18.7. A hand of 13 cards is chosen randomly from a bridge deck of 52 cards. Compute the probability of each of the following events.

(a) The hand contains no spades.

(b) The hand contains only spades.

(c) The hand contains no red cards.

(d) The hand contains only red cards.

(e) The hand contains no aces.

(f) The hand contains all four aces.

PROBLEM 18.8. Ninety lottery tickets are numbered from 1 to 90. Assume that two tickets are chosen at random from the ninety, without replacement. Compute the probability of each of the following events.

(a) Each of the tickets drawn has a number less than 10.

(b) Each of the tickets drawn has an even number.

(c) The first ticket has an even number and the second ticket has an odd number.

(d) One of the tickets has an even number and one of the tickets has an odd number.

(e) The number on the second ticket is one more than the number on the first ticket.

(f) The two numbers are consecutive.

PROBLEM 18.9. Ninety lottery tickets are numbered from 1 to 90. Assume that three tickets are chosen at random from the ninety, without replacement. Compute the probability of each of the following events.

(a) Each of the three tickets has a number less than 10.

(b) Each of the three tickets has an even number.

(c) The first two tickets have even numbers and the third ticket has an odd number.

(d) Two of the tickets have even numbers and one of the tickets has an odd number.

(e) The number on the second ticket is one more than the number on the first ticket, and the number on the third ticket is two more than the number on the first ticket.

(f) The three numbers are consecutive.

PROBLEM 18.10. Three tickets are drawn at random, without replacement, from a collection of lottery tickets numbered from 1 to n $(n \geq 3)$. What is the probability that the three numbers are consecutive? (Compare Problem 18.9(f).)

§19. Coin-Tossing Experiments

In Example 15.3 we computed probabilities for various events associated with three tosses of a coin. We now want to generalize that example to events associated with n tosses of a coin, where n is any positive integer. The importance of studying such coin-tossing experiments comes from their conceptual similarity with other experiments that may have nothing to do with coin tossing. Any experiment that consists of a sequence of trials, where each trial has only two possible equally likely outcomes (as H or T), is probabilistically the same as a coin-tossing experiment; examples are given in the problems. And we shall see in the next section that a much wider class of experiments can be analyzed with only slightly more general arguments. We begin by answering the following question.

PROBLEM 19A. What is the probability of obtaining exactly k heads in n tosses of a coin ($0 \leq k \leq n$)? (Assume the coin to be fair, so that the probability of a head on any single toss is $1/2$.)

Solution

The total number of possible outcomes is 2^n, a typical outcome being a sequence of H's and T's like $HHTH \cdots TH$. The number of these sequences corresponding to the event 'exactly k heads' is going to be the number of these sequences that contain exactly k H's, and this is just the number of different ways of specifying k particular places to put the H's (out of the n places); that is, it is $C(n, k)$. Therefore the probability of obtaining exactly k heads in n tosses of a coin is

$$\frac{C(n, k)}{2^n}.$$

Thus, for instance, in six tosses of a coin it follows, using the sixth row from Pascal's triangle (Section 18), that the probabilities of obtaining various numbers of heads are as follows.

TABLE 19.1

Six Tosses of a Coin	
Number of Heads	Probability
0	$1/2^6 = 0.0156$
1	$6/2^6 = 0.0938$
2	$15/2^6 = 0.2344$
3	$20/2^6 = 0.3125$
4	$15/2^6 = 0.2344$
5	$6/2^6 = 0.0938$
6	$1/2^6 = 0.0156$

These probabilities can be shown graphically by drawing a *histogram* in which the horizontal scale shows the various numbers of heads, and the area of the bar centered over each number shows the probability of getting exactly that many heads (Figure 19.1). (Equivalently, the heights of the bars show the probabilities, since the width of each bar is one unit. But for later purposes we want to emphasize the area.) Notice that the sum of the areas of these bars is 1.

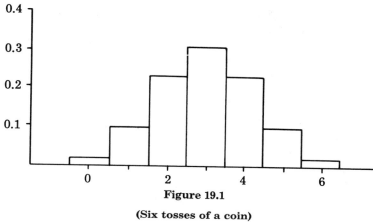

Figure 19.1

(Six tosses of a coin)

     When the number n becomes large, the computation of $C(n, k)/2^n$ becomes laborious, and so one uses a computer or logarithms or book of tables (such as [2] or [4]). It is then a routine matter to carry out the relevant computations. Here are the probabilities and corresponding histograms (Figures 19.2 and 19.3) for ten and twenty tosses of a coin.

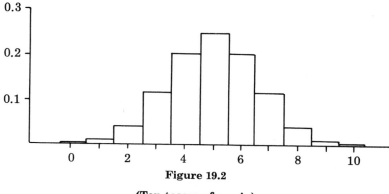

Figure 19.2

(Ten tosses of a coin)

     Now that we have the probability of obtaining *exactly* k heads in n tosses of a coin, it is easy to get the probability of obtaining *at least* (or *at most*) k heads in n tosses of a coin.

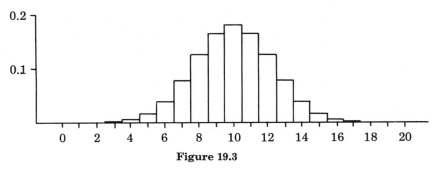

Figure 19.3

(Twenty tosses of a coin)

PROBLEM 19B. What is the probability of obtaining at least k heads in n tosses of a coin ($0 \leq k \leq n$)? (Again assume the coin to be fair.)

Solution

The total number of possible outcomes is still 2^n. The outcomes corresponding to 'at least k heads' are those which yield either k heads, or $k + 1$ heads, . . . , or n heads, and the number of these is

$$C(n, k) + C(n, k + 1) + \cdots + C(n, n).$$

Therefore the probability of obtaining *at least* k heads in n tosses of a coin is

$$[C(n, k) + C(n, k + 1) + \cdots + C(n, n)]/2^n.$$

Similarly, the probability of obtaining *at most* k heads in n tosses of a coin is

$$[C(n, 0) + C(n, 1) + \cdots + C(n, k)]/2^n.$$

EXAMPLE 19.1. The probability of obtaining at least 2 heads in 3 tosses of a coin is

$$[C(3, 2) + C(3, 3)]/2^3 = [3 + 1]/8 = 1/2$$

in agreement with Example 15.3.

Because the answer to Problem 19B can be written in the form

$$C(n, k)/2^n + C(n, k + 1)/2^n + \cdots + C(n, n)/2^n,$$

we see that the probability of obtaining at least k heads is the sum of the probabilities of obtaining k, or $k + 1$, . . . , or n heads. (Warning: One must use care in computing probabilities of complex events by adding the probabilities of simpler events. See Problem 15.11).

TABLE 19.2

Ten Tosses of a Coin	
Number of Heads	Probability
0	0.0010
1	0.0098
2	0.0439
3	0.1172
4	0.2051
5	0.2461
6	0.2051
7	0.1172
8	0.0439
9	0.0098
10	0.0010

TABLE 19.3

Twenty Tosses of a Coin	
Number of Heads	Probability*
0	0.0000
1	0.0000
2	0.0002
3	0.0011
4	0.0046
5	0.0148
6	0.0370
7	0.0739
8	0.1201
9	0.1602
10	0.1762
11	0.1602
12	0.1201
13	0.0739
14	0.0370
15	0.0148
16	0.0046
17	0.0011
18	0.0002
19	0.0000
20	0.0000

* The probabilities have been rounded to the fourth decimal place. The probability of 1 head is not exactly equal to zero, for instance; it is 0.000019073486328125.

EXAMPLE 19.2. Using Table 19.3, we see that the probability of obtaining at least 14 heads in 20 tosses of a coin is

$$0.0370 + 0.0148 + 0.0046 + 0.0011 + 0.0002 + 0.0000 + 0.0000,$$

or approximately 0.058. Thus if we toss a coin 20 times and obtain 14 or more heads, we observe an event that would happen only about 6 percent of the time in experiments with a fair coin. We might suspect that the coin is biased (not fair) in such a case, but of course we could not be sure.

We now see how to approach Problem 15B, which was: If a coin is tossed 10,000 times and 5,200 heads are obtained, is it reasonable to assume that the coin is not a fair one? We must test the hypothesis: The coin is fair. To do this we compute the probability of obtaining 5,200 or more heads in 10,000 tosses of a *fair* coin. If this probability turns out to be quite small, then we should reject our hypothesis. That is, it would then be reasonable to assume that the coin is biased. Of course the words 'small' and 'reasonable' are indefinite, but a probability can be small enough to be very convincing. The difficulty with the present problem is that the probability of 5,200 or more heads is

$$[C(10000, 5200) + C(10000, 5201) + \cdots + C(10000, 10000)]/2^{10000},$$

and unless one has an electronic computer, this offers an exceedingly nasty computational problem. For this reason we shall leave Problem 15B until Section 21; the theory we discuss there will yield an answer with a negligible amount of computation.

PROBLEM SET 19

PROBLEM 19.1. Compute the probability of each of the following events.
  (a) Obtaining exactly 4 heads in 7 tosses of a coin.
  (b) Obtaining exactly 3 heads in 8 tosses of a coin.
  (c) Obtaining exactly 6 tails in 8 tosses of a coin.
  (d) Obtaining at least 4 heads in 6 tosses of a coin.
  (e) Obtaining at least 8 heads in 10 tosses of a coin.
  (f) Obtaining at least 12 heads in 20 tosses of a coin.
  (g) Obtaining at most 12 heads in 20 tosses of a coin.
  (h) Obtaining at least 3 tails in 4 tosses of a coin.

PROBLEM 19.2. Compute the probability of obtaining at least 75 percent heads in each of the following cases.
  (a) Four tosses of a coin.
  (b) Eight tosses of a coin.
  (c) Twenty tosses of a coin.
  Compare the answers in (a), (b), and (c), and state, without calculation, whether you would expect the probability of at least 75 percent heads in 100 tosses of a coin to be greater than or less than the probabilities in these three cases. Why?

PROBLEM 19.3. What is the probability of getting exactly five questions correct on a ten-question true-false examination if the questions are answered randomly?

PROBLEM 19.4. (a) A fair coin is tossed twice. Draw the relevant tree. Given that the coin landed head on the first toss, what is the probability that it will land head on the second toss?
(b) A fair coin is tossed twenty times. Given that the coin landed head on each of the first nineteen tosses, what is the probability that it will land head on the twentieth toss? (A coin has no memory.)

PROBLEM 19.5. (a) through (h). Same as Problem 15.9 with three children replaced by ten children. Note the similarity with the experiment of tossing a coin ten times; this will allow the use of Table 19.2.

PROBLEM 19.6. Assume that 50 percent of the eligible voters in a certain precinct are Democrats, and that six eligible voters are selected at random from the precinct.
(a) What is the probability that all six are Democrats?
(b) What is the probability that exactly three of the six are Democrats?
(c) What is the probability that none of the six is a Democrat?

PROBLEM 19.7. (a) In a city with streets numbered as in Problem 16.10, how many different twenty-block routes are there from $1,A$ to $11,K$? (There are twenty decisions to be made, ten of which involve going north one block and ten of which involve going east one block.)
(b) A route is chosen randomly from among those in part (a). What is the probability that it passes through $11,A$?
(c) Same as (b) with $11,A$ replaced by $6,A$.
(d) Same as (b) with $11,A$ replaced by $6,F$.

PROBLEM 19.8. If an experiment has n possible outcomes with respective probabilities $p_1, p_2, \ldots, p_n$ and respective values $v_1, v_2, \ldots, v_n$, then the *mathematical expectation* for the experiment is defined to be $p_1 v_1 + p_2 v_2 + \cdots + p_n v_n$. (Compare Problem 15.13, in which there are only two outcomes, one of which has value zero.) In the case of a game, where the value denotes the prize, the mathematical expectation can be thought of as the reasonable amount to pay for the privilege of playing.
(a) What is a player's mathematical expectation in a game in which a fair die is thrown and the player receives as many dollars as the number that appears?
(b) What is a player's mathematical expectation in a game in which a coin is tossed two times and the player receives as many dollars as the number of heads obtained?
(c) Same as (b) with 2 tosses replaced by 4 tosses.
(d) Same as (b) with 2 tosses replaced by 6 tosses.
(e) Paul asks Peter to pay one dollar for the privilege of playing a game in which Paul will pay Peter four dollars if either 3 or 4 heads are obtained in 4 tosses of a coin; otherwise Peter will receive nothing. Should Peter agree to play?
(f) Assuming Peter is to pay one dollar for the privilege of playing in part (e), what should the prize be so as to be fair to both Peter and Paul?

§20. Binomial Experiments

Coin-tossing experiments can be characterized by four properties:

(1)   there is a sequence of repeated trials of some kind (repeated tosses of a coin);
(2)   there are only two possible outcomes for each trial (head or tail), and these are mutually exclusive*;
(3)   the probability of each of the two possible outcomes remains the same throughout the trials;
(4)   for each trial, the two possible outcomes have equal probabilities (probability of head equals probability of tail).

There are many experiments that are the same as coin-tossing except possibly for property (4). Such experiments satisfying (1), (2), and (3) are called *binomial experiments* (or *Bernoulli experiments*, after James Bernoulli (Swiss, 1654–1705), whose *Ars Conjectandi*, published posthumously in 1713, was the first substantial book on probability). We shall denote the two possible outcomes for each trial by S (for success) and F (for failure), and their respective probabilities by p and q. Thus if we are concerned with the number of heads in coin tossing, we use H for S, T for F, and $p = q = 0.5$. Before analyzing binomial experiments in general, let us look at another specific example.

EXAMPLE 20.1. Suppose we are interested in the number of 6's obtained in 3 rolls of a die. Then let S denote '6 comes up' and F denote '1, 2, 3, 4, or 5 comes up'. In this case $p = \Pr(S) = 1/6$ on each roll, and $q = \Pr(F) = 5/6$ on each roll. (We are assuming a fair die.)
(a) What is the probability of obtaining 6 on the first roll together with something other than 6 on the second and third rolls? In other words, what is the probability of SFF?
    The total number of possible outcomes is 6^3, a typical outcome being a sequence of three numbers each either 1, 2, 3, 4, 5, or 6. The number of these sequences corresponding to the event SFF is the number of sequences $6xy$, where x and y each can be any one of 1, 2, 3, 4, or 5. There are 5^2 sequences of this latter kind. Therefore the probability of the event SFF is $5^2/6^3 = 25/216$, or approximately 0.116. (Problem 20.1 exposes a trap to be avoided in solving problems such as this.)
(b) What is the probability of FSF? FFS?
    The total number of possible outcomes is again 6^3, and the number of sequences $x6y$ where x and y each can be any one of 1, 2, 3, 4, or 5, is 5^2. Therefore the probability of FSF is also $25/216$. Similarly, the probability of FFS is $25/216$.
(c) What is the probability of obtaining exactly one 6 in 3 rolls of a die?

---

* That is, they cannot both occur (we get head or tail, but never both, on a single trial). In drawing a card from a bridge deck, the outcomes 'draw an ace' and 'draw a spade' are not mutually exclusive.

The total number of possible outcomes is still 6^3. The number of sequences corresponding to 'exactly one 6' is the sum of the number corresponding to *SFF*, *FSF*, and *FFS*, or 3 times 5^2. Therefore the probability of obtaining exactly one 6 is $(3 \cdot 5^2)/6^3 = 75/216$.

(d) What is the probability of *SSF*?

Reasoning as in part (a), we get the probability 5/216.

(e) What is the probability of obtaining exactly two 6's in 3 rolls of a die?

Using (d) and reasoning as in part (c), we get $(3 \cdot 5)/6^3 = 15/216$.

(f) The probability of *FFF* is $5^3/6^3 = 125/216$.

(g) The probability of *SSS* is 1/216.

The key to computing probabilities for binomial experiments is in the solution of the following two problems.

PROBLEM 20A.   What is the probability of obtaining k successes followed by $n - k$ failures in a binomial experiment with n trials $(0 \le k \le n)$?

PROBLEM 20B. What is the probability of obtaining exactly k successes in a binomial experiment with n trials $(0 \le k \le n)$?

Example 20.1 settles these questions for the following special cases (each with $p = 1/6$, $q = 5/6$):

(a)   is Problem 20A with $n = 3$, $k = 1$;
(c)   is Problem 20B with $n = 3$, $k = 1$;
(d)   is Problem 20A with $n = 3$, $k = 2$;
(e)   is Problem 20B with $n = 3$, $k = 2$;
(f)   is Problem 20A (or 20B) with $n = 3$, $k = 0$;
(g)   is Problem 20A (or 20B) with $n = 3$, $k = 3$.

Problem 20A asks for the probability of the event

$$SS \cdots SFF \cdots F \qquad (k \text{ S's, } n - k \text{ F's}),$$

given that for each trial $\Pr(S) = p$ and $\Pr(F) = q$. We shall now deduce that this probability is $p^k q^{n-k}$.

If the number of possible outcomes for each trial is t, then the total number of possible outcomes for the sequence of n trials is t^n, by the Basic Counting Principle. Assume that (for each trial) the number of outcomes corresponding to S is u (thus $p = u/t$). Then the number of outcomes corresponding to F must be $t - u$, because of defining property (2) for binomial experiments, given at the beginning of this section. Therefore, by the Basic Counting Principle again, the number of outcomes corresponding to $SS \cdots SFF \cdots F$ for the sequence of n trials is

$$u \times u \times \cdots \times u \times (t - u) \times (t - u) \times \cdots \times (t - u) = u^k(t - u)^{n-k}.$$

Thus

$$\Pr(SS \cdots SFF \cdots F) = u^k(t - u)^{n-k}/t^n = (u/t)^k \cdot ((t - u)/t)^{n-k} = p^k q^{n-k},$$

as claimed. (Note that $p + q = u/t + (t - u)/t = 1$.)

Applying this to the question in Example 20.1(a), we get $(1/6)^1(5/6)^2 = 25/216$, as before.

Now consider Problem 20B. The total number of possible outcomes for the sequence of n trials is t^n, as before. But this time we want the probability of the event k S's and $n - k$ F's and we do not insist that the S's come first, as we did in Problem 20A. To compute the number of sequences corresponding to k S's, we first note that (by the Basic Counting Principle) the number of outcomes corresponding to k S's and $n - k$ F's in any particular order is $u^k(t - u)^{n-k}$, just as for the order $SS \cdots SFF \cdots F$. (For instance, in the case $n = 6$, $k = 2$, the number of ways of getting $SFFFSF$ is $u(t - u)(t - u)(t - u)u(t - u) = u^2(t - u)^4$.) Therefore the number of outcomes corresponding to k S's and $n - k$ F's is $u^k(t - u)^{n-k}$ multiplied by the number of possible orders for k S's and $n - k$ F's in a sequence. (For instance, in the case $n = 3$, $k = 2$, there are three different orders: SSF, SFS, FSS.) The number of these possible orders is just $C(n, k)$, the number of ways of selecting k places to put the S's among the n total places. Therefore the answer to Problem 20B is

$$\frac{C(n, k)\ u^k(t - u)^{n-k}}{t^n} = C(n, k)(u/t)^k((t - u)/t)^{n-k}.$$

Using $p = u/t$ and $q = (t - u)/t$, this probability is

$$C(n, k)p^k q^{n-k}.$$

This result is of such importance that we state it as a theorem.

THEOREM 20.1

In n trials of a binomial experiment, with each trial having probabilities p for success and q for failure, the probability of obtaining exactly k successes and $n - k$ failures is

$$C(n, k)p^k q^{n-k}.$$

Notice that by the Binomial Theorem these probabilities are the terms in the expansion of $(p + q)^n$.

EXAMPLE 20.2. (a) In coin-tossing experiments, $p = q = 1/2$, and the probability in Theorem 20.1 reduces to $C(n, k)/2^n$. This agrees with the solution to Problem 19A.
(b) With $p = 1/6$, $q = 5/6$, and $n = 3$, Theorem 20.1 agrees with the results of Example 20.1(f), (c), (e), and (g) when we use $k = 0, 1, 2,$ and 3.

PROBLEM 20C. Theorem 20.1 gives the probability of obtaining *exactly* k successes in an n-trial binomial experiment. What is the probability of *at least* k successes?

Solution

For $p = q = 1/2$ this is Problem 19B, and the solution here is like the one there. The outcomes corresponding to 'at least k successes' are those that yield either k successes, or $k + 1$ successes, ..., or n successes, and the number of these is

$$C(n, k)u^k (t - u)^{n-k} + C(n, k + 1)u^{k+1}(t - u)^{n-(k+1)} + \cdots$$
$$+ C(n, n)u^n(t - u)^0.$$

Dividing this number by the total number of possible outcomes, t^n, and simplifying, we get that the probability of at least k successes is

$$C(n, k)p^k q^{n-k} + C(n, k + 1)p^{k+1}q^{n-(k+1)} + \cdots + C(n, n)p^n q^0,$$

which is the sum of the probabilities of obtaining k successes, $k + 1$ successes, ..., n successes.

EXAMPLE 20.3. The probability of obtaining at least two 6's in 3 rolls of a die is $15/216 + 1/216 = 16/216$, where $15/216$ is the probability of obtaining exactly two 6's and $1/216$ is the probability of obtaining exactly three 6's, as computed in (e) and (g) of Example 20.1. The histogram for this experiment (3 rolls of a die) is shown in Figure 20.1. The probability of at least two 6's is the sum of the areas of the rectangles centered over 2 and 3. Note the lack of symmetry, as compared with the histograms for coin-tossing experiments in Section 19. Histograms for binomial experiments will be completely symmetric only for $p = q = 0.5$. However, they will be nearly symmetric whenever np and nq are sufficiently large (we shall say more about this in the next section).

Other illustrations of binomial experiments are contained in Problem Set 20. For our last example we turn to Problem 15C: Suppose

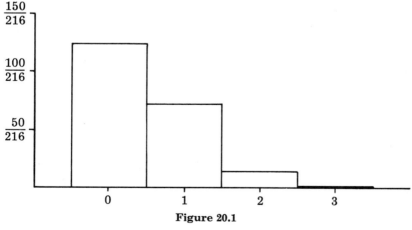

Figure 20.1

(Three rolls of a die)

that the normal rate of death from a certain disease is 25 percent. If 10 victims of the disease are given injections of a new vaccine, and all of them recover, is it reasonable to assume that the vaccine is effective? What if 25 victims are given the vaccine and 23 recover? Which of these two sets of data would be the more convincing?

Choosing 10 victims of the disease can be thought of as a binomial experiment with 10 trials and $p = 0.75$, since 75 percent of the victims of the disease can be expected to recover if no extraneous factors are present (such as other health problems or the use of the vaccine we are testing). By Theorem 20.1, the probability that 10 out of 10 victims would recover if only chance were operating is

$$C(10, 10) \times (0.75)^{10} \times (0.25)^0 = (0.75)^{10} = 0.056.$$

In other words, if the hypothesis 'the vaccine has no effect' were true, then 10 recoveries out of 10 victims would happen less than 6 percent of the time. Thus it is reasonable to assume that the vaccine is effective, although that is not certain.

The probability that 23 or more out of 25 would recover if only chance were operating is

$$C(25, 23) \times (0.75)^{23} \times (0.25)^2 + C(25, 24) \times (0.75)^{24} \times (0.25)^1$$
$$+ C(25, 25) \times (0.75)^{25} \times (0.25)^0 = 0.032,$$

approximately. Thus 23 recoveries out of 25 injections would be more convincing than 10 recoveries out of 10 injections, since as many as 23 recoveries out of 25 victims would be less likely than 10 recoveries out of 10 victims, if only chance were operating.

Figures 20.2 and 20.3 show the histograms corresponding to these two binomial experiments.

It must be realized that our conclusions lose meaning to the extent to which the assumptions about the random nature of the experiment are incorrect: if the victims are not representative of all those with the

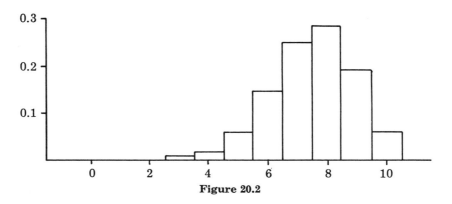

Figure 20.2

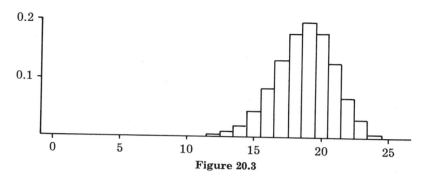

Figure 20.3

disease, or if they are also undergoing other treatment, then these things must be taken into account. There are two critical factors in any application of mathematics—we observed them in applying mathematical geometry to describe physical geometry. An abstract mathematical model is being used to describe a particular experiment: we must make certain that the model is mathematically sound (internally consistent), and we must make certain that the facts underlying the experiment match (are consistent with) the assumptions underlying the model.

PROBLEM SET 20

PROBLEM 20.1. Find the flaw in the following solution for Example 20.1 (a): The probability of obtaining *SFF* from among the outcomes *FFF, SFF, FSF, FFS, SSF, SFS, FSS, SSS* is 1/8. Therefore the probability of obtaining 6 on the first roll together with something other than 6 on the second and third rolls is 1/8.

PROBLEM 20.2. A multiple choice exam contains ten questions, and there are five possible choices for each question, only one of which is correct. Assume the ten questions are answered randomly.
(a) What is the probability of getting all ten correct?
(b) What is the probability of getting exactly seven correct?
(c) What is the probability of getting at least seven correct?
(d) What is the probability of getting at most two correct?

PROBLEM 20.3. Fifteen letters are chosen randomly from the English alphabet, with replacement. (Compare Problem 16.9.)
(a) What is the probability that exactly one is a vowel?
(b) What is the probability that exactly three are vowels?
(c) What is the probability that at most three are vowels?
(d) Answer (a), (b), and (c) if the experiment is without replacement. (Theorem 20.1 does not apply in part (d). Why?)

PROBLEM 20.4. A pollster is told that 20 percent of the eligible voters in a certain precinct are Republicans. He chooses four eligible voters at random from the precinct and finds that three are Republicans. Is he justified in feeling that he has been misinformed? What if he chooses seven and finds that six are Republicans? What are the relevant probabilities? (Assume the precinct to be large enough so that the difference between selecting with or without replacement is negligible.)

PROBLEM 20.5. Assume that a triple of dice is thrown ten times.

(a) What is the probability of obtaining (6, 6, 6) exactly once?

(b) What is the probability of obtaining (6, 6, 6) at least once?

(c) What is the probability of obtaining at least one odd number on every throw?

PROBLEM 20.6. A pair of coins is tossed five times. Compute the probability of each of the following events.

(a) Obtaining exactly two double heads.

(b) Obtaining exactly four double heads.

(c) Obtaining at least one double head.

(d) Obtaining at most one double head.

(e) Obtaining a double head on the first toss and no double head on the remaining tosses.

PROBLEM 20.7. A machine turns out parts of which 5 percent are defective, on the average. Ten parts are chosen randomly from among those produced by the machine. Write an expression for the probability of each of the following.

(a) None of the ten is defective.

(b) Exactly one of the ten is defective.

(c) At least one of the ten is defective.

(d) More than five are defective.

(e) All ten are defective.

PROBLEM 20.8. Suppose that the normal rate of death from a certain disease is 25 percent, and that ten victims of the disease are chosen at random. Write expressions for each of the following probabilities.

(a) None recovers.

(b) Exactly two recover.

(c) At least two recover.

(d) Exactly five recover.

(e) At most five recover.

§21. Normal Approximation

Recall that by the end of Section 19 we were able to solve Problem 15B—in theory. But the computational problem that arose was such that we were unable to follow through to a practical answer. We shall now describe a method for obtaining approximate answers for such problems. The method is useful for any binomial experiment having np and nq sufficiently large, and in particular gives quite accurate approximations for coin-tossing experiments involving large numbers of tosses.

The histograms shown in Figures 19.1, 19.2, and 19.3 (representing tosses of six, ten, and twenty coins, respectively) have several common characteristics: they are symmetric, relatively high in the center and flat at the ends, and tend to a bell-shape if the tops of the rectangles are smoothed out. These characteristics are preserved in histograms representing larger numbers of tosses. The fact we shall exploit is that these histograms can be approximated by a curve known as the *normal curve*. This curve, or strictly speaking the equation that defines it, is of immense importance in probability and statistics; not only for approximations, as we shall use it, but in more theoretical work as well. The proofs of the relevant facts about this curve involve the use of calculus, so we shall not be able to present them; the way these facts are used in problems such as those we have been discussing is what we shall describe.

The normal curve is obtained by plotting pairs of corresponding values of t and y, given by the equation

$$y = \frac{1}{\sqrt{2\pi}} e^{-(t^2/2)},$$

with t measured along a horizontal axis and y measured along a vertical axis (Figure 21.1). Pairs of some corresponding t and y values are shown in Table 21.1, where $h(t)$ has been used instead of y, $h(t)$ representing the height of the curve at t. The height above $-t$ is the same as the height above t, and so in Table 21.1 it has not been necessary to list negative values of t. Although Table 21.1 shows $h(t) = 0.0000$ for all values of t beyond 4.2, $h(t)$ is never exactly zero (for example, $h(4.5) = 0.000016$ to the nearest millionth). The number e is irrational, like π, and is approximately equal to 2.71828; it arises in a natural way in many situations in mathematics (see Problem 21.10). We shall not discuss the details of how the y values can be computed from given t values (see Example 45.7).

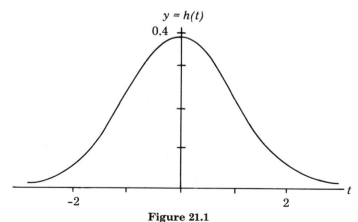

$y = h(t)$

Figure 21.1

(normal curve)

TABLE 21.1

Normal Distribution Table

t	h(t)	A(t)	t	h(t)	A(t)
0.0	0.3989	0.5000	2.3	0.0283	0.0107
0.1	0.3970	0.4602	2.4	0.0224	0.0082
0.2	0.3910	0.4207	2.5	0.0175	0.0062
0.3	0.3814	0.3821	2.6	0.0136	0.0047
0.4	0.3683	0.3446	2.7	0.0104	0.0035
0.5	0.3521	0.3085	2.8	0.0079	0.0026
0.6	0.3332	0.2743	2.9	0.0060	0.0019
0.7	0.3123	0.2420	3.0	0.0044	0.0013
0.8	0.2897	0.2119	3.1	0.0033	0.0010
0.9	0.2661	0.1841	3.2	0.0024	0.0007
1.0	0.2420	0.1587	3.3	0.0017	0.0005
1.1	0.2179	0.1357	3.4	0.0012	0.0003
1.2	0.1942	0.1151	3.5	0.0009	0.0002
1.3	0.1714	0.0968	3.6	0.0006	0.0002
1.4	0.1497	0.0808	3.7	0.0004	0.0001
1.5	0.1295	0.0668	3.8	0.0003	0.0001
1.6	0.1109	0.0548	3.9	0.0002	0.0000
1.7	0.0940	0.0446	4.0	0.0001	0.0000
1.8	0.0790	0.0359	4.1	0.0001	0.0000
1.9	0.0656	0.0287	4.2	0.0001	0.0000
2.0	0.0540	0.0228	4.3	0.0000	0.0000
2.1	0.0440	0.0179	4.4	0.0000	0.0000
2.2	0.0355	0.0139	4.5	0.0000	0.0000

The normal curve is used to approximate probabilities, and it will be recalled that with histograms it was area that represented probability. For example, in Figure 19.2 the area of the rectangle centered on 7 is equal to the probability of obtaining exactly 7 heads in 10 tosses of a coin, and the area of that rectangle together with those to the right of it is equal to the probability of obtaining at least 7 heads in 10 tosses of a coin. Similarly, it is area that will represent probability when using the normal curve, and so we will need to be able to compute the area under various parts of the curve. Again, this is a job for calculus. The columns labelled $A(t)$ in Table 21.1 give samples of such areas. Specifically, for each positive value of t, $A(t)$ is the area under the normal curve, above the (horizontal) t-axis, and to the right of the given value of t (Figure 21.2). Thus $A(0) = 0.5000$ means that the area under the right half of the curve is 0.5000, and so the area under the entire curve is 1.0000 (as it should be, since it is the probability corresponding to all possibilities). Similarly, the area to the right of 1.0 is 0.1587 and the area to the right of 2.0 is 0.0228, so that the area under the curve and

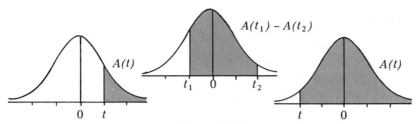

Figure 21.2

between 1.0 and 2.0 is $A(1.0) - A(2.0) = 0.1587 - 0.0228 = 0.1359$. For negative values of t, the area under the curve and to the right of t is $1 - A(-t)$ (because if t is negative then $A(-t)$ is the area to the right of $-t$, which is the same as the area to the left of t, and the total area under the curve is 1). For example, the area to the right of -0.50 is $1.0000 - 0.3085 = 0.6915$.

We have claimed that the normal curve would be useful to us for approximating histograms for binomial experiments. A glance at Figures 19.1, 19.2, 19.3, and 21.1 will reveal a technical difficulty that must be overcome before using the normal curve for this purpose. Although the histograms for coin-tossing, when smoothed out, have the same general shape as the normal curve, they have different heights and are symmetric about different values (heights roughly 0.31, 0.25, 0.18, 0.40, respectively, and centered about 3, 5, 10, 0, respectively, for the figures mentioned above). In order to fit any such histogram to the normal curve, two conversions must be made: one to shift the center of symmetry to the left or right, one to change the height. This can be done in one step, making use of the three numbers n, p, and q for the particular binomial experiment to be approximated. That is the content of the following theorem.

THEOREM 21.1
    In a binomial experiment of n trials with each trial having success probability p, the probability of obtaining at least k successes is approximately equal to A(t), where A(t) is the area under the normal curve to the right of t, and

$$t = \frac{k - \frac{1}{2} - np}{\sqrt{npq}}.$$

Just how close this approximation is depends on the particular values k, n, p, and q. The approximation is fairly good whenever $np > 5$ and $nq > 5$, particularly if k is near np. In the case of a coin-tossing experiment with $n = 100$, the approximations agree with the exact probabilities to within at least 0.001, for all values of k. We shall make some further remarks about the terms 1/2, np, and npq appearing in the theorem, but first we give several applications.

EXAMPLE 21.1. Use Theorem 21.1 to approximate the probability of obtaining 100 or more sixes in 500 throws of a fair die.

Here $n = 500, p = 1/6, q = 5/6, k = 100$. Therefore
$$t = (100 - 1/2 - 500 \times 1/6)/\sqrt{500 \times 1/6 \times 5/6}$$
$$= [(600 - 3 - 500)/6]/\sqrt{2500/36}$$
$$= (97/6)/(50/6)$$
$$= 97/50 = 1.94.$$

Thus the probability is approximately $A(1.94)$. Table 21.1 shows $A(1.9) = 0.0287$ and $A(2.0) = 0.0228$, so $A(1.94)$ is between these two values. It is approximately 0.026.

EXAMPLE 21.1 (continued). What is the probability of obtaining at least 65 but fewer than 100 sixes in 500 throws of a fair die? This probability will be represented by the area under the normal curve to the right of the t-value corresponding to $k = 65$, but excluding that to the right of the t-value corresponding to $k = 100$ ($n = 500, p = 1/6, q = 5/6$ in each case). The latter area is 0.026, from the first part of the example. For the second, $t = -2.26$. And $A(-2.26) = 1 - A(2.26) = 1 - 0.012 = 0.988$, approximately. Therefore the probability in question is $0.988 - 0.026 = 0.96$, approximately.

EXAMPLE 21.2. Use Theorem 21.1 to approximate the probability of obtaining at least 14 heads in 20 tosses of a coin.

Here $n = 20, p = q = 1/2, k = 14$. Therefore
$$t = (14 - 1/2 - 20 \times 1/2)/\sqrt{20 \times 1/2 \times 1/2}$$
$$= (7/2)/\sqrt{5}$$
$$= 7\sqrt{5}/10$$
$$= 1.57,$$

where we have used $\sqrt{5} = 2.24$ (approximation). Since 1.57 is between 1.5 and 1.6, the best we can do using Table 21.1 is to compare $A(1.5) = 0.0668$ and $A(1.6) = 0.0548$. A more extensive table, such as [4], would show $A(1.57) = 0.0582$, or rounded to the nearest thousandth, 0.058, in agreement with the value 0.058 computed for this problem in Example 19.2.

EXAMPLE 21.3. Compare the probabilities for a coin-tossing experiment for $n = 6$ (Table 19.1), and the corresponding approximations as given by Theorem 21.1.

In this case $n = 6, p = q = 1/2$, and so
$$t = (k - 1/2 - 6 \times 1/2)/\sqrt{6 \times 1/2 \times 1/2}$$
$$= (k - 7/2)/(\sqrt{6}/2)$$
$$= (2k - 7)/\sqrt{6}$$
$$= (2k - 7)\sqrt{6}/6.$$

Using $\sqrt{6} = 2.45$ (approximation), we can compute t for each value of k and then read $A(t)$ from Table 21.1. For comparison, we add values given by the table accompanying Figure 19.1 to obtain probabilities for at least 0 heads, 1 head, 2 heads, and so forth. Here are the results:

k	t	Probability of at least k heads	$A(t)$ or $1 - A(-t)$*
0	-2.90	1.0000	0.9981
1	-2.10	0.9844	0.9821
2	-1.20	0.8906	0.8849
3	-0.40	0.6562	0.6554
4	0.40	0.3438	0.3446
5	1.20	0.1094	0.1151
6	2.10	0.0156	0.0179

* Recall that the area to the right of t is given by $1 - A(-t)$ if $t < 0$.

EXAMPLE 21.4. Use Theorem 21.1 to approximate the probability involved in Problem 15B.

We deduced after Example 19.2 that the relevant probability here is the probability of obtaining at least 5,200 heads in 10,000 tosses of a fair coin. Thus we use Theorem 21.1 with $n = 10{,}000$, $p = q = 1/2$, $k = 5{,}200$. Then

$$t = (5200 - 1/2 - 10000 \times 1/2)/\sqrt{10000 \times 1/2 \times 1/2}$$
$$= (200 - 1/2)/50$$
$$= 3.99.$$

Table 21.1 gives $A(4.00) = 0.0000$. A more accurate table, such as [4], gives $A(4.00) = 0.000032$. In other words, we have an event that would happen only about 3 times out of 100,000 with a fair coin. With such a small probability, it is certainly likely that something other than chance is present, and so it is reasonable to assume that the coin is not a fair one.

We shall now make some general remarks about the normal curve and normal approximation. The normal curve is the proper mathematical object for describing many phenomena in addition to binomial experiments. For instance, heights of men, IQ scores, and sizes of parts produced by a machine, are all distributed in a way that is characterized by the normal curve. In all such cases there are two numbers that must be taken into account that are determined by the particular experiment or set of data being considered; these two numbers adjust the normal curve to the curve describing the experiment or data. One is the *mean*, denoted μ (Greek letter mu), and the other is the *standard deviation*, denoted σ (Greek letter sigma).

For binomial experiments, Theorem 21.1 tells us how to convert the data for a particular experiment so that it will fit the normal curve as given by Figure 21.1. Alternatively, we could convert the normal curve so that it fits the given data. The proper equation for this converted normal curve is

$$y = \frac{1}{\sigma\sqrt{2\pi}} \, e^{-\frac{1}{2}((x-\mu)/\sigma)^2},$$

where μ and σ are the mean and standard deviation for the given experiment or data (Figure 21.3). It can be seen that μ corresponds to the line

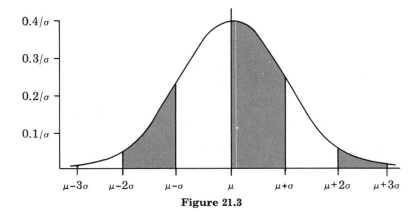

Figure 21.3

of symmetry for the curve. Changes in σ have the effect of making the curve relatively higher or flatter (the highest point is always approximately $0.4/\sigma$, and the area under the curve is always 1, so a larger σ will necessarily make the curve flatter). The mean is an 'average' value, and the standard deviation measures the amount of spread or deviation from the mean. Table 21.1 can be used to compute areas under various parts of this curve: the area under the curve and to the right of $\mu + t$ is $A(t)$.

We shall not discuss the methods for computing particular μ and σ. For binomial experiments it can be shown that the relevant values are $\mu = np$ and $\sigma = \sqrt{npq}$; this is the essential content of Theorem 21.1. The term $1/2$ appearing in the numerator in the expression for t in Theorem 21.1 comes from the fact that in finding the probability of at least k successes in a binomial experiment, we must approximate the areas of all rectangles beginning $1/2$ unit to the left of k.

The normal curve is often called the *Gaussian curve*, although it was used by Laplace and DeMoivre (1667–1754) before Gauss. The use of this curve in probability theory requires a more general definition of probability than that given in Section 15; among other things, one must allow for an infinite number of possible outcomes.

PROBLEM SET 21

PROBLEM 21.1. Use Table 21.1 to find each of the following numbers.
(a) $h(2.5)$ (b) $h(-2.5)$
(c) $h(-0.7)$ (d) $A(0.9)$
(e) $A(-0.9)$ (f) $A(0) - A(1.0)$
(g) $A(-1.0) - A(0)$ (h) $A(-1.0) - A(1.0)$
(i) $A(-2.0) - A(0)$ (j) $A(-3.0) - A(3.0)$

PROBLEM 21.2. Use Theorem 21.1 to compute the (approximate) probability of obtaining 60 or more heads in 100 tosses of a fair coin.

PROBLEM 21.3. Use Theorem 21.1 to compute the (approximate) probability of obtaining less than 6 heads in 25 tosses of a fair coin.

PROBLEM 21.4. Use Theorem 21.1 to compute the (approximate) probability of obtaining more than 40 but fewer than 60 heads in 100 tosses of a fair coin.

PROBLEM 21.5. If a student knows the answers to half of the questions on a 100-question true-false exam, and answers the others randomly, what is the probability he (or she) will get at least 80 correct?

PROBLEM 21.6. A pollster is told that 20 percent of the eligible voters in a precinct are Republicans. He chooses 16 eligible voters at random from the precinct, and finds that 12 are Republicans. Is he justified in feeling that he has been misinformed? What if he chooses 16 and finds that 8 are Republicans? Use Theorem 21.1. (Notice that 8 out of 16 (50 percent) is more significant than 3 out of 4 (75 percent). Compare Problem 20.4.)

PROBLEM 21.7. (Continuation of Example 21.1.) (a) What is the probability of obtaining 80 or more sixes in 500 throws of a fair die?
(b) What is the probability of obtaining 90 or more sixes in 500 throws of a fair die?
(c) What is the probability of obtaining at least 80 but fewer than 90 sixes in 500 throws of a fair die?

PROBLEM 21.8. Assume that birthdays are equally distributed among the months of the year, and that the month of birth of each of 100 randomly chosen persons is recorded. Use Theorem 21.1 to approximate each of the following probabilities. (Suggestion: In computing t, use 3.3 for $\sqrt{11}$.)
(a) At least 10 of the 100 have November birthdays.
(b) At least 5 of the 100 have November birthdays.
(c) At least 20 of the 100 have November birthdays.

PROBLEM 21.9. A machine turns out parts of which 5 percent are defective, on the average. One hundred parts are chosen randomly from among those produced by the machine. Use Theorem 21.1 to approximate each of the following probabilities. (Suggestion: In computing t, use 4.36 for $\sqrt{19}$.)
(a) None of the one hundred is defective.
(b) At least five are defective.
(c) Fewer than five are defective.
(d) Fewer than ten are defective.
(e) Twenty or more are defective.
(f) Four or five or six are defective.

PROBLEM 21.10. The number e appearing in the defining equation for the normal curve can be considered the sum of the series

$$1 + \frac{1}{1!} + \frac{1}{2!} + \frac{1}{3!} + \frac{1}{4!} + \cdots + \frac{1}{n!} + \cdots,$$

in the same sense in which 1 can be considered the sum of either the series

$$\frac{1}{2} + \frac{1}{4} + \frac{1}{8} + \frac{1}{16} + \cdots + \frac{1}{2^n} + \cdots$$

or the series

$$\frac{9}{10} + \frac{9}{100} + \frac{9}{1000} + \cdots + \frac{9}{10^n} + \cdots.$$

(Compare Problem 5.2(c), for $0.\bar{9}$.) Compute decimal approximations for each of 1, 1/1!, 1/2!, 1/3!, 1/4!, 1/5!, and 1/6!, and then compare the sums obtained from adding the first two of these; the first three; ... ; all of them. Compare with the approximation 2.71828 given in the text. (See Section 39 for more on the number e.)

REFERENCES

1. BELL, E. T., *Men of Mathematics,* Simon and Schuster, New York, 1937.
2. BURINGTON, R. S., and D. S. MAY, Jr., *Handbook of Probability and Statistics with Tables,* Handbook Publishers, Sandusky, Ohio, 1953.
3. FELLER, WILLIAM, *An Introduction to Probability Theory and Its Applications,* 2 vols., John Wiley and Sons, New York, 1957 and 1966.
4. *Handbook of Mathematical Functions,* National Bureau of Standards Applied Mathematics Series (55), 1964.
5. KOLMOGOROV, A. N., *Foundations of the Theory of Probability,* trans. edited by N. Morrison, Chelsea, New York, 1950.
6. MOSTELLER, F., R. E. K. ROURKE, and G. B. THOMAS, Jr., *Probability with Statistical Applications,* Addison-Wesley, Reading, Mass., 1961.
7. NEWMAN, J., ed., *The World of Mathematics,* 4 vols., Simon and Schuster, New York, 1956.
8. TODHUNTER, I., *A History of the Mathematical Theory of Probability from the Time of Pascal to that of Laplace,* Chelsea, New York, 1949.
9. WEAVER, W., *Lady Luck,* Anchor, Garden City, New York, 1963.

CHAPTER IV

Cardinal Numbers

§22. Equivalent Sets

OBSERVATION A

If a lecturer enters an auditorium in which each seat is occupied by one person and in which each person is seated, he can conclude that there is the same number of persons as seats in the auditorium—without knowing how many there are of either. In the same way, we can agree that the sets $\{a, b, c\}$ and $\{x, y, z\}$ have the same number of elements because we can pair off their elements

$$
\begin{array}{ccc}
a & b & c \\
\updownarrow & \updownarrow & \updownarrow \\
x & y & z
\end{array}
$$

—and this does not require the concept 'three'.

OBSERVATION B (Galileo (1638))

$$
\begin{array}{cccccccc}
1 & 2 & 3 & 4 & \cdots & n & & \cdots \\
\updownarrow & \updownarrow & \updownarrow & \updownarrow & & \updownarrow & & \\
1 & 4 & 9 & 16 & \cdots & n^2 & & \cdots
\end{array}
$$

Interpreting Observation B in the light of Observation A, we could say that there is the same number of natural numbers as squares of natural numbers. On the other hand, there are many natural numbers that are not squares of natural numbers (2, 3, 5, 6, 7, 8, 10, . . .), and so the first set is certainly larger than the second. Thus we have two sets having the same number of elements, with one of the two sets larger than the other. How can we explain this apparent contradiction?

We first notice that the sets in Observation B are infinite. What we have tried to do is compare the size of these two sets by using two natural but conceptually different notions. One is the notion that two sets have the same number of elements if their elements can be paired off; the other is the notion that if we remove elements from a set, then we make the set smaller. The key is that while these notions agree for finite sets, they do not agree for infinite sets. The safe conclusion—and until the latter part of the nineteenth century the only conclusion—is that we cannot compare the size of infinite sets. What we shall discuss in this chapter is a more imaginative conclusion due primarily to Georg Cantor (1845–1918). We begin by formalizing the idea behind Observation A.

By a *one-to-one correspondence* between sets A and B is meant a pairing of the elements of A with the elements of B, in such a way that each element of A is paired with exactly one element of B and each element of B is paired with exactly one element of A. Thus the first example in Observation A describes a one-to-one correspondence between the set of persons in the auditorium and the set of seats in the auditorium; the second example in Observation A gives a schematic representation of a one-to-one correspondence between the sets $\{a, b, c\}$ and $\{x, y, z\}$; and Observation B gives a one-to-one correspondence between $\{1, 2, 3, . . .\}$ and $\{1, 4, 9, . . .\}$.

For convenience, we shall call two sets *equivalent* if their elements can be put in one-to-one correspondence. It is clear, then, that two finite sets are equivalent if and only if they have the same number of elements—this is the substance of Observation A. Cantor had the genius and courage to apply this notion of equivalence to sets that were not necessarily finite, and to follow through to a theory that allows us to speak of and compare the 'number' of elements in infinite sets. Later we shall discuss the appropriate definition of 'number'. For now, we simply mention that it will turn out that equivalent sets 'have the same number of elements'.

Before giving further examples of equivalent sets, let us apply the idea of equivalence to give a definition of 'infinite'. We do this by capitalizing on the apparent contradiction that followed Observation B. We call a subset S of a set T a *proper* subset of T if T contains at least one element that is not in S (thus the only subset of T that is not proper is T itself).* Then: a set is said to be *infinite* if it is equivalent with some

---

* Subsets are discussed in Section 17.

proper subset of itself. The set of natural numbers is infinite according to this definition, by Observation B. Of course, we used 'infinite' in the discussion above before it was defined, but had we been willing to sacrifice motivation for pedantry, that could have been avoided just by giving all definitions first.

The next three examples illustrate the scope of equivalence. Notice, with the first of these, the surprising conclusion that although the set of all rational numbers would appear to be much larger than the set of all natural numbers, the two sets are in fact equivalent.

EXAMPLE 22.1 (Cantor). The set of all positive rational numbers is equivalent with the set of all natural numbers.

Proof

List the positive fractions systematically, as shown.

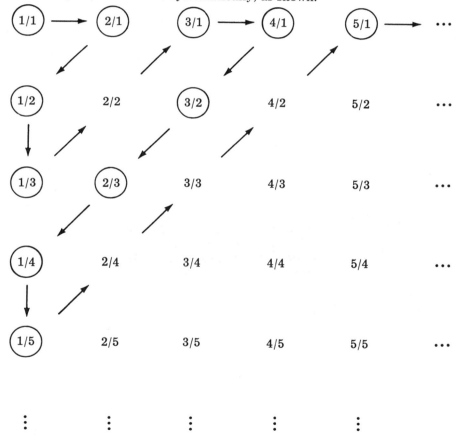

Now follow the path indicated, circling an entry if it is not equal to some entry previously circled. Finally, write down the circled entries, in order, to obtain the one-to-one correspondence

1	2	3	4	5	6	7	8	$\cdots$
$\updownarrow$	$\updownarrow$	$\updownarrow$	$\updownarrow$	$\updownarrow$	$\updownarrow$	$\updownarrow$	$\updownarrow$	
1/1	2/1	1/2	1/3	3/1	4/1	3/2	2/3	$\cdots$

It can be seen that each positive rational number will ultimately appear in the second row of the last diagram, and none will appear more than once because only one fraction representing each rational number has been circled. $\square$

EXAMPLE 22.2. The sets of points on any two line segments are equivalent.

Proof

Given segments MN and PQ, with MN longer than PQ, place them parallel, as in Figure 22.1, and extend MP and NQ to get a triangle AMN. Now draw

Figure 22.1

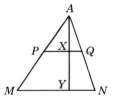

lines from A and pair the points where these lines intersect MN and PQ: thus in the case shown point X would correspond with point Y.

   If MN and PQ are of equal length, simply place one on top of the other and pair coincident points. $\square$

EXAMPLE 22.3. The set of points on any line segment, with endpoints omitted, is equivalent with the set of points on any line.

Proof

Given a line segment RS and a line l, bend RS at its midpoint T and place T on l, as shown in Figure 22.2. Now let O be the point halfway between the positions of R and S. Finally, pair points such as X_1 and Y_1, and X_2 and Y_2, obtained by using lines through point O. $\square$

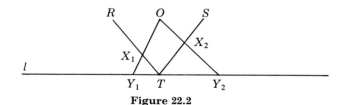

Figure 22.2

With regard to Examples 22.2 and 22.3, it can be shown that the set of points on a line segment is equivalent with the set of points on the line segment with endpoints omitted (see Problem 24.3 or Problem 25.7).

In the next section we shall show that not all infinite sets are equivalent.

The notion of a theory of infinite sets was just as revolutionary as the notion of non-Euclidean geometry. It was felt by some that use of Cantor's methods might lead to inconsistencies in mathematics, and their objection was violent. The details of the unfair treatment he received from other mathematicians furnish an excellent reminder that, even in such an objective field as mathematics, judgment is not always just; this story is told in E. T. Bell's book *Men of Mathematics* [2]. It is true that Cantor's ideas lead to difficulties if they are not handled with care; we shall consider some of these problems in Section 26.

The infinite had been contemplated and debated by philosophers for over two thousand years, but only with Cantor was it put in terms precise enough to be handled by mathematicians. Cantor did not develop his ideas from philosophical considerations or for mere entertainment. He was motivated in the beginning by delicate questions about sets of real numbers, and the origin of these questions can be traced back to the early nineteenth century when the French mathematician Fourier, and others, became involved with the mathematics of vibrating strings. By the time Cantor had finished his work on infinite sets, however, it had clearly become worth investigating for its own sake, and it is now an integral part of mathematics. We are presenting Cantor's theory as a product of mathematical imagination in the purest form— we could be grateful for it even if it had no application whatsoever.

PROBLEM SET 22

PROBLEM 22.1. Describe one-to-one correspondences between each of these pairs of sets.
(a) Natural numbers and negative integers.
(b) Natural numbers and even natural numbers.
(c) Natural numbers and all integers.
(d) Natural numbers and even integers.
(e) Natural numbers and the integers greater than 1,000,000.
(f) Natural numbers and the integers less than 1,000,000.
(g) Natural numbers and all rational numbers.
(h) Natural numbers and the rational numbers greater than 1.
(i) Natural numbers and the rational numbers between 0 and 1.
(j) Natural numbers and some proper subset of the set of real numbers between 1 and 2.

PROBLEM 22.2. Which of the following relations describe one-to-one correspondences between the indicated sets? Why?

(a) $n \leftrightarrow 3n$ for each n (natural numbers versus natural numbers).

(b) $n \leftrightarrow 3n$ for each n (natural numbers versus rational numbers).

(c) $n \leftrightarrow 3n$ for each n (rational numbers versus rational numbers).

(d) $n \leftrightarrow n + 1$ for each n (natural numbers versus natural numbers).

(e) $n \leftrightarrow n + 1$ for each n (integers versus integers).

(f) $x \leftrightarrow x^2$ for each x (real numbers versus real numbers).

(g) $x \leftrightarrow x^2$ for each x (real numbers versus positive real numbers).

(h) $x \leftrightarrow \dfrac{1}{x}$ for each x (positive rational numbers versus positive rational
numbers).

PROBLEM 22.3. Does there exist a one-to-one correspondence between the
set of positive integers and the set of positive integers less than 1,000,000?
Explain.

PROBLEM 22.4. Continue the correspondence in Example 22.1, determining
which rational numbers correspond with each of the natural numbers 9
through 15.

PROBLEM 22.5. Describe a one-to-one correspondence between the set of all
positive rational numbers and the set of all natural numbers, different
from that given in Example 22.1.

PROBLEM 22.6. The proof in Example 22.1 shows that the positive rational
numbers can be listed in a sequence (a first, a second, a third, and so on).
Explain why they cannot be listed in a sequence with each number in the
sequence greater than the one before it.

PROBLEM 22.7. (a) Write out all of the proper subsets of $\{x, y\}$.

(b) Write out all of the proper subsets of $\{x, y, z\}$.

(c) Describe an infinite number of different proper subsets of the set of
natural numbers.

PROBLEM 22.8. Using the definition of 'infinite' given in the text, show that
each of the following sets is infinite.

(a) Natural numbers greater than 100.

(b) All integers.

(c) All rational numbers.

(d) All real numbers.

PROBLEM 22.9. Write a definition of 'finite' set using the idea of equivalence,
so that a set is finite if and only if it is not infinite in the sense of the text.

PROBLEM 22.10. Two sets are said to be *disjoint* if they have no elements
in common. For example, the set of even integers and the set of odd
integers are disjoint.

(a) Describe two infinite disjoint subsets of the set of natural numbers,
other than the sets of even and odd integers.

(b) Describe three infinite subsets of the set of natural numbers such that
each pair of the three is disjoint.

(c) Do (b) with three replaced by four.

(d) Do (b) with three replaced by one hundred.

(e) Describe an infinite number of infinite subsets of the set of natural numbers such that each pair of the subsets is disjoint.

PROBLEM 22.11. It is a fact that if x is a rational number and y is an irrational number then $x + y$ is an irrational number (Problem 4.2). Criticize the following statement: The set of rational numbers is equivalent with the set of irrational numbers because of the one-to-one correspondence $x \leftrightarrow x + \sqrt{2}$ for each rational number x.

§23. Some Nonequivalent Sets

We have given examples of equivalent infinite sets, and it might be thought that any two infinite sets are equivalent; especially as some of the sets we have shown to be equivalent differ from each other so much in terms of other possible ways that sets can be compared. The next example shows that nonequivalent infinite sets do exist. It is the existence of such examples that gives our subject its interest.

EXAMPLE 23.1 (Cantor). The set of natural numbers is not equivalent with the set of real numbers between 0 and 1.

Proof

We first recall from Section 5 that the real numbers are those numbers that can be represented in the decimal system. In the present case we are concerned with those that are positive and have 0 to the left of the decimal point. (It turns out that it does matter whether 0 and 1 are included here; see Problem 24.4 or Problem 25.7.)

Two sets are equivalent if their elements can be put in one-to-one correspondence; to show they are not equivalent we must show there can be no such correspondence. We shall show that in any attempt to pair the elements of the two sets given, some real number between 0 and 1 is necessarily omitted.

Thus assume that there is a one-to-one correspondence

$$
\begin{array}{ccl}
1 & \leftrightarrow & 0.a_1 a_2 a_3 a_4 \cdots \\
2 & \leftrightarrow & 0.b_1 b_2 b_3 b_4 \cdots \\
3 & \leftrightarrow & 0.c_1 c_2 c_3 c_4 \cdots \\
4 & \leftrightarrow & 0.d_1 d_2 d_3 d_4 \cdots \\
\vdots & & \vdots
\end{array}
$$

(One should not be distracted by the fact that the alphabet does not have enough letters to carry this diagram past 26. It is the idea of the proof that we are trying to get across, and there are quite enough letters for that.) What we must show is that there is some real number between 0 and 1 not appearing on the right in the diagram. Here is how to construct such a number. Let the digits $x_1, x_2, x_3, \ldots$ in the number $0.x_1 x_2 x_3 \cdots$ be determined as follows:

$$
\begin{array}{ll}
\text{If } a_1 \neq 1, \text{ let } x_1 = 1. & \text{If } a_1 = 1, \text{ let } x_1 = 2. \\
\text{If } b_2 \neq 1, \text{ let } x_2 = 1. & \text{If } b_2 = 1, \text{ let } x_2 = 2. \\
\text{If } c_3 \neq 1, \text{ let } x_3 = 1. & \text{If } c_3 = 1, \text{ let } x_3 = 2.
\end{array}
$$

$$\cdots$$

(For example, if our diagram were

1	$\leftrightarrow$	$0.5178\cdots$
2	$\leftrightarrow$	$0.3164\cdots$
3	$\leftrightarrow$	$0.2317\cdots$
4	$\leftrightarrow$	$0.8334\cdots$

then the number $0.x_1x_2x_3\cdots$ would be $0.1221\cdots$.) We now claim that the number $0.x_1x_2x_3\cdots$ appears nowhere on the right in the original pairing. For instance, $0.x_1x_2x_3\cdots \neq 0.c_1c_2c_3\cdots$, because $x_3 \neq c_3$. Similarly, $0.x_1x_2x_3\cdots$ could not appear in the nth row for any n, because $0.x_1x_2x_3\cdots$ disagrees, in the nth place to the right of the decimal point, with the real number in the nth row of our original diagram.

As we have already pointed out, showing that $0.x_1x_2x_3\cdots$ does not appear is enough to prove the theorem. $\square$

We can combine Example 23.1 with those in the previous section to obtain other examples of nonequivalent sets. In order to do this, we point out three properties of equivalence: (1) any set is equivalent with itself (pair each individual element with itself); (2) if a set S is equivalent with a set T, then T is equivalent with S (replace each pair $x \leftrightarrow y$ by the pair $y \leftrightarrow x$); (3) if S, T, and U are sets, and S is equivalent with T and T is equivalent with U, then S is equivalent with U (if $x \leftrightarrow y$ and $y \leftrightarrow z$, then use $x \leftrightarrow z$).

EXAMPLE 23.2. The set of natural numbers is not equivalent with the set of points on a line segment.

Proof

By Example 22.2 it does not matter which line segment we use here. By the fundamental assumption made in Section 5, the set of points on the line segment between 0 and 1 is equivalent with the set of real numbers between 0 and 1 (Figure 5.1). Therefore, if the set of natural numbers were equivalent with the set of points on a line segment, then the set of natural numbers would be equivalent with the set of real numbers between 0 and 1. But this would contradict Example 23.1. Therefore, by *reductio*, the statement in Example 23.2 is proved. $\square$

The correspondence between real numbers and points on a line can be used to give the following geometric example of equivalent sets; this example moved Cantor to write, 'I see it, but I don't believe it.'

EXAMPLE 23.3. The set of points in a square is equivalent with the set of points on a line segment.

Proof

Choose a unit of length equal to a side of the square. Then the points along the bottom edge of the square can be labelled (put in one-to-one correspondence) with the real numbers between 0 and 1; and the points along the left edge of the square also can be labelled with the real numbers between 0 and 1 (see Figure 23.1). Now each point in the square determines (and is determined by) a unique pair of real numbers, the first giving its distance from the left edge of the square, the second giving its distance from the bottom edge of the square. (Figure 23.1 shows the point corresponding to the pair (0.3, 0.7).) This gives a one-to-one correspondence between the

Figure 23.1

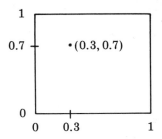

points in the square and the set of *pairs* of real numbers between 0 and 1. It now suffices to prove the following statement:

> *The set of real numbers between 0 and 1 is equivalent with the set of pairs of real numbers, each between 0 and 1.*

To prove this, let S denote the set of pairs in question and T the set of real numbers between 0 and 1. Let $(0.a_1a_2a_3 \cdots, 0.b_1b_2b_3 \cdots)$ in S correspond with $0.a_1b_1a_2b_2a_3b_3 \cdots$ in T. This yields a one-to-one correspondence of S with a subset of T, if we disallow representations ending with repeating nine (see the footnote on page 32). However, not every number in S corresponds to a pair in this way (this was once overlooked by Cantor); consider $0.\overline{09}$, for instance. Thus we complete the proof by appealing to the Equivalence Theorem in Section 24; after observing that $0.a_1a_2a_3 \cdots \leftrightarrow (0.1, \ 0.a_1a_2a_3 \cdots)$ yields a one-to-one correspondence of T with a subset of S. $\square$

PROBLEM SET 23

PROBLEM 23.1. Which real number will each of the following pairs of real numbers correspond with in the proof in Example 23.3?

(a) (0.5, 0.1)   (b) $(0.\overline{3}, 0.2)$

(c) $(0.\overline{3}, 0.\overline{6})$ (d) $(0.\overline{3}, 0.\overline{47})$

PROBLEM 23.2. Apply the idea in Example 23.3 to show that the set of points in a cube is equivalent with the set of points on a line segment.

PROBLEM 23.3. Let S denote the set of all pairs of rational numbers between 0 and 1. Using an idea like that in the proof in Example 23.3, prove that S is equivalent with the set of all rational numbers between 0 and 1. (Suggestion: There are four cases, depending on whether the decimal representations of the numbers in a pair terminate or become periodic.)

PROBLEM 23.4. Prove: If A and B are subsets of a set S, each of A and B is equivalent with the set of natural numbers, and each element of S is in A

or B (but not both), then S is equivalent with the set of natural numbers. (Suggestion: A can be written as $\{a_1, a_2, a_3, \ldots\}$. Similarly for B. Now use a scheme like that in Example 23.3.)

PROBLEM 23.5. Prove: The set of irrational numbers between 0 and 1 is not equivalent with the set of natural numbers. (Suggestion: Use Problem 22.1(i), Problem 23.4, Example 23.1, and *reductio*.)

PROBLEM 23.6. Show that the set of real numbers between 0 and 1 is equivalent with the set of all real numbers. (Suggestion: Use the previous examples, and the remarks preceding Example 23.2.)

§24. Cardinal Numbers

We pointed out in Section 22 that two finite sets will be equivalent if and only if they have the same number of elements. The central idea of this chapter is that we can extend this to define a notion of 'number' for infinite sets as well. The appropriate concept is that of 'cardinal number'. Our primary concern here is not with the concept of cardinal number itself, however, but rather with its use for comparison of sets. This is merely an extension of the way numbers are used with respect to finite sets: we do not often dwell on the meaning on the concept 'three'; what matters is that three represents something less than four, and something more than two, and so on. Thus we shall first define what it means to say that two sets 'have the same cardinal number', and then what it means to say that one set has 'smaller' or 'larger' cardinal number than another set. After that we shall discuss the meaning of 'cardinal number' itself.

DEFINITION
Two sets have the same *(or* equal*) cardinal number* if and only if they are equivalent.

For example, $\{a, b, c\}$ and $\{x, y, z\}$ have the same cardinal number. And, by Example 22.1, the set of positive rational numbers has the same cardinal number as the set of all natural numbers.

DEFINITION
A set S has smaller *cardinal number than a set T if S has the same cardinal number as some proper subset of T but does not have the same cardinal number as T. In this case we also say that T has* larger *cardinal number than S.*

Or, directly in terms of equivalence: a set S has smaller cardinal number than a set T if S is equivalent with some proper subset of T but S is not equivalent with T.

Thus $\{x, y\}$ has smaller cardinal number than $\{a, b, c\}$, as could be expected. By Example 23.1, the set of real numbers between 0 and 1 does not have the same cardinal number as the set of natural numbers. Therefore it will follow that the set of real numbers between 0 and 1 has larger cardinal number than the set of natural numbers, if we can show that the latter set is equivalent with some subset of the former. For this we can use the correspondence

$$
\begin{array}{ccccccc}
1 & 2 & 3 & 4 & 5 & \cdots & n & \cdots \\
\updownarrow & \updownarrow & \updownarrow & \updownarrow & \updownarrow & & \updownarrow & \\
1/2 & 1/3 & 1/4 & 1/5 & 1/6 & \cdots & 1/(n+1) & \cdots.
\end{array}
$$

If S and T are any two sets, then precisely one of the following is true: (1) S has the same cardinal number as T; (2) S has smaller cardinal number than T; (3) S has larger cardinal number than T. This seems reasonable, but it is not completely trivial; it is logically equivalent with the Axiom of Choice, which we shall discuss briefly in Section 26.

The following theorem offers a method for showing sets equivalent through use of the ideas just given. We used the theorem in Example 23.3 and shall refer to it in problems, but we omit its proof, which can be found in any extensive treatment of the theory of infinite sets. The theorem was conjectured by Cantor and proved independently by F. Bernstein and E. Schröder in the 1890's.

EQUIVALENCE THEOREM

If S is equivalent with a subset of T and T is equivalent with a subset of S, then S and T are equivalent.

Let us now consider briefly the meaning of 'cardinal number'. One possible definition is the following: The *cardinal number of a set S* is the set of all sets that are equivalent with S. For example, by this definition, the cardinal number of $\{x, y\}$, or what we would normally call 'two', is the set of all pairs. This definition was first given by G. Frege (German, 1848–1925) in 1884, and again by Bertrand Russell (1872–1970) in 1901. The idea behind it is simple: a satisfactory definition of the 'number' of elements in (for example) the set $\{a, b, c\}$ must consist of some property that is possessed by those sets, and only those sets, whose elements can be put in one-to-one correspondence with the elements of the set $\{a, b, c\}$. Thus we take the collection of all such sets as the cardinal number of $\{a, b, c\}$.

The Frege-Russell definition leads to subtle logical difficulties of the kind to be discussed in Section 26, however. In an attempt to avoid such difficulties, John von Neumann (1903–1957) suggested another definition in 1928. With von Neumann's definition, a set is distinguished among all the sets that are equivalent with any given set, and then the cardinal number of each of those equivalent sets is defined to be that distinguished set. Thus $\{a, b\}$ might be used as the cardinal number of each pair. Any attempt to define 'cardinal number' of a set is designed to associate some single object with all of the sets that are equivalent with that set. Rather than pursue these definitions further, however, we now return to specific examples of sets and their comparison.

Figure 24.1 shows some of the relations between cardinal numbers that follow from various examples and exercises in this and the previous

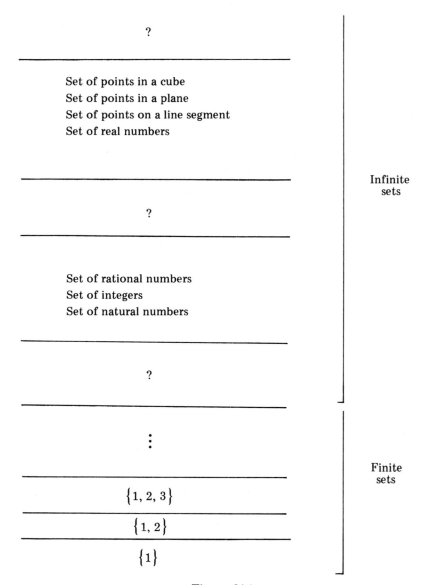

Figure 24.1

two sections. Sets separated by lines in Figure 24.1 have different cardinal numbers.

Figure 24.1 suggests three questions:

QUESTION 24A. Is there an infinite set having cardinal number smaller than that of the set of natural numbers?

QUESTION 24B. Is there a set having cardinal number larger than that of the set of natural numbers and smaller than that of the set of real numbers?

QUESTION 24C. Is there a set having cardinal number larger than that of the set of real numbers?

We shall discuss these questions in the next two sections.

PROBLEM SET 24

PROBLEM 24.1. Reproduce Figure 24.1, inserting in the appropriate places each of the following sets. Make use of previous examples and problems as needed.
(a) Set of even integers.
(b) Set of real numbers between 0 and 1.
(c) Set of real numbers between 0.1 and 0.2.
(d) Set of integers greater than 1,000,000.
(e) Set of all prime numbers.
(f) Set of irrational numbers.
(g) Set of points in a square.
(h) Set of negative integers.

PROBLEM 24.2. If S and T are sets, then $S = T$, $S \subset T$, and $S \supset T$ mean S is equal to T, S is a subset of T, and T is a subset of S, respectively. Find two subsets A and B of $\{x, y\}$ such that $A = B$, $A \subset B$, and $A \supset B$ are all false. (Thus sets are not necessarily comparable with respect to $=$, $\subset$, $\supset$. As stated in Section 24, however, their cardinal numbers are always comparable even if they are infinite.)

PROBLEM 24.3. Use the Equivalence Theorem and Example 22.2 to prove that the set of points on a line segment is equivalent with the set of points on the line segment with endpoints omitted.

PROBLEM 24.4. Use Problem 23.6 and the Equivalence Theorem to show why the following four sets are equivalent: set of real numbers between 0 and 1 inclusive, set of real numbers between 0 and 1 exclusive, set of positive real numbers, set of all real numbers.

PROBLEM 24.5. Given two sets S and T, precisely one of the following two conditions, I or II, is true:
    I. S is equivalent with some subset of T;
    II. S is equivalent with no subset of T.

Similarly, precisely one of the following two conditions, A or B, is true:
   A. T is equivalent with some subset of S;
   B. T is equivalent with no subset of S.
By a remark preceding the Equivalence Theorem, II and B cannot hold simultaneously. The combinations I,A and I,B and II,A are possible, however. What can be said about the relative cardinal numbers of S and T in each of the latter three cases?

PROBLEM 24.6. (a) Describe a one-to-one correspondence between the set of natural numbers and the set of 2-element subsets of the set of natural numbers. (Suggestion: See Example 22.1.)
(b) Use (a) to deduce that the set of natural numbers is equivalent with the set of all 2-element subsets of the set of natural numbers. Now explain why the set of natural numbers is equivalent with the set of all 3-element subsets of the set of natural numbers.
(c) State, but do not prove, the extension of (b) to n-element subsets.
(d) Show that the set of natural numbers is equivalent with the set of all finite subsets of the set of natural numbers. (Suggestion: Use part (c), and the ideas in Problem 23.4 and Example 22.1.) Compare Theorem 25.2.

§25. More Cardinal Numbers

The following theorem answers Question 24A. It shows that, although there is no largest finite cardinal number, there is a smallest infinite cardinal number.

THEOREM 25.1
   Any infinite set has cardinal number equal to, or larger than, that of the set of natural numbers.

Proof
   Let S denote an infinite set. By the remarks on page 139, S will have cardinal number either equal to, or smaller than, or larger than, that of the set of natural numbers. Therefore, the theorem will be proved if we can show that S does not have cardinal number smaller than that of the set of natural numbers.
   Let N denote the set of natural numbers. It will follow that S does not have cardinal number smaller than that of N, if we can show that S cannot be equivalent with a subset of N without being equivalent with N itself.
   Assume S is equivalent with a subset M of N. Then M is infinite because S is infinite. We shall show that M is equivalent with N, and it will follow that S is equivalent with N by remark (3) on page 136. To prove that M is equivalent with N we simply make repeated use of a fundamental fact about the set N: any subset of natural numbers (other than ϕ) contains a smallest number. Thus M

contains a smallest number, which we denote x_1. Then the subset remaining if we remove x_1 from M also will contain a smallest number, which we denote x_2. We continue in this way, getting numbers x_1, x_2, x_3, x_4, ... We now use the correspondence

$$
\begin{array}{ccccc}
1 & 2 & 3 & \cdots & n & \cdots \\
\updownarrow & \updownarrow & \updownarrow & & \updownarrow & \\
x_1 & x_2 & x_3 & \cdots & x_n & \cdots .
\end{array}
$$

Each natural number will be paired with some element of M, because M is infinite. And each element of M will ultimately appear in the second row (in fact, $x_n \geq n$ for each n, so x_n will appear no later than the nth position). This proves the theorem. $\square$

We shall discuss Question 24B in the next section. We now answer Question 25C in the affirmative. In fact, we prove something much more general than that there is a set having cardinal number larger than that of the set of real numbers. For Theorem 25.2 will show if S is any set whatsoever, then the power set of S has cardinal number larger than that of S.* Thus there is no largest cardinal number.

We recall that in Section 17 it was proved that if a finite set contains n elements then its power set contains 2^n elements. Here is a form of that theorem which applies to infinite sets as well. The proof of this theorem deserves careful study.

THEOREM 25.2 (Cantor)
If S is any set, then the power set of S has cardinal number larger than that of S.

Proof
For convenience, we shall denote the power set of S by $P(S)$. Thus $P(S)$ is the set of all subsets of S. We must show: (i) S is equivalent with some subset of $P(S)$, and (ii) S is not equivalent with $P(S)$.

(i) is easy. We simply let each element x in the set S correspond to the element $\{x\}$ in the set $P(S)$.

In order to prove (ii), we must show that in any attempt to put the elements of S in one-to-one correspondence with the elements of $P(S)$, some element of $P(S)$ will necessarily be omitted. The trick here is, just as it was in the proof of Example 23.1, to get our hands on an omitted element.

Assume then that there is a one-to-one correspondence between S and $P(S)$, and for convenience, let the element of $P(S)$ corresponding to a given x in S be denoted by S_x, that is, $x \leftrightarrow S_x$.

---

* Power sets are discussed in Section 17. Problems 17.1 and 17.5 will help smooth the way for the proof of Theorem 25.2.

Now each S_x, being an element of $P(S)$, is a subset of S, and so we can ask the following question for each element x in S: Is x an element of S_x? (Example: If $S = \{1, 2, 3\}$, and

$$1 \leftrightarrow S_1 = \{2, 3\}$$
$$2 \leftrightarrow S_2 = \{1, 3\}$$
$$3 \leftrightarrow S_3 = \{1, 2, 3\},$$

then 1 is not an element of S_1 but 3 is an element of S_3.) Consider the subset of S made up of all those elements for which the answer to the question is No, and denote this subset of S by the letter T. (In the example, $T = \{1, 2\}$.) The claim now is that T is an 'omitted' element. That is, we claim that $S_y \neq T$ for each y in S. This is true because if y is in S_y then y is not in T (so $S_y \neq T$), while if y is not in S_y then y is in T (so $S_y \neq T$). Thus in either case S_y is different from T.

This completes the proof. $\square$

Theorem 25.2 raises a question related to Question 24B. If N denotes the set of natural numbers, then by Theorem 25.2 the power set of N has cardinal number larger than that of N. And we proved in Example 23.1 that the set of real numbers has cardinal number larger than that of N. Thus we are led to ask: How does the cardinal number of the set of real numbers compare with the cardinal number of the power set of N?

EXAMPLE 25.1. The cardinal number of the set of real numbers is equal to the cardinal number of the power set of the set of natural numbers.

Proof

For this proof we recall an idea that was introduced in Problem 2.4. We indicated there that any *natural* number can be represented in the binary system (numeration system based on 2), as well as in the decimal system. More generally, any *real* number can be represented in the binary system. For example, 1011.10101 in the binary system would translate in the decimal system to

$$1 \times 8 + 0 \times 4 + 1 \times 2 + 1 \times 1 + 1 \times \tfrac{1}{2} + 0 \times \tfrac{1}{4} + 1 \times \tfrac{1}{8} + 0 \times \tfrac{1}{16}$$
$$+ 1 \times \tfrac{1}{32} = 8 + 2 + 1 + 0.5 + 0.125 + 0.03125 = 11.65625.$$

Instead of defining a real number as any number that can be represented in the decimal system (as in Section 5), we could equally well have defined a real number as any number that can be represented in the binary system.

Now the real numbers between 0 and 1 are those positive real numbers that have 0 to the left of the 'binary point'. As this set has cardinal number equal to that of the set of all real numbers (Problem 23.6), we will have proved the statement in Example 25.1 if we show that the set of positive real (binary) numbers having 0 to the left of the binary point can be put in one-to-one correspondence with the set of all subsets of the set of natural numbers. Here is a rule that defines such a correspondence*:

> Let the binary number $0.a_1a_2a_3a_4 \cdots$
> (each subscripted a either 0 or 1)
> correspond with
> the subset of N that contains exactly
> those n for which $a_n = 1$.

For example,

$$0.1101 \leftrightarrow \{1, 2, 4\} \text{ and } 0.\overline{01} \leftrightarrow \{2, 4, 6, 8, \ldots\}. \quad \square$$

Another example of the ideas in this chapter, including an application, is given in Theorem 47.2.

PROBLEM SET 25

PROBLEM 25.1. (a) Describe examples of three infinite sets R, S, and T such that the cardinal number of R is smaller than the cardinal number of S and the cardinal number of S is smaller than the cardinal number of T.
(b) Describe examples of five infinite sets such that no two have the same cardinal number.
(c) Can (b) be done if five is replaced by five hundred?
(d) Describe an infinite number of infinite sets such that no two have the same cardinal number.

PROBLEM 25.2. The cardinal number of the power set of a set cannot have the same cardinal number as the set of natural numbers. Why?

PROBLEM 25.3. Adopting the notation in the proof of Theorem 25.2, let $S = \{1, 2, 3\}$ and describe the set T in each of the following cases.
(a) $S_1 = \{1\}$, $S_2 = \{2\}$, $S_3 = \{3\}$.
(b) $S_1 = \{1\}$, $S_2 = \{1, 2\}$, $S_3 = \{1, 2, 3\}$.
(c) $S_1 = \{2, 3\}$, $S_2 = \{1, 3\}$, $S_3 = \{1, 2\}$.
(d) $S_1 = \phi$, $S_2 = \{1, 2, 3\}$, $S_3 = \{3\}$.

PROBLEM 25.4. Refer to the correspondence given at the end of the proof for Example 25.1, and describe the set of natural numbers that corresponds with each of the following real numbers.
(a) 0.1   (b) 0.11111   (c) $0.\overline{1}$
(d) 0.0   (e) $0.00\overline{1}$ (f) $0.1\overline{01}$

PROBLEM 25.5. Write each of the following binary numbers in decimal form.
(a) 0.11   (b) 11.11   (c) 111.101
(d) 0.000101   (e) $0.\overline{1}$ (f) $0.\overline{01}$

PROBLEM 25.6. Write each of the following decimal numbers in binary form.
(a) 0.5   (b) 0.25   (c) 1.5
(d) 4.5   (e) 2.75   (f) 7.875

---

* A remark like that in the footnote on page 32 applies to binary representations. The ideas in Problems 25.7 and 25.8 can be used to modify the proof in Example 25.1 taking this remark into account.

PROBLEM 25.7. Prove: If $\{x_1, x_2, \ldots, x_n\}$ is a finite subset of an infinite set S, and S' denotes the set obtained by removing $\{x_1, x_2, \ldots, x_n\}$ from S, then S and S' are equivalent. That is, if a finite subset is removed from an infinite set then what remains has the same cardinal number as the original set. (Suggestion: By Theorem 25.1, S' contains a subset $T = \{y_1, y_2, \ldots\}$ that is equivalent with the set of natural numbers. T is also a subset S. Make use of a one-to-one correspondence between $\{x_1, x_2, \ldots, x_n, y_1, y_2, \ldots\}$ (in S), and $\{y_1, y_2, \ldots\}$ (in S').)

PROBLEM 25.8. Let S denote a set, R a subset of S, and S' the subset of S obtained by removing the elements of R from S. By Problem 25.7, if S is infinite and R is finite then S and S' are equivalent.
(a) Give an example to show that if R is not assumed finite then S and S' are not necessarily equivalent. (Thus removing a subset from an infinite set may or may not change the cardinal number of the set.)
(b) Give an example to show that it is possible to have S, R, S' all infinite with S and S' equivalent.

PROBLEM 25.9. By Theorem 25.2 the set of all subsets of the set of natural numbers has larger cardinal number than that of the set of natural numbers. By Problem 24.6(d) the set of all *finite* subsets of the set of natural numbers has the same cardinal number as the set of natural numbers. Deduce that the set of all *infinite* subsets of the set of natural numbers has larger cardinal number than that of the set of natural numbers. (Suggestion: Use *reductio* and Problem 23.4.)

§26. Foundations

Question 24B is a celebrated one, first stated by Cantor in 1878. Although Cantor conjectured that the answer is No, he was not able to prove it. His conjecture eventually became known as the continuum hypothesis.*

CONTINUUM HYPOTHESIS
There does not exist a set having cardinal number larger than that of the set of natural numbers and smaller than that of the set of real numbers.

The question of whether the continuum hypothesis is, in fact, true, has received a great deal of attention from mathematicians. Before discussing it further, let us look at another type of problem that arose concerning the theory of sets.

We have mentioned that Cantor's ideas lead to difficulties if they are not handled with care, and Cantor himself pointed out one of these difficulties; it concerned the matter of what kinds of objects one should admit as sets.

---

* The word 'continuum' is sometimes used to describe any set having the same cardinal number as the set of real numbers.

CANTOR'S PARADOX

Let U denote the set of all sets. Then P(U) (the power set of U), being a set of sets, is a subset of U, and thus has either the same cardinal number as that of U or smaller cardinal number than that of U. On the other hand, we know by Theorem 25.2 that P(U) has cardinal number larger than that of U.

A similar difficulty is the following, discovered by Bertrand Russell in 1901.

RUSSELL'S PARADOX

Let R denote the set of all those sets that do not contain themselves as an element. Example of a set in R: the set of natural numbers. Examples of non-R sets: the set of abstract ideas; the set of all objects describable in exactly eleven English words. Question: Does the set R contain itself as an element? If the answer is Yes, then R, being a set that contains itself as an element, is a non-R set, and thus is not an element of itself. If the answer is No, then R, being a set that does not contain itself as an element, is a set in R, and thus is an element of itself.

The moral of such paradoxes is that restrictions must be placed on the objects that are to be called sets, if inconsistencies (contradictions) are to be avoided. In particular, Cantor's Paradox shows that a contradiction follows from the notion of 'the set of all sets'. A more basic, philosophical, question was raised by Cantor's critics: Do infinite sets exist? Some, including Cantor and most present-day mathematicians, treat infinite sets as something completed or actual; others treat them as only potential or becoming.

Because of problems arising from too-free use of terms such as 'set' and 'element', various systems of axioms have been developed as bases for theorems proved about set theory (for instance, about such things as cardinal numbers). The first such axiom system was given by Ernst Zermelo (1871–1956) in 1908. Each of these systems establishes set theory as a strict deductive science, just as the axioms of Euclid and Hilbert did for geometry, and the axioms are designed in such a way as to avoid inconsistencies such as those uncovered by the paradoxes of Cantor and Russell. Thus the axioms prohibit use of 'the set of all sets', and preclude a set from being an element of itself. The question 'Do infinite sets exist?' is answered with an axiom, the Axiom of Infinity, which guarantees the existence of infinite sets in the deductive systems; the question of whether this agrees with what one wants to believe about the real world or the world of one's imagination is a separate matter.

The consistency of any axiom system for set theory is subject to the same uncertainty as the consistency of the axiom systems for geometry, mentioned at the end of Section 14. That is, the theorem of

Gödel, asserting that consistency proofs are necessarily relative, applies to set theory as well as to geometry. What concerns us now, however, is a different theorem of Gödel, this one relating to the continuum hypothesis.

One way to prove the continuum hypothesis true, if it were true, would be to prove that a contradiction could be obtained if it were assumed false. Similarly, the continuum hypothesis would be proved false if a contradiction could be obtained from the assumption of its truth. This is analogous to the situation in geometry, where Saccheri and others attempted to prove the Fifth Postulate true by proving that a contradiction could be obtained if it were assumed false. In the case of geometry, the underlying assumptions for any such work were the five common notions and first four postulates of Euclid; in the case of set theory, they are the axioms for set theory (again, there are several possible axiom systems for set theory, but their details and differences are not important for our discussion). Gödel's contribution to this was his proof, in 1938, that the continuum hypothesis could never be disproved on the basis of the usual axioms for set theory. In other words, if a contradiction could be obtained on the basis of the usual axioms for set theory together with the continuum hypothesis, then a contradiction could be obtained on the basis of the usual axioms for set theory alone. Part of the significance of this result was that mathematicians could now use the continuum hypothesis in proving other theorems, with the knowledge that in doing so they were not in danger of introducing any inconsistencies if there were none before.

Gödel's theorem left open the possibility that the continuum hypothesis might someday be proved true. However, any hope of that was dispelled in 1963, when the U.S. mathematician Paul Cohen showed that the continuum hypothesis could not be proved on the basis of the usual axioms for set theory. Thus the status of the continuum hypothesis in set theory is like that of Euclid's Fifth Postulate in geometry: a (relatively) consistent theory of sets will be obtained if we assume, in addition to the other axioms, either the continuum hypothesis or the contradictory of the continuum hypothesis.

We close our discussion of these questions with two statements from set theory that have logical status similar to that of the continuum hypothesis. The first is the *generalized continuum hypothesis*: if S is an infinite set, then there does not exist a set having cardinal number larger than that of S and smaller than that of $P(S)$ (if S is the set of natural numbers, this is the continuum hypothesis). The second is the *axiom of choice*: if C is a nonempty collection of nonempty sets, no two of which have an element in common, then there is a set S containing exactly one element from each set. Again, these statements have logical status similar to that of the continuum hypothesis: Gödel showed they could not be disproved; Cohen has shown they cannot be proved.

REFERENCES

1. BARKER, S. F., *Philosophy of Mathematics*, Prentice-Hall, Englewood Cliffs, N. J., 1964.

2. BELL, E. T., *Men of Mathematics,* Simon and Schuster, New York, 1937.

3. CANTOR, G., *Contributions to the Founding of the Theory of Transfinite Numbers,* trans. by P. E. B. Jourdain, Open Court, Chicago and London, 1915; paperback edition, Dover, New York.

4. HILBERT, D., 'Mathematical Problems', trans. by M. W. Newson, Bulletin of the American Mathematical Society, vol. 8, 1902, pp. 437–445, 478–479. Reprinted in part in reference [12] of Chapter II.

5. KAMKE, E., *Theory of Sets,* trans. by F. Bagemihl, Dover, New York, 1950.

6. *The Mathematical Sciences*, The MIT Press, Cambridge, Mass., 1969.

7. *Mathematics in the Modern World,* with introductions by M. Kline, W. H. Freeman, San Francisco, 1968.

8. RUSSELL, B., *Introduction to Mathematical Philosophy,* Macmillan, New York, 1920.

9. VILENKIN, N. YA., *Stories about Sets,* trans. by Scripta Technica, Academic Press, New York, 1968.

10. WILDER, R. L., *Introduction to the Foundations of Mathematics,* John Wiley & Sons, New York, 1965.

CHAPTER V

Groups

§27. Group Defined

Abstract mathematical objects are so much a part of our culture that we often are not aware when we are using them. 'Circle' is not the same as wheel or coin or outline of a ball; it is an abstraction from such things. 'Two' is not $\{x, y\}$ or any other particular pair; it is an abstract property characteristic of all pairs. On a more technical level, the system of real numbers, which we have discussed in several earlier chapters, is not the same as length or time or probability; it is an abstract system useful for representing such things. Mathematics is in large part concerned with abstracting essential properties and ideas common to different kinds of natural or mathematical phenomena, and with studying the abstract objects that result. The power of this process comes, first of all, because abstraction serves as a filter to screen out things that are not pertinent to a particular problem or investigation. Second, by studying the single object that results from the abstraction, one is in reality studying all of the particular objects that it represents: for example, an engineer is free to apply the Pythagorean Theorem to any right-angled triangle, wood or steel or whatever, without stopping to verify the theorem for each such triangle. The task for mathematicians is to discover properties and ideas that can be abstracted, and to study those that are worth studying after they have been abstracted. The question of what is worth studying can be subjective, as was mentioned in Section 3. Some properties and ideas are of such universal occurrence, however, as to be of obvious importance. The concept of group, which we shall discuss in this chapter, is an abstract mathematical idea of that kind.

The main interest in groups during their early development, which began in the second half of the eighteenth century, arose from their connection with the solution of algebraic equations; we shall discuss that connection later in this section. The concept of group arises naturally in other places in mathematics, such as in geometry, and it is also useful in physics, chemistry, and crystallography; we shall touch on some of these applications in Section 29. Beginning with Section 30 we shall prove some of the elementary theorems of group theory and show how they can be used to help answer some fundamental questions in the subject. Before doing any of this, however, we must define 'group' and give several different types of examples.

The definition of group requires the notion of operation between elements of a set.

DEFINITION

> If G is any set, then an operation on G is a relationship that assigns to each ordered pair (x, y) of elements in G an element $x * y$ in G.

The term 'ordered' pair is used to convey that (x, y) is to be distinguished from (y, x): if $x \neq y$ then $x * y$, the element assigned to (x, y), may differ from $y * x$, the element assigned to (y, x).

The exact nature of the operation $*$ can take many different forms. If the set G happens to consist of numbers, then $*$ might be addition or multiplication, for instance, and then we would use the usual symbol ($+$ or $\times$) in place of $*$.

EXAMPLE 27.1. (a) Each of addition, subtraction, and multiplication is an operation on the set of integers.

(b) Division ($\div$) is not an operation on the set of integers, because $x \div 0$ is meaningless. Furthermore, $x \div y$ is not necessarily an integer, even if $y \neq 0$ (for instance, $1 \div 2 = \frac{1}{2}$ is not an integer).

(c) Division is an operation on the set of rational numbers other than 0 $((x/y) \div (z/w) = (x/y)/(z/w) = xw/yz)$.

(d) For each pair of natural numbers (m, n) let $m * n$ mean m^n. (For instance, $3 * 2 = 3^2 = 9$ and $2 * 3 = 2^3 = 8$.) This $*$ is an operation on the set of natural numbers.

(e) If G is a finite set, then we can specify an operation on G by means of a table. We form a square with the elements of the given set listed across the top and also down the left-hand side, and put $x * y$ at the intersection of the (horizontal) row with x at the left and the (vertical) column with y at the top. For example, if $G = \{u, v, w\}$, then

*	u	v	w
u	u	v	w
v	w	u	v
w	v	w	u

means that $u * u = u$, $u * v = v$, $v * u = w$, and so forth. Any way of filling in the nine spaces in the table, with entries chosen from the set $\{u, v, w\}$, will define an operation on $\{u, v, w\}$. Such tables are called *Cayley* tables, after Arthur Cayley.

Examples of other operations will be given in the next section. We now move on to the definition of group.

DEFINITION
A group is a set G together with an operation $*$ on G such that each of the following conditions is fulfilled:
(1) $x * (y * z) = (x * y) * z$ for all elements x, y, z in G;
(2) there is an element e in G such that $e * x = x * e = x$ for each element x in G; and
(3) for each element x in G there is an element y in G such that $x * y = y * x = e$.

Property (1) in the definition is called the *associative law*. The element e whose existence is decreed in (2) is called the *identity element* of the group (we shall prove eventually that a group has only one such element)†. The element y such that $x * y = y * x = e$, which exists by (3), is called the *inverse* of the element x. It is sometimes convenient to refer to 'the group G', but it should be stressed that a group consists of two things, a set and an operation on that set.

EXAMPLE 27.2. (a) The set of integers together with $+$ is a group. The identity element is 0, and the inverse of an element x is $-x$.
(b) The set of rational numbers other than 0, together with multiplication, is a group. The identity element is 1, and the inverse of an element r/s is $(r/s)^{-1} = s/r$.
(c) The set of natural numbers together with $+$ is not a group, because there is no identity element. Even if we used the natural numbers and 0, together with $+$, we would not get a group, for although 0 would be an identity element nothing other than 0 would have an inverse.
(d) The set of natural numbers together with the operation defined in Example 27.1(d) is not a group, because that operation is not associative (among

---

† This e should not be confused with the constant real number e appearing in the defining equation for the normal curve in Chapter III. The e we are using here is simply a symbol to denote a specific element in a group, and will be different things in different groups.

other things). For instance, $(2 * 3) * 2 = (2^3) * 2 = 8 * 2 = 8^2 = 64$ while $2 * (3 * 2) = 2 * (3^2) = 2 * 9 = 2^9 = 512$.

(e) The set $\{1, -1\}$ together with multiplication is a group.

(f) The set $\{u, v, w\}$ together with the operation $*$ defined in Example 27.1 (e) is not a group. For instance, there is no identity element.

(g) Here is a Cayley table for a group with three elements:

$*$	a	b	c
a	a	b	c
b	b	c	a
c	c	a	b

The identity element is a, and the inverses of a, b, and c are a, c, and b, respectively.

In the next section we shall describe a wide class of groups in which the sets are something other than numbers and the operations something other than the usual operations of arithmetic. But first let us discuss the connection between groups and algebraic equations; for our purposes this is of historical interest, and we shall not use specific facts from this discussion later in the chapter.

The simplest kinds of algebraic equations involving an unknown x are those of first degree, that is, those of the form

$$ax + b = 0,$$

where a and b are given coefficients (real numbers, for instance) with $a \neq 0$. The solution of such an equation is $x = -b/a$. Thus the solution of $2x + 3 = 0$ is $x = -3/2$.

The quadratic (second degree) equations are those of the form

$$ax^2 + bx + c = 0,$$

where a, b, and c are given coefficients with $a \neq 0$. These have two solutions, and they can be obtained by use of the quadratic formula,

$$x = \frac{-b \pm \sqrt{b^2 - 4ac}}{2a},$$

the $+$ sign giving one solution, the $-$ sign the other. Thus the solutions of $x^2 + 3x + 1 = 0$ are

$$x = \frac{-3 \pm \sqrt{3^2 - 4 \cdot 1 \cdot 1}}{2 \cdot 1} = \frac{-3 \pm \sqrt{5}}{2}.$$

(There is a special problem if the term $b^2 - 4ac$ in the square root is negative. We shall ignore this for the present and return to it in Section 46.)

Methods for solving first and second degree equations were known by the sixteenth century; particular types of quadratics had been handled by the Egyptians, Babylonians, and Greeks, and by the Hindus and Arabs in the Middle Ages. But the problem of solving the general cubic (third degree) equation,

$$ax^3 + bx^2 + cx + d = 0,$$

was much more difficult. It was solved, however, by sixteenth century Italian algebraists, who went on to discover formulas for solving the general quartic (fourth degree) equation,

$$ax^4 + bx^3 + cx^2 + dx + e = 0,$$

as well. (The names associated with these discoveries are del Ferro, Cardan, Tartaglia, and Ferrari, with a controversy over priorities which is discussed in any extensive history of mathematics.) The detailed form of these solutions is fairly complicated, and it is not important here. The point is that it is possible to write the solutions of the equations by combining the coefficients $a, b, \ldots$ in a perfectly well-determined way using the fundamental operations of arithmetic—addition, subtraction, multiplication, division, and extraction of roots—much as with the quadratic formula[†]. The discovery of these general solutions is sometimes taken as the beginning of the modern period of mathematics.

It should be stressed that the solutions we are discussing here are exact solutions; the problem of obtaining approximate solutions is a different matter. For instance, an exact solution of $x^2 - 2 = 0$ is $\sqrt{2}$; an approximate solution is 1.414. The latter would be preferable for some purposes, but it is not satisfactory if we are looking for exact solutions. This distinction marks an extremely important contrast in points of view. For many practical applications of mathematics approximate answers are sufficient, and they are often the only answers that can be obtained. But exact answers are what one would like, and it is the dissatisfaction with settling for less that has raised mathematics above the level of simple calculations with numbers.

In the broadest sense it is the general algebraic equation,

$$a_n x^n + a_{n-1} x^{n-1} + \cdots + a_1 x + a_0 = 0,$$

which is of interest; this equation is said to be of degree n if $a_n \neq 0$. After finding methods for solving algebraic equations of degrees up through four, one would obviously like to extend the results to equations of degree five and higher. It is in passing from equations of degree four to equations of higher degree that the theory of groups becomes important. In 1770–1771 the Frenchman J. L. Lagrange (1736–1813), regarded by many as the best mathematician of the eighteenth century, introduced methods of studying algebraic equations that in reality involved group theory. Lagrange was able to show by these methods that certain systematic techniques for deriving solutions of equations of

---

[†] The operations are to be applied only a finite number of times. Thus, for instance, the use of infinite series (Section 45) is disallowed.

degree less than five could not be extended to equations of degree five or higher; there remained the possibility that some other techniques for deriving solutions might be found. However, in 1824 the Norwegian mathematician N. H. Abel (1802–1829) used ideas introduced by Lagrange to show that there can be no formulas for solving general equations of degree higher than four. Thus, the efforts to extend the results on third and fourth degree equations to general equations of higher degree had failed for the same reasons efforts to prove Euclid's Fifth Postulate had failed: success was logically impossible in both cases.

Abel's theorem showed that the solutions to the most general equations of degree higher than four could not be written by combining the coefficients through use of the fundamental operations of arithmetic. Still, the solutions for some particular equations of degree higher than four can be written in that way: for example, the solutions of $x^5 - 5x^3 + 4x = 0$ are 0, 1, -1, 2, -2, and they can be written in terms of the coefficients 1, -5, 4 by repeated use of the fundamental operations. The problem of deciding which higher degree equations can be solved in this way led the French mathematician Evariste Galois (1811–1832) to an understanding of the basic connection between groups and algebraic equations. Galois theory, as the study of this connection is now called, gives a method, making use of properties of groups related to the equations, for deciding which equations have solutions derivable from their coefficients by use of the fundamental operations. (Galois theory reveals, for example, that the solutions of the equation $x^5 + x - 3 = 0$ cannot be expressed in terms of the coefficients 1, 1, -3 by repeated use of the fundamental operations.) Regrettably, the details of Galois theory are too complicated to be discussed here.

The general concept of group grew out of this work with algebraic equations. Although Lagrange made use of the ideas of group theory, it was not until Galois that the group concept was made clear; groups then became objects of independent interest with the work of A. L. Cauchy (1789–1867), another Frenchman, in the mid-1840's. The early period of group theory was marred by the premature deaths of Abel and Galois, Abel of tuberculosis at age 26, Galois as a result of a duel at age 20; both had shown enormous mathematical potential. We shall later make some remarks about more recent history of group theory.

PROBLEM SET 27

PROBLEM 27.1. Decide in each of the following cases whether the given set together with the given operation is a group. If it is not a group, state at least one of the conditions in the definition of group that is violated. If it is a group, give the identity element and describe the inverse of each element.

(a) Set of all even integers, addition $(+)$.

(b) Set of all integer multiples of 5 $(\ldots, -10, -5, 0, 5, 10, \ldots)$, addition $(+)$.

(c) Set of all integers, multiplication $(\times)$.

(d) Set of all integers other than 0, multiplication $(\times)$.

(e) Set of all integers, subtraction $(-)$.

(f) Set of all positive rational numbers, multiplication $(\times)$.

(g) Set of all rational numbers other than 0, division $(\div)$.

(h) Set of all irrational numbers, addition $(+)$.

(i) Set of all irrational numbers, multiplication $(\times)$.

PROBLEM 27.2. Verify that the operation in Example 27.1(e) does not satisfy the associative law.

PROBLEM 27.3. Determine whether each of the following determines an operation on the set of integers. For those which do, state whether the associative law is satisfied and whether there is an identity element. Give reasons.

(a) $m * n = m + n + 1$ (b) $m * n = m - n$

(c) $m * n = 2mn$ (d) $m * n = 5$

(e) $m * n = mn + 1$ (f) $m * n = m$

(g) $m * n = \sqrt{mn}$ (h) $m * n = 5m + n$

PROBLEM 27.4. An operation $*$ on a set G is said to satisfy the *commutative law* (or to be *commutative*) if $x * y = y * x$ for all elements x and y in G. Thus the operation in Example 27.1(e) is not commutative because $u * v \neq v * u$, for instance. State whether each of the following operations is commutative.

(a)–(h) The operations in Problem 27.3.

(i) Addition of integers.

(j) Subtraction of integers.

(k) Multiplication of rational numbers.

(l) The operation in Example 27.1(d).

PROBLEM 27.5. Construct an operation (table) for the set $\{a, b\}$ so that $\{a, b\}$ together with this operation is a group.

PROBLEM 27.6. Construct a new operation (table) for the set $\{u, v, w\}$ in Example 27.1(e) so that $\{u, v, w\}$ together with this new operation is a group. (Suggestion: See Example 27.2(g).)

PROBLEM 27.7. In terms of Cayley tables, two operations on a finite set G are different if the tables differ in at least one entry (assuming the outside rows and columns to be the same for the two tables). Thus the two operations $*$ and $\circ$ shown here are different because $v * u = u$ while $v \circ u = v$.

$*$	u	v
u	u	v
v	u	u

$\circ$	u	v
u	u	v
v	v	u

(a) How many different operations are there on $\{u, v\}$?

(b) How many different operations are there on $\{u, v, w\}$?

(c) Of the operations in (a), how many yield a group?

(d) Of the operations in (b), how many have u as an identity element?

(e) How many different operations are there on a finite set having n elements? (Suggestion: See Section 16.)

PROBLEM 27.8. For x an element of a group, x^2 is defined to mean $x * x$, x^3 to mean $x^2 * x$, and, in general, x^{n+1} to mean $x^n * x$ (n a positive integer). For the group in Example 27.2(g), compute a^2, a^3, b^2, b^3, c^2, and c^3.

PROBLEM 27.9. In Example 27.1(b) it is stated that $x \div 0$, that is, division by zero, is meaningless. Why is that so? (Suggestion: $x \div y = z$ means $x = yz$.)

PROBLEM 27.10. If $*$ is an operation on a set G, then an element e in G is said to be a *left identity element* for the operation if $e * x = x$ for each element x in G; e is said to be a *right identity element* if $x * e = x$ for each element x in G. Thus an identity element in a group is both a left identity element and a right identity element.

(a) The operation in Example 27.1(d) has a right identity element. What is it?

(b) The operation in Example 27.1(e) has a left identity element. What is it? (Compare Example 27.2(f).)

(c) Construct a new operation (table) for the set $\{u, v, w\}$ in Example 27.1(e) so that there is a right identity element but no left identity element.

(d) Construct a new operation (table) for the set $\{u, v, w\}$ in Example 27.1(e) so that there is a left identity element and a right identity element.

(e) For the table constructed in (d), the left identity element and the right identity element were necessarily the same. Prove that this must always be the case. That is, prove that if e is a left identity for an operation $*$ on a set G, and f is a right identity for the same operation, then $e = f$. (Suggestion: What is $e * f$?)

PROBLEM 27.11. The associative law (the first property in the definition of group) states that the 'product' of three elements is determined by the order in which they are written and not by the way in which parentheses are inserted between them. It follows from this that the same is true of products of more than three elements. Thus $t * (u * (v * w)) = (t * u) * (v * w)$, as can be seen from the associative law by treating $v * w$ as a single element (which it is).

(a) Use the associative law to verify that $(t * u) * (v * w) = ((t * u) * v) * w$ for t, u, v, and w elements of a group.

(b) Do the same for $((t * u) * v) * w = t * ((u * v) * w)$.

(c) If the associative law is not assumed, how many different products could be obtained from t, u, v, and w, combined in that order? (How many ways are there of inserting two sets of parentheses in $t * u * v * w$?)

§28. Permutation Groups

By a *permutation* of a set S is meant a one-to-one correspondence of the elements of S with themselves.† For example, each of the following is a permutation of the set $\{1, 2, 3\}$:

$$
\begin{array}{ccc}
1 & 2 & 3 \\
\updownarrow & \updownarrow & \updownarrow \\
1 & 2 & 3
\end{array}
\qquad
\begin{array}{ccc}
1 & 2 & 3 \\
\updownarrow & \updownarrow & \updownarrow \\
2 & 3 & 1.
\end{array}
$$

---

† One-to-one correspondence is defined in Section 22.

If we agree to write the numbers in the top row in increasing order, as in the two cases shown, then the correspondence is completely determined by the arrangement of the numbers in the second row. Thus these one-to-one correspondences can be thought of as 'permutations of 3 elements taken 3 at a time', in the sense of the definition in Section 18; this justifies use of the word 'permutation' here.

We shall be concerned in this section only with finite sets, and in fact we shall restrict attention to permutations of sets of the form $\{1, 2, 3, \ldots, n\}$, where n will be a positive integer. To simplify notation,

$$
\begin{array}{cccc}
1 & 2 & 3 & n \\
\updownarrow & \updownarrow & \updownarrow & \cdots \quad \updownarrow \\
k_1 & k_2 & k_3 & k_n
\end{array}
$$

will be written as

$$
\begin{pmatrix}
1 & 2 & 3 & \cdots & n \\
k_1 & k_2 & k_3 & \cdots & k_n
\end{pmatrix}.
$$

Here $k_1, k_2, k_3, \ldots, k_n$ are just the numbers $1, 2, 3, \ldots, n$ in some order.

By the formula for $P(n, k)$, in Section 18, we know that there are $P(n, n) = n!$ permutations of the set $\{1, 2, 3, \ldots, n\}$. Let us write all of these for the case $\{1, 2, 3,\}$.

EXAMPLE 28.1. Here are the $3! = 6$ permutations of the set $\{1, 2, 3,\}$ (we label them $P_1, \ldots, P_6$ so that we can refer to them later):

$$
P_1 = \begin{pmatrix} 1 & 2 & 3 \\ 1 & 2 & 3 \end{pmatrix}, \qquad
P_2 = \begin{pmatrix} 1 & 2 & 3 \\ 2 & 3 & 1 \end{pmatrix}, \qquad
P_3 = \begin{pmatrix} 1 & 2 & 3 \\ 3 & 1 & 2 \end{pmatrix},
$$

$$
P_4 = \begin{pmatrix} 1 & 2 & 3 \\ 1 & 3 & 2 \end{pmatrix}, \qquad
P_5 = \begin{pmatrix} 1 & 2 & 3 \\ 3 & 2 & 1 \end{pmatrix}, \qquad
P_6 = \begin{pmatrix} 1 & 2 & 3 \\ 2 & 1 & 3 \end{pmatrix}.
$$

We now want to introduce a class of groups whose elements will be permutations. In order to do this, we must have an operation on the set of permutations of $\{1, 2, 3, \ldots, n\}$. That is, we must have some way of combining two given permutations to obtain a third permutation. The operation we shall use is called the *composition* of the permutations. If we think of a permutation as giving a rearrangement of the numbers $1, 2, \ldots, n$, then the composition of two given permutations can be described as follows: perform the first rearrangement, then the second; the resulting rearrangement is the composition of the two. We shall use the symbol $\circ$ to denote this operation (composition).

EXAMPLE 28.2. (a)

$$
\begin{pmatrix} 1 & 2 & 3 \\ 2 & 3 & 1 \end{pmatrix} \circ \begin{pmatrix} 1 & 2 & 3 \\ 1 & 3 & 2 \end{pmatrix} = \begin{pmatrix} 1 & 2 & 3 \\ 3 & 2 & 1 \end{pmatrix}
$$

Here the first permutation moves 1 to 2, and the second permutation moves 2 to 3; therefore the composition moves 1 to 3. The first moves 2 to 3, and the second moves 3 to 2; therefore the composition moves 2 to 2 (leaves 2 fixed). The first moves 3 to 1, the second moves 1 to 1; therefore the composition moves 3 to 1. Thus the composition of the two permutations on the left has the same effect on 1, 2, and 3 as the permutation on the right, and that is what is meant by equality of the two sides.

(b)

$$\begin{pmatrix} 1 & 2 & 3 & 4 \\ 2 & 4 & 3 & 1 \end{pmatrix} \circ \begin{pmatrix} 1 & 2 & 3 & 4 \\ 4 & 1 & 2 & 3 \end{pmatrix} = \begin{pmatrix} 1 & 2 & 3 & 4 \\ 1 & 3 & 2 & 4 \end{pmatrix}$$

EXAMPLE 28.3. Here is the Cayley table for the operation $\circ$ on the set $\{P_1, \ldots, P_6\}$ of all permutations of $\{1, 2, 3\}$ (Example 28.1):

$\circ$	P_1	P_2	P_3	P_4	P_5	P_6
P_1	P_1	P_2	P_3	P_4	P_5	P_6
P_2	P_2	P_3	P_1	P_5	P_6	P_4
P_3	P_3	P_1	P_2	P_6	P_4	P_5
P_4	P_4	P_6	P_5	P_1	P_3	P_2
P_5	P_5	P_4	P_6	P_2	P_1	P_3
P_6	P_6	P_5	P_4	P_3	P_2	P_1

We observe that P_1 is an identity element with respect to this operation. That is, $P_1 \circ P_k = P_k \circ P_1 = P_k$ for each $k = 1, 2, \ldots, 6$. The operation is associative, also. This could be verified by direct computation, but that would be laborious. It is simpler and more efficient to observe the following general fact about compositions of permutations.

If P, Q, R are any permutations of a set, then

$$P \circ (Q \circ R) = (P \circ Q) \circ R.$$

In the special case of P_2, P_3, and P_6, above,

$$P_2 \circ (P_3 \circ P_6) = P_2 \circ P_5 = P_6,$$

and also

$$(P_2 \circ P_3) \circ P_6 = P_1 \circ P_6 = P_6.$$

More generally, assume that w is an arbitrary element of the set permuted by P, Q, and R, and assume that P moves w to x, Q moves x to y, and R moves y to z. Then $Q \circ R$ moves x to z, so $P \circ (Q \circ R)$ moves w to z. And $P \circ Q$ moves

w to y, so $(P \circ Q) \circ R$ also moves w to z. Thus $P \circ (Q \circ R)$ and $(P \circ Q) \circ R$ have the same effect on each element on which they act, and so they are equal. Thus the associative law for the Cayley table above is a special case of the associative law for the operation $\circ$ in general.

If we now recall the definition of group from the previous section, we see that the table above defines a group if each element has an inverse. That is, we have verified (1) and (2) in the definition of group, so only (3) remains: the inverses of $P_1, P_2, P_3, P_4, P_5, P_6$ are $P_1, P_3, P_2, P_4, P_5, P_6$, respectively.

Summarizing, we have proved that the set of all permutations of the set $\{1, 2, 3\}$ is a group with respect to the operation $\circ$ (composition). This is a special case of the following theorem.

THEOREM 28.1

The set of all permutations of the set $\{1, 2, \ldots, n\}$ is a group with respect to the operation $\circ$ (composition). This group will be denoted by S_n and will be called the symmetric group of degree n.

Proof

The associative law is a consequence of the general remark in Example 28.3. The identity element of the group is

$$\begin{pmatrix} 1 & 2 & 3 & \cdots & n \\ 1 & 2 & 3 & \cdots & n \end{pmatrix}.$$

The inverse of a permutation, thought of as a rearrangement, is the permutation that moves each number back to its original position: if the permutation P moves t to n_t, then the inverse of P moves n_t to t. $\square$

In constructing the group S_n we used the operation $\circ$ and all $n!$ of the permutations of the set $\{1, 2, \ldots, n\}$. It is possible to construct groups by using some subset of permutations of $\{1, 2, \ldots, n\}$, together with $\circ$, if the subset is chosen with care. Such groups are called *permutation groups*, and they are simply the subgroups of S_n, in the sense of the following general definition.

DEFINITION

If G together with $*$ is a group, then H is a subgroup of G (with respect to $*$) if:
(1) H is a subset of G; and
(2) H together with $*$ is a group.

Before presenting examples of subgroups, we stress that for H to be a subgroup of G it is necessary that $x * y$ be in H whenever x and y are in H. Also, the identity of G must be in H and the inverse of each element in H must be in H. The associative law automatically will be satisfied for a subset H of G: if $x * (y * z) = (x * y) * z$ is true for all elements of G, then it is certainly true for all elements of H.

EXAMPLE 28.4. (a) The set of all even integers is a subgroup of the group of all integers with respect to $+$.

(b) The group in Example 27.2(e) is a subgroup of the group in Example 27.2(b).
(c) If e is the identity element of a group, then $\{e\}$ is a subgroup of the group. Thus $\{0\}$ is a subgroup of the group of all integers with respect to $+$.
(d) If G together with $*$ is a group, then G is a subgroup of G (with respect to $*$).
(e) S_3, the group in Example 28.3, has six different subgroups:

$$\{P_1\}, \ \{P_1, P_4\}, \ \{P_1, P_5\}, \ \{P_1, P_6\}, \ \{P_1, P_2, P_3\}, \ \{P_1, P_2, P_3, P_4, P_5, P_6\}.$$

There are no others (Problem 28.5). Thus S_3 has 6 different sub*groups*, but $2^6 = 64$ sub*sets* (Theorem 17.1). It is true in general that few of the subsets of a group are subgroups. In Section 31 we shall obtain more precise information concerning which subsets of a group can be subgroups.

Assume that G is a group and that S is a subset of G. Then, as pointed out in the last example, S may not be a subgroup of G. We shall see in the next section that it is useful to associate with S the smallest subgroup of G containing S. There is such a subgroup, and it is referred to as the subgroup of G *generated* by the set S. This subgroup will be denoted by $\langle S \rangle$, or, if S is a set consisting of x, y, $\ldots$, then it will be denoted by $\langle x, y, \ldots \rangle$. The remarks preceding Example 28.4 are helpful in determining $\langle S \rangle$ from S.

EXAMPLE 28.5. (a) Because $\{e\}$ is already a subgroup of any group for which e denotes the identity element, $\langle e \rangle = \{e\}$.
(b) What is the subgroup $\langle 2 \rangle$ in the group of integers? Making use of the remark preceding Example 28.4, we see that $\langle 2 \rangle$ must contain $2 + 2 = 4$, then $2 + 4 = 6$, then $2 + 6 = 8$, and so on, so that $\langle 2 \rangle$ must contain all positive even integers. Also, $\langle 2 \rangle$ must contain the identity element 0, and the negative (inverse) of each of its elements, that is, it must contain the negative even integers. Thus $\langle 2 \rangle$ is the subgroup of even integers (Example 28.4(a)).
(c) Referring to Example 28.4(e), we see that in S_3,

$$\begin{aligned}
\langle P_2 \rangle &= \{P_1, P_2, P_3\}, \\
\langle P_3 \rangle &= \{P_1, P_2, P_3\}, \\
\langle P_4 \rangle &= \{P_1, P_4\}, \\
\langle P_2, P_3 \rangle &= \{P_1, P_2, P_3\}, \\
\langle P_2, P_4 \rangle &= S_3.
\end{aligned}$$

There is a special kind of permutation group that we shall need in the next section. We illustrate it here in the case of subgroups of S_n. If T is a subset of $\{1, 2, \ldots, n\}$, then we say that a permutation in S_n leaves T *invariant* if it permutes the elements of T among themselves. Thus a permutation leaving T invariant moves no element of T outside of T.

EXAMPLE 28.6. (a) Consider the subset of S_3 consisting of the permutations that leave $\{1\}$ invariant. Referring to Example 28.1, we see that this subset is $\{P_1, P_4\}$, and it is a subgroup of S_3.

(b) Consider the subset of S_4 consisting of the permutations that leave the set $\{2, 3\}$ invariant. This subset is

$$\left\{ \begin{pmatrix} 1 & 2 & 3 & 4 \\ 1 & 2 & 3 & 4 \end{pmatrix}, \begin{pmatrix} 1 & 2 & 3 & 4 \\ 1 & 3 & 2 & 4 \end{pmatrix}, \begin{pmatrix} 1 & 2 & 3 & 4 \\ 4 & 2 & 3 & 1 \end{pmatrix}, \begin{pmatrix} 1 & 2 & 3 & 4 \\ 4 & 3 & 2 & 1 \end{pmatrix} \right\},$$

and it is a subgroup of S_4.

(c) In general, if T is any subset of $\{1, 2, \ldots, n\}$, then the subset of S_n consisting of the permutations that leave T invariant is a subgroup of S_n. (Compare Theorem 29.2.)

PROBLEM SET 28

PROBLEM 28.1. Assume

$$Q_1 = \begin{pmatrix} 1 & 2 & 3 & 4 \\ 2 & 3 & 1 & 4 \end{pmatrix}, \quad Q_2 = \begin{pmatrix} 1 & 2 & 3 & 4 \\ 1 & 3 & 2 & 4 \end{pmatrix}, \quad Q_3 = \begin{pmatrix} 1 & 2 & 3 & 4 \\ 4 & 1 & 2 & 3 \end{pmatrix}.$$

Compute each of the following.

(a) $Q_1 \circ Q_2$

(b) $Q_2 \circ Q_1$

(c) $Q_2 \circ Q_3$

(d) $Q_3 \circ Q_2$

(e) $Q_1 \circ (Q_2 \circ Q_3)$

(f) $(Q_1 \circ Q_2) \circ Q_3$

(g) Q_1^{-1} (inverse of Q_1)

(h) Q_2^{-1}

(i) Q_3^{-1}

(j) $Q_3^2 = Q_3 \circ Q_3$ (See Problem 27.8.)

(k) Q_3^3

(l) Q_3^4

PROBLEM 28.2. Verify that $\{Q_3, Q_3^2, Q_3^3, Q_3^4\}$ is a subgroup of S_4 (see Problem 28.1). What is the inverse of each of the elements in the subgroup?

PROBLEM 28.3. Which elements in S_3 are their own inverse? (Make use of the table in Example 28.3.)

PROBLEM 28.4. Use the table in Example 28.3 to compute the following, in S_3.

(a) $P_2 \circ P_3$

(b) $P_2^2 = P_2 \circ P_2$

(c) $P_2^4 = P_2 \circ P_2 \circ P_2 \circ P_2$

(d) $P_1 \circ P_2 \circ P_3$

(e) $P_1 \circ P_2 \circ P_3 \circ P_4$

(f) $P_4 \circ P_3 \circ P_2 \circ P_1$

(g) $P_1 \circ P_2 \circ P_3 \circ P_4 \circ P_5$

(h) $P_5 \circ P_4 \circ P_3 \circ P_2 \circ P_1$

PROBLEM 28.5. Verify that S_3 has no subgroups other than those listed in Example 28.4(e).

PROBLEM 28.6. List all of the elements in each of the following subgroups. (See Example 28.5 and the paragraph preceding it.)

(a) $\left\langle \begin{pmatrix} 1 & 2 & 3 & 4 \\ 2 & 1 & 4 & 3 \end{pmatrix} \right\rangle$

(b) $\left\langle \begin{pmatrix} 1 & 2 & 3 & 4 \\ 2 & 3 & 4 & 1 \end{pmatrix} \right\rangle$

(c) $\left\langle \begin{pmatrix} 1 & 2 & 3 & 4 \\ 1 & 3 & 4 & 2 \end{pmatrix} \right\rangle$

(d) $\left\langle \begin{pmatrix} 1 & 2 & 3 & 4 \\ 1 & 4 & 3 & 2 \end{pmatrix} \right\rangle$

(e) $\left\langle \begin{pmatrix} 1 & 2 & 3 & 4 \\ 2 & 1 & 4 & 3 \end{pmatrix}, \begin{pmatrix} 1 & 2 & 3 & 4 \\ 3 & 4 & 1 & 2 \end{pmatrix} \right\rangle$

(f) $\left\langle \begin{pmatrix} 1 & 2 & 3 & 4 \\ 1 & 3 & 4 & 2 \end{pmatrix}, \begin{pmatrix} 1 & 2 & 3 & 4 \\ 1 & 2 & 4 & 3 \end{pmatrix} \right\rangle$

(g) $\left\langle \begin{pmatrix} 1 & 2 & 3 & 4 \\ 2 & 3 & 4 & 1 \end{pmatrix}, \begin{pmatrix} 1 & 2 & 3 & 4 \\ 2 & 1 & 4 & 3 \end{pmatrix} \right\rangle$

(h) $\left\langle \begin{pmatrix} 1 & 2 & 3 & 4 \\ 1 & 3 & 4 & 2 \end{pmatrix}, \begin{pmatrix} 1 & 2 & 3 & 4 \\ 1 & 3 & 2 & 4 \end{pmatrix} \right\rangle$

PROBLEM 28.7. Determine the subgroups of S_3 consisting of the permutations that leave the following sets invariant. (See Example 28.6 and the paragraph preceding it.)

(a) $\{2\}$ (b) $\{3\}$
(c) $\{1, 2\}$ (d) $\{1, 3\}$
(e) $\{2, 3\}$ (f) $\{1, 2, 3\}$

PROBLEM 28.8. Determine the subgroups of S_4 consisting of the permutations that leave the following sets invariant. (See Example 28.6 and the paragraph preceding it.)

(a) $\{1\}$ (b) $\{1, 2\}$
(c) $\{1, 3\}$ (d) $\{2, 3, 4\}$
(e) $\{1, 3, 4\}$ (f) $\{1, 2, 3, 4\}$

PROBLEM 28.9. A group G is said to be *cyclic* if it is generated by a single element, that is, if $G = \langle g \rangle$ for some g in G. Which subgroups of S_3 are cyclic? (See Example 28.4(e).)

PROBLEM 28.10. It can be proved that every subgroup of the group of integers (operation addition) is cyclic, as defined in Problem 28.9. Verify this for each of the following subgroups by finding a generator for each.

(a) $\langle 2, 3 \rangle$ (b) $\langle 2, 4 \rangle$
(c) $\langle 3, 5 \rangle$ (d) $\langle 4, 6 \rangle$
(e) $\langle -1, 2 \rangle$ (f) $\langle 6, 10, 15 \rangle$
(g) $\langle -2, 2 \rangle$ (h) $\langle 0, 5 \rangle$

PROBLEM 28.11. Not every subgroup of the group of rational numbers (operation addition) is cyclic, as defined in Problem 28.9. Verify, however, that each of the following is cyclic, by finding a generator for each.

(a) $\langle \frac{1}{2}, 1 \rangle$ (b) $\langle \frac{1}{4}, \frac{1}{2} \rangle$
(c) $\langle 2, 3 \rangle$ (d) $\langle \frac{1}{2}, \frac{1}{3} \rangle$
(e) $\langle \frac{1}{2}, \frac{1}{3}, \frac{1}{5} \rangle$ (f) $\langle 0, \frac{1}{3} \rangle$
(g) $\langle -\frac{1}{6}, -\frac{1}{4} \rangle$ (h) $\langle \frac{1}{7}, 14 \rangle$

PROBLEM 28.12. Prove that the group of all rational numbers (operation addition) is not cyclic, as defined in Problem 28.9. (Suggestion: Denote the group by R, assume $R = \langle r \rangle$, and use a *reductio* proof, considering $\frac{1}{2}r$.)

PROBLEM 28.13. The *center* of a group G is defined to be the set of elements g in G for which $x * g = g * x$ for every x in G.

(a) Verify that the center of S_3 is $\{P_1\}$, by observing that $P_1 \circ P_k = P_k \circ P_1$ for each k, and then finding an element P_m in S_3 such that $P_2 \circ P_m \neq P_m \circ P_2$, and so on for P_3, P_4, P_5, P_6. (Make use of the table in Example 28.3.)

(b) What is the center of a group whose operation is commutative, as defined in Problem 27.4?

(c) Prove that the center of any group is a subgroup of that group.

§29. Symmetry

We have said that group theory is useful in physics, chemistry, and crystallography, as well as in the study of algebraic equations. In each case the usefulness of groups comes about because they are the appropriate mathematical objects for analyzing symmetry. In crystallography, groups are used to describe in a precise way the kinds of symmetries that can arise in crystals, each kind of symmetry giving rise to a different group; a crystal can then be classified according to the group describing its symmetry. In the study of algebraic equations, a group is associated with each equation, and this group characterizes a type of symmetry involving the roots of the equation; it is possible to answer questions about the solvability of an equation by studying the group associated with the equation. The details of how groups are used in these applications tend to be complicated and require more information about groups and the particular fields of application than can be discussed here. We can, however, indicate the way in which groups are used to characterize some familiar kinds of ornamental symmetry. But first we must examine our intuitive notion of symmetry and turn it into something that can be handled mathematically. We shall restrict our attention to plane figures; the extension to three-dimensional figures, while more complex, would not add anything significant for our purposes.

The two figures shown in Figure 29.1 are symmetric, but they are symmetric in different ways. Figure 29.1(a) is symmetric with respect to the vertical line l dividing it in half, and Figure 29.1(b) is symmetric

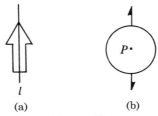

(a)   (b)

Figure 29.1

with respect to the point P in its center. To make these notions more precise, let us agree that *two points A and B are symmetric with respect to a line m* if m is perpendicular to AB and bisects AB. Thus the points A and B in Figure 29.2 are symmetric with respect to the line m. We say that *a geometric figure is symmetric with respect to a line* if whenever the figure contains one of a pair of points symmetric with respect to the line then it contains the other as well.

The symmetry of Figure 29.1(b) can be described in a similar way, by agreeing that *two points are symmetric with respect to a third point*

A •

_____ C E D
m •   •   •

B •

Figure 29.2

if the third point is midway between the other two. Thus C and D are symmetric with respect to E in Figure 29.2. *A geometric figure is symmetric with respect to a given point* if whenever the figure contains one of a pair of points symmetric with respect to the given point then it contains the other as well.

These two kinds of symmetry can also be characterized by using the notions of reflection and rotation. Given a line in the plane, the permutation of the points in the plane that moves each point to its symmetric point with respect to the line is called *the reflection of the plane through the line*. Thus reflection through m in Figure 29.2 interchanges A and B. The two sides of the arrow in Figure 29.1 are interchanged under reflection through line l. Another way of saying that the arrow is symmetric with respect to line l is to say that the arrow remains invariant (is carried into itself) under reflection through l.

Similarly, given a point in the plane, the permutation of the points in the plane that moves each point to its symmetric point with respect to the given point is called *the reflection of the plane through the given point*. Thus reflection through E in Figure 29.2 interchanges C and D. We could say that Figure 29.1(b) is symmetric with respect to P because it remains invariant under reflection through P. A different way of describing this symmetry, one that will be useful in other examples, is to say that the figure remains invariant under rotation of $180°$ around the point P.

Figure 29.3 illustrates symmetry of reflection and symmetry of rotation still further. The square is symmetric with respect to reflection

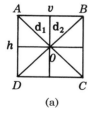 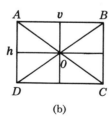 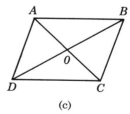

       (a)   (b)   (c)

Figure 29.3

through its horizontal and vertical lines h and v, and also its diagonals d_1 and d_2; it is also symmetric with respect to rotation (clockwise, say) of $90°$, $180°$, $270°$, or $360°$ about its point O. The rectangle is symmetric with respect to reflection through its lines h and v, but not its diagonals; it is symmetric with respect to rotation of $180°$ or $360°$ about its point O, but not $90°$ or $270°$. The parallelogram is not symmetric with respect to reflection through any line; it is symmetric with respect to rotation of $180°$ or $360°$ about its point O, but not $90°$ or $270°$.

Now that we have seen examples of symmetry of reflection and rotation we are ready to generalize to further types of symmetry. Either reflection through a line or rotation about a point yields a permutation of the set of points in the plane, in the sense of Section 28, and it is in the context of permutations that symmetry can be studied in its most general form. In order to show this we need the following generalization of Theorem 28.1.

THEOREM 29.1

If S is any set, then the set of all permutations of S is a group with respect to the operation $\circ$ (composition). In particular, the set of all permutations of the set of points in a plane is a group.

Let us first explain the theorem. The operation $\circ$ was defined in Section 28 only between permutations of $\{1, 2, \ldots, n\}$, but the idea is the same for other sets; it is as follows. If P is a permutation of a set S, and x is an element of S, let xP denote the element of S that P places in correspondence with x. If Q is a second permutation of S, then by definition $P \circ Q$ will place x in correspondence with $(xP)Q$. In other words, $P \circ Q$ is defined to be the permutation of S given by: $x \leftrightarrow (xP)Q$ for each x in S.

EXAMPLE 29.1. (a) If $S = \{1, 2, 3\}$, and P_2 and P_5 are as in Example 28.1, then $1(P_2 \circ P_5) = (1P_2)P_5 = 2P_5 = 2$ and $1(P_5 \circ P_2) = (1P_5)P_2 = 3P_2 = 1$.
(b) If R denotes reflection of the square through line v in Figure 29.3, then $AR = B$ and $BR = A$, and so $A(R \circ R) = (AR)R = BR = A$.
(c) Consider the square in Figure 29.3, and let M_2 denote 90° clockwise rotation around O, and M_5 denote reflection of the square through line h. (We are anticipating some later examples in using the symbols M_2 and M_5.) Figure 29.4 shows $M_2 \circ M_5$ and $M_5 \circ M_2$. We see that $M_2 \circ M_5$ is the same as reflection through d_2, and that $M_5 \circ M_2$ is the same as reflection through d_1.

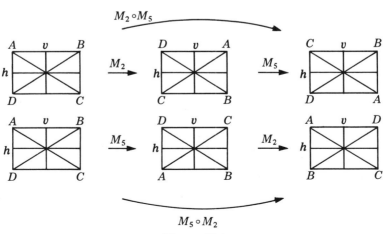

Figure 29.4

Proof of Theorem 29.1

The verification of the associative law is the same as in Example 28.3; here it is using the notation just introduced. If x is any element of S, and P, Q, and R are any permutations of the set S, then

$$\begin{aligned}
x((P \circ Q) \circ R) &= (x(P \circ Q))R \\
&= ((xP)Q)R \\
&= (xP)(Q \circ R) \\
&= x(P \circ (Q \circ R)).
\end{aligned}$$

Therefore

$$(P \circ Q) \circ R = P \circ (Q \circ R).$$

The identity element of the group is the permutation I defined by $xI = x$ for each x in S.

If P is any permutation of S, then P^{-1} is the permutation defined by:

$$xP^{-1} = y \text{ if and only if } x = yP.$$

Then $P^{-1} \circ P = I$ and $P \circ P^{-1} = I$, so that P^{-1} is an inverse for P.   □

In the previous section we used the term permutation group to mean any subgroup of some S_n. In general the term refers to any group of permutations. That is, any subgroup of a group of the type in Theorem 29.1 is called a *permutation group*.

In discussing symmetry in terms of permutations we are not interested in all possible permutations of the plane, but only those having the property of preserving distance between points; let us call such permutations *motions* of the plane. Thus, if x and y are two points in the plane, and P is a motion of the plane, then the distance between xP and yP is the same as the distance between x and y. Reflections and rotations are motions; but if we interchange only A and B in the square in Figure 29.3 and leave the remainder of the points fixed, then the resulting permutation will not be a motion (for instance, the distance from D to B (new position of A) will not be the same as the distance from D to A (original position of A)). It is not difficult to see that the set of all motions of the plane is a subgroup of the group of all permutations of the plane.

We are now ready for the key to the use of groups for characterizing symmetry. We first formalize the meaning of invariant, by saying that if S is a set of points in the plane and M is a motion of the plane, then M leaves S *invariant* if M permutes the elements of S among themselves; compare Example 28.6 and the paragraph preceding it. Thus if M is a motion leaving S invariant, then xM belongs to S whenever x belongs to S. (The latter condition is not always equivalent with invariance of M under S. See Problem 29.13.) The connection between group theory and symmetry of plane figures rests on the following theorem.

THEOREM 29.2

If S is any set of points in the plane (such as the set of points making up a figure), then the set of all motions of the plane that leave the set S invariant is a group.

Proof

It suffices to observe: (i) if M and N are motions leaving S invariant, then $M \circ N$ is a motion leaving S invariant; (ii) the identity permutation of the plane is a motion leaving S invariant; (iii) if M is a motion leaving S invariant, then M^{-1} is also. □

The group in Theorem 29.2, a subgroup of the group of motions of the plane, is called the *group of symmetries* of the set S. We can best see that the group of symmetries of a figure does characterize the symmetry of the figure by looking at examples.

EXAMPLE 29.2.   Let us find the group of symmetries for Figures 29.3(a) through (c). It is helpful to notice, first of all, that any motion of one of the figures will necessarily permute the vertices of the figure and the sides of the figure. As there are only 4 vertices for each figure, there are at most $4! = 24$ (total number of permutations of 4 things) symmetries for each figure; the symmetries (motions) will be completely determined by what they do to the vertices. Here are the groups of symmetries for the three figures; it can be seen that not every one of the 24 permutations of the vertices corresponds to a symmetry of the figure (see Problem 29.3). Notice that the more symmetric the figure, in the intuitive sense, the larger its group of symmetries.

> *Group of symmetries of square (Figure 29.3(a))*
> M_1 = no motion (identity permutation)
> M_2 = rotate 90° clockwise around O
> M_3 = rotate 180° clockwise around O
> M_4 = rotate 270° clockwise around O
> M_5 = reflect through h
> M_6 = reflect through v
> M_7 = reflect through d_1
> M_8 = reflect through d_2

> *Group of symmetries of rectangle (Figure 29.3(b))*
> M_1 = no motion (identity permutation)
> M_3 = rotate 180° around O
> M_5 = reflect through h
> M_6 = reflect through v

> *Group of symmetries of parallelogram (Figure 29.3(c))*
> M_1 = no motion (identity permutation)
> M_3 = rotate 180° around O

Here is the Cayley table for the group of symmetries of the square.   The entries $M_2 \circ M_5 = M_8$ and $M_5 \circ M_2 = M_7$ were computed in Example 29.1(c), and the others can be computed in the same way.

	M_1	M_2	M_3	M_4	M_5	M_6	M_7	M_8
M_1	M_1	M_2	M_3	M_4	M_5	M_6	M_7	M_8
M_2	M_2	M_3	M_4	M_1	M_8	M_7	M_5	M_6
M_3	M_3	M_4	M_1	M_2	M_6	M_5	M_8	M_7
M_4	M_4	M_1	M_2	M_3	M_7	M_8	M_6	M_5
M_5	M_5	M_7	M_6	M_8	M_1	M_3	M_2	M_4
M_6	M_6	M_8	M_5	M_7	M_3	M_1	M_4	M_2
M_7	M_7	M_6	M_8	M_5	M_4	M_2	M_1	M_3
M_8	M_8	M_5	M_7	M_6	M_2	M_4	M_3	M_1

The basic type of symmetry of the plane other than reflection and rotation is translational symmetry. This type of symmetry corresponds to the motion of shifting each point in the plane a given distance in a given direction; for example, one unit to the right. For a figure to be symmetric with respect to this motion, the figure must be considered infinite in extent.

EXAMPLE 29.3. Figure 29.5 is symmetric with respect to translation through t units to the left or right. *It is assumed in this and later examples and problems in this section that such figures extend infinitely far to the left and right.*

Figure 29.5

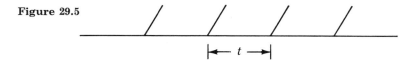

Using symmetries of translation and reflection, we can characterize all motions of the plane associated with so-called band ornaments. These are ornaments of the kind shown in Figure 29.8, where the first requirement in each case is that the figure be invariant under translation to the left and right through multiples of some smallest distance; Figure 29.5 (Example 29.3) has this type of symmetry, with corresponding smallest distance t. Band ornaments are known to have existed in many ancient civilizations, and an extensive collection of pictures of such ornaments can be found in Owen Jones' book *The Grammar of Ornament* [4], from which the samples in Figure 29.8 have been taken. There is, of course, an unlimited number of possible designs for such ornaments, but in terms of symmetry there can be only seven different types. These seven types are shown in both Figure 29.7 and Figure 29.8. Examples of each of these types of symmetry can be found in ancient decorative works, those in Figure 29.8 being from Greece. It is a theorem about groups of motions that permits us to say precisely which types of band symmetry are possible. We now describe these possibilities.

EXAMPLE 29.4. The following can be proved.

Assume given a plane figure lying wholly between two parallel lines, and invariant under a motion T translating the figure t units to the right, and assume that the figure is not invariant under translation through any smaller distance. Then the group of symmetries of the figure must be one of the seven groups I through VII which follow.

We shall give each group by listing motions that generate it; we first describe these generating motions. (See Figure 29.6.) The dot on each line is to serve as a point of reference to show the effects of the motion, and thus has not itself been subjected to the motion.

T: Translation t units to the right (Example 29.3).

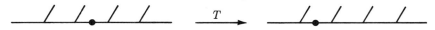

R: Reflection through a horizontal line.

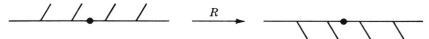

R': Reflection through a vertical line.

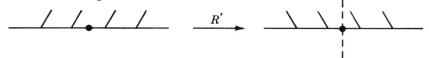

C: A single motion consisting of R followed by R'.

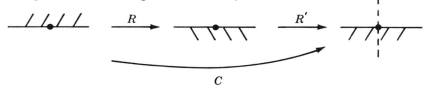

C': A single motion consisting of translation through $\frac{1}{2}\,t$, followed by R.

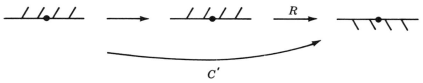

Figure 29.6

Here are the seven possible groups of symmetry for band ornaments:

$$\text{I. } \langle T \rangle$$
$$\text{II. } \langle T, R \rangle$$
$$\text{III. } \langle T, R' \rangle$$
$$\text{IV. } \langle T, C \rangle$$
$$\text{V. } \langle T, C' \rangle$$
$$\text{VI. } \langle T, R, R' \rangle$$
$$\text{VII. } \langle T, R', C' \rangle.$$

We point out the following relationships:

A figure having the type of symmetry associated with VII has the symmetries associated with each of III, IV, and V.

A figure having the type of symmetry associated with VI has the symmetries associated with each of II, III, and IV.

A figure having any of the types of symmetry has all of the symmetries associated with I.

The latter relationships are indicated in Figure 29.7, where each type of symmetry is represented and where one figure has all of the types of symmetries of another figure if there is an arrow from the first to the second. Thus the figures at the top have greatest symmetry in the sense of having largest groups of symmetry.

Hermann Weyl's book *Symmetry* [6] and Chapter XX of the survey work [1] are recommended for further information on groups of symmetry and their various applications.

Figure 29.7

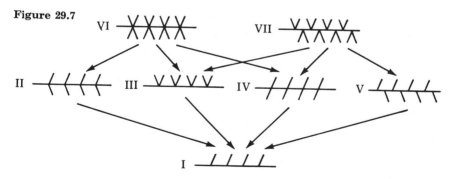

PROBLEM SET 29

PROBLEM 29.1. Verify the following entries of the table in Example 29.2, using the method of Example 29.1(c).

(a) $M_3 \circ M_4$

(b) $M_4 \circ M_3$

(c) $M_4 \circ M_4$

(d) $M_5 \circ M_6$

(e) $M_6 \circ M_7$

(f) $M_7 \circ M_6$

(g) $M_2 \circ M_8$

(h) $M_8 \circ M_3$

Reproduced by permission of Bernard Quaritch Ltd.

Figure 29.8

172

PROBLEM 29.2. Each of the symmetries of the square (Example 29.2) induces
a permutation of the vertices of the square. For example, M_4 induces
$\begin{pmatrix} A & B & C & D \\ D & A & B & C \end{pmatrix}$. Determine the permutations induced by each of the other
symmetries of the square.

PROBLEM 29.3. Why is there no motion of the square in Figure 29.3 inducing
the permutation $\begin{pmatrix} A & B & C & D \\ A & C & B & D \end{pmatrix}$ on the vertices of the square? (Compare
Problem 29.2.)

PROBLEM 29.4. List all of the elements in each of the following subgroups
of the group given by the Cayley table in Example 29.2. (The notation $\langle \ \rangle$
was introduced in Section 28.)

(a) $\langle M_1 \rangle$ (b) $\langle M_2 \rangle$
(c) $\langle M_3 \rangle$ (d) $\langle M_4 \rangle$
(e) $\langle M_2, M_5 \rangle$ (f) $\langle M_3, M_5 \rangle$
(g) $\langle M_5, M_6 \rangle$ (h) $\langle M_6, M_7 \rangle$

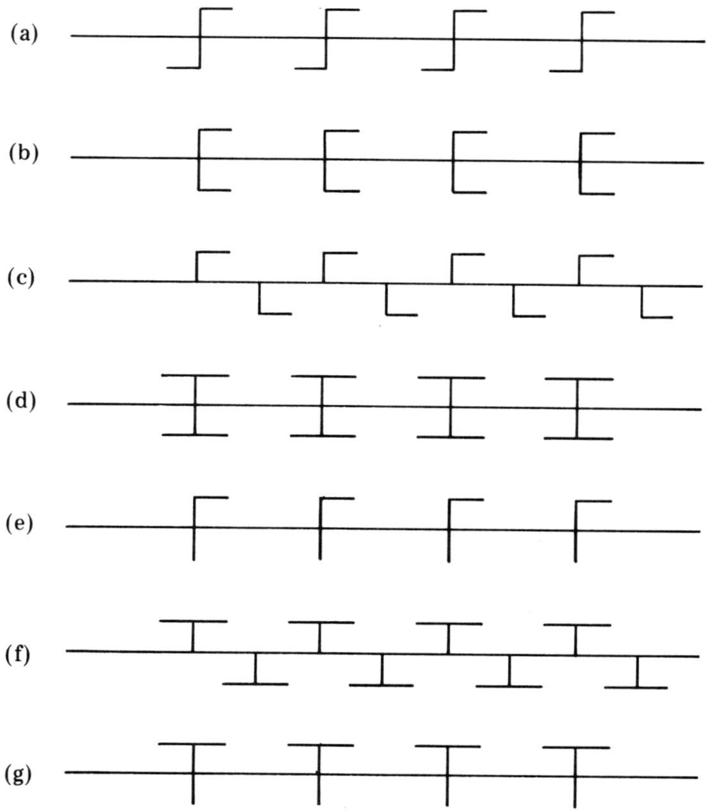

Figure 29.9

PROBLEM 29.5. Using the notation of Example 29.2, determine the group of symmetries of a rhombus. (Suggestion: Assume the parallelogram in Figure 29.3(c) to have $AB = AD$.)

PROBLEM 29.6. Determine the group of symmetries of an equilateral triangle ABC. (The group will contain at least one rotation, at least one reflection, and six total elements.)

PROBLEM 29.7. Determine the group of symmetries of an isosceles triangle ABC with $AB = AC$. (Compare Problem 29.6.)

PROBLEM 29.8. The group of symmetries for each part of Figure 29.9 is among the seven in Example 29.4, and no two correspond to the same group. Match the figures with the groups.

PROBLEM 29.9. The group of symmetries for each part of Figure 29.10 is among the seven in Example 29.4. Find the appropriate group for each part.

PROBLEM 29.10. Draw seven figures, different from those in the book, illustrating the seven types of symmetry shown in Figure 29.7.

(a)    (f)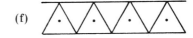

(b)    (g)

(c)    (h)

(d)    (i)

(e)    (j)

Figure 29.10

PROBLEM 29.11. Considered as geometric objects, the twenty-six capital letters of the alphabet fall into five sets, with the letters in each set having the same group of symmetries. Determine the letters in the five sets. (Suggestion: A, B, N, H, and F belong to different sets.)

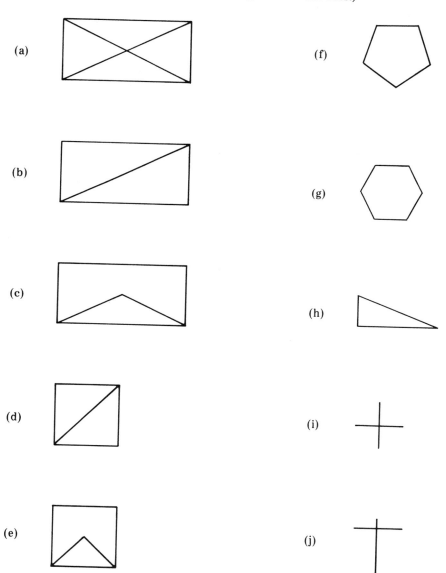

Figure 29.11

PROBLEM 29.12. Determine the group of symmetries for each part of Figure 29.11. (Suggestion: It suffices in each case to use motions similar to those found in Example 29.2.)

PROBLEM 29.13. Let l denote a fixed horizontal line, let S denote the set of all points in the plane below l, and let M denote the motion of the plane shifting each point one unit down. Explain why S is not invariant under M, in the sense of the definition preceding Theorem 29.2, even though xM belongs to S for each x in S.

PROBLEM 29.14. Which elements are in the center of the group given by the Cayley table in Example 29.2? (The center of a group is defined in Problem 28.13.)

PROBLEM 29.15. Verify that in Example 29.4 I is a subgroup of II through VII; each of II, III, and IV is a subgroup of VI; and each of III, IV, and V is a subgroup of VII. (Suggestion: If A and B are subsets of a group and A is a subset of B, then $\langle A \rangle$ is a subgroup of $\langle B \rangle$.) (In showing IV is a subgroup of VII; the vertical lines arising with IV and VII must be chosen to be different.)

§30. Elementary Properties

The following theorem gives some properties that are useful in the study of groups. We shall illustrate their use in this and the following section.

THEOREM 30.1

Assume that G together with $*$ is a group. Then each of the following is true.

(a) If x, y, and z are elements of G and $x * y = x * z$, then $y = z$ (left cancellation law).

(b) If x, y, and z are elements of G and $y * x = z * x$, then $y = z$ (right cancellation law).

(c) If e and f are elements of G and $e * x = x * e = x$ for each x in G and $f * x = x * f = x$ for each x in G, then $e = f$. (Briefly, a group has only one identity element.)

(d) If x, y, and z are elements of G, e is the identity element of G, and $x * y = y * x = e$ and $x * z = z * x = e$, then $y = z$. (Briefly, an element of a group has only one inverse element.)

Proof

(a) Assume $x * y = x * z$, and let w denote an element such that $w * x = e$, where e is an identity element for G. Such an element w exists by condition (3) in the definition of group. Then

$$
\begin{aligned}
y &= e * y && (e \text{ is identity element}) \\
&= (w * x) * y && (e = w * x) \\
&= w * (x * y) && (\text{associative law}) \\
&= w * (x * z) && (x * y = x * z) \\
&= (w * x) * z && (\text{associative law}) \\
&= e * z && (w * x = e) \\
&= z && (e \text{ is the identity element}).
\end{aligned}
$$

(b) The proof is similar to that of (a).

(c) Assume e and f satisfy the given conditions. Then $e = e * f = f$, that is, $e = f$.

(d) Assume x, y, and z as stated. Then

$$\begin{aligned}
y = e * y &= (z * x) * y \\
&= z * (x * y) \\
&= z * e \\
&= z,
\end{aligned}$$

that is, $y = z$. $\square$

It is (c) in Theorem 30.1 that permits us to speak of *the* identity element in a group. Similarly, (d) permits us to speak of *the* inverse of an element in a group. The (unique) inverse of an element x in a group is commonly denoted x^{-1}, in accordance with the usual multiplicative notation for numbers (if x is a real number other than 0, then $x \cdot x^{-1} = x^{-1} \cdot x = 1$). However, in a group in which there is already an established notation for the inverse of an element, that established notation is used (thus in the group of integers together with $+$, the inverse of x is denoted $-x$).

A group is said to be *finite* if the set of its elements is finite; otherwise it is *infinite*. The *order* of a group is the (cardinal) number of its set of elements. Thus the order of S_n is $n!$, and the group of integers with respect to $+$ is infinite.

We shall be concerned primarily with finite groups, our goal being to develop an idea of how abstract mathematical objects are studied. In particular we want to say as much as we can about the principal problem of the theory of finite groups, which is, roughly speaking, to determine all Cayley tables that define groups; for instance, the table in Example 27.1(e) does not define a group, but the table in Example 27.2(g) does define a group. We can begin by interpreting (a) and (b) of Theorem 30.1 in terms of Cayley tables.

If x, y, and z are elements of a finite group, then $x * y$ and $x * z$ will be in the same row (x) of the Cayley table for the group. Theorem 30.1(a) ensures that $x * y \neq x * z$ if $y \neq z$. Thus

>   *an element can appear only once in any given row of a Cayley table for a group.*

Similarly, Theorem 30.1(b) insures that $y * x \neq z * x$ if $y \neq z$. Thus

>   *an element can appear only once in any given column of a Cayley table for a group.*

Since the number of spaces in each row is the same as the number of elements in the group, it follows that each element must appear exactly once in each row of the Cayley table for a group; similarly, it must appear exactly once in each column.

We shall use some of these properties in the next section to prove a very powerful theorem concerning the subgroups of a finite group. We close this section by showing how the properties can be used to complete a Cayley table for a group.

EXAMPLE 30.1. If we wish to make a group with the set $\{a, b, c\}$, then one of the three elements must be the identity element; assume it to be a. Then the table must have the form shown, with the four ?'s to be determined. Because

$*$	a	b	c
a	a	b	c
b	b	?	?
c	c	?	?

each element must appear exactly once in the column headed b, and b already appears there, the two ?'s in that column must be a and c. But the bottom one cannot be c, because c already appears in that row. Thus necessarily $b * b = c$ and $c * b = a$. Finally, the remaining element in the b row, $b * c$, must be a, and the remaining element in the c row, $c * c$, must be b. Therefore the table for the group must be

$*$	a	b	c
a	a	b	c
b	b	c	a
c	c	a	b

It can be verified that this table does indeed yield a group, as was claimed in Example 27.2(g).

Problems 30.2 and 30.3 illustrate that with larger sets there is more arbitrariness than in the last example.

PROBLEM SET 30

PROBLEM 30.1. If $\{a, b\}$ together with $*$ is to be a group, with a the identity element, then what must the Cayley table be?

PROBLEM 30.2. Assume that $\{x, y, z, w\}$ together with $*$ is to be a group, with x the identity element. In contrast with Example 30.1, there are a number of ways a Cayley table can be completed here so as to yield a group. However, with any one of the additional assumptions (a), (b), (c), or (d) below, there is only one Cayley table yielding a group. Determine that Cayley table in each case.

(a) $y * y = z$ (b) $y * y = w$

(c) $y * y = x$ and $z * z = x$ (d) $y * y = x$ and $z * z = y$

PROBLEM 30.3. Assume that $\{x, y, z, w\}$ together with $*$ is to be a group, with x the identity element. Show that the four cases (a), (b), (c), and (d) in Problem 30.2 are the only possible ones.

PROBLEM 30.4. Prove that if G together with $*$ is a group, then $(a * b)^{-1} = b^{-1} * a^{-1}$, for all a and b in G. (Suggestion: $(a * b)^{-1}$ is the *unique* element in G such that $(a * b) * (a * b)^{-1} = e$.)

PROBLEM 30.5. Prove that if $x * y = z$ in a group, then $y = x^{-1} * z$ and $x = z * y^{-1}$.

PROBLEM 30.6. Assume that H is a subgroup of the group G (operation $*$). Prove that if x and y are elements of H, then $x * y^{-1}$ is an element of H.

PROBLEM 30.7. Assume that g is a fixed element of a group G with operation $*$. Associate each x in G with the element $x * g$ in G: $x \leftrightarrow x * g$. Prove that this association gives a permutation of the set of elements in G. (Suggestion: Use Theorem 30.1(b).)

PROBLEM 30.8. Prove that if $x * x = e$ for each x in a group G, then $y * z = z * y$ for all y and z in G. (Groups having the latter property are said to be *commutative*, or *Abelian*; see Problem 27.4 and Example 31.2. Suggestion: $(y * z) * (y * z) = e$. Multiply this on the left by y, and then on the right by z.)

PROBLEM 30.9. Let S be the set $\{e, a, b, c, x, y, z, w\}$. Write a Cayley table for an operation $*$ on the set S in such a way that S together with $*$ is a group with identity element e, and such that each element is its own inverse and $a * b = x$, $a * c = y$, $b * c = z$. (Suggestion: Notice that $a * x = a * a * b = e * b = b$, and so forth. Also use Problem 30.8.)

§31. Lagrange's Theorem

We have observed that, in general, not every subset of a group will be a subgroup. Lagrange's Theorem, to be proved below, states that the order of any subgroup of a finite group must divide (evenly) the order of the group. Thus, since S_3 has order $3! = 6$, any subgroup of S_3 must have order 1, 2, 3, or 6; S_3 cannot have subgroups of order 4 or 5. A group of order 7 has only two subgroups, one of order 1 ($\{e\}$), and the other of order 7 (the group itself).

Lagrange did not prove this theorem in the form applying to all finite groups, but he did use it in significant special cases and so it is fitting that it be named for him.

LAGRANGE'S THEOREM

If G together with $*$ is a finite group, and H is a subgroup of G, then the order of H divides the order of G.

Proof

Assume the elements of H to be $x_1, x_2, \ldots, x_k$, with $x_1 = e$, and assume the order of G to be n.

We must prove that k divides n, that is, we must prove that $n = sk$ for some integer s. We shall do this by showing that the set G can be divided into a number of subsets, to be written in rows below, in such a way that:

(i)   each of the rows has k elements, and
(ii)   no element of G appears in more than one row.

If we succeed in doing this we will have proved the theorem, for then the order of G, which is n, will be the number of rows, say s, times the number of elements in each row, which is k.

We begin by putting the elements of H in a row:

Row 1

$$x_1, x_2, \ldots, x_k.$$

If $H = G$, then we are through, that is, $n = k$. If $H \neq G$, then there is at least one element in G that is not in H; in this case choose any such element and call it r_2 (it will help determine our second row). Write

Row 2

$$r_2 * x_1, r_2 * x_2, \ldots, r_2 * x_k.$$

We now want to show that

(iii) Row 2 has k different elements (that is, no two of the different elements in Row 2 are equal), and
(iv)   no element in Row 2 is also in Row 1.

To prove (iii), assume that $r_2 * x_1 = r_2 * x_2$, for instance. Then by the left cancellation law, $x_1 = x_2$, which is a contradiction of the fact that $x_1, x_2, \ldots, x_k$ are all different. Similarly, no other two different elements in Row 2 are equal.

To prove (iv), assume that some element in Row 1 is also in Row 2, say $x_u = r_2 * x_v$, where u is $1, 2, \ldots,$ or k and v is $1, 2, \ldots,$ or k. Then if x_v^{-1} is the inverse element of x_v, it follows that $x_u * x_v^{-1} = r_2$ (Problem 30.5). But x_u and x_v belong to H, so $x_u * x_v^{-1}$ does also, since H is a subgroup (Problem 30.6). Thus we have that r_2 is an element of H, which is a contradiction. Therefore we cannot have $x_u = r_2 * x_v$, so (iv) is proved.

If each element of G is in either Row 1 or Row 2, then $n = 2k$. If not, then choose an element in G that is not in Row 1 or Row 2, call in r_3, and write

Row 3

$$r_3 * x_1, r_3 * x_2, \ldots, r_3 * x_k.$$

Now using the same technique as in proving (iii) and (iv), we can prove that the elements in Row 3 are different from each other and that none of them is in Row 1 or Row 2.

Now either each element of G is in Row 1, 2, or 3 (in which case $n = 3k$), or else we can choose a new element r_4 and form

Row 4

$$r_4 * x_1, r_4 * x_2, \ldots, r_4 * x_k.$$

We continue this process until we have used up all of the elements in G. If this happens with Row s, then $n = sk$. This proves the theorem. □

It is important to point out that the converse of Lagrange's Theorem is false. That is, it is not necessarily true that a group of order n has a subgroup of order k when k divides n. For instance, there is a group of order 12 possessing no subgroup of order 6. On the other hand, the Norwegian mathematician L. Sylow (1832–1918) proved in 1872 that if k is some power of a single prime (such as $8 = 2^3$ or $625 = 5^4$), then a group of order n does necessarily have a subgroup of order k if k divides n. Knowledge of subgroups turns out to be vital in the study of groups, and so these theorems of Lagrange and Sylow are especially important.

We also mention that a group may have more than one subgroup of a given order. For example, S_3 has three subgroups of order 2, as we saw in Example 28.4(e).

We have noted that any group of order 2 or more has at least two subgroups: namely, the subgroup consisting of the identity element alone, and the group itself. Some groups have no subgroups other than these two; we observed this above for groups of order 7. The following corollary furnishes a large number of such groups.

COROLLARY

> Any group G of prime order contains no subgroups other than $\{e\}$ and G.

Proof

This is a direct consequence of Lagrange's Theorem, since a prime has no divisors other than 1 and itself. □

The converse of this corollary is true: if a group of order larger than 1 possesses only two subgroups, then it is of prime order. We shall not prove this.

We complete this section by giving further examples of groups. The first example shows that there is at least one group of order n for each finite cardinal number n.

EXAMPLE 31.1. If g is an element of a group G, then $\langle g \rangle$, the subgroup generated by g, is called a *cyclic* group, as was stated in Problem 28.9. Note that the subgroup of S_3 generated by

$$P_3 = \begin{pmatrix} 1 & 2 & 3 \\ 3 & 1 & 2 \end{pmatrix}$$

is of order 3. More generally, it can be verified that the subgroup of S_n generated by

$$\begin{pmatrix} 1 & 2 & 3 & \cdots & k & \cdots & n \\ n & 1 & 2 & \cdots & k-1 & \cdots & n-1 \end{pmatrix}$$

is of order n. Thus there is at least one group of order n for each n. (See Problem 31.3 for a special case in detail.)

EXAMPLE 31.2. A group G with operation $*$ is said to be *Abelian* (after N. H. Abel) if $x * y = y * x$ for all x, y in G. Thus in the terminology of Problem 27.4 a group is Abelian if the underlying operation is commutative. The group of integers, with operation $+$, is Abelian, because $m + n = n + m$ for all integers m and n. The group S_3 is not Abelian, because (for example) $P_3 \circ P_4 = P_6$ while $P_4 \circ P_3 = P_5$. Any cyclic group is Abelian. In terms of its Cayley table a group will be Abelian if the entries in the table are symmetric about the diagonal running from the upper left-hand corner to the lower right-hand corner. Here is a Cayley table for an Abelian group of order 4.

$*$	e	a	b	c
e	e	a	b	c
a	a	e	c	b
b	b	c	e	a
c	c	b	a	e

PROBLEM SET 31

PROBLEM 31.1. Apply Lagrange's Theorem to determine the possible orders for subgroups of groups of each of the following orders.

    (a) 10   (b) 12   (c) 16
    (d) 17   (e) 18   (f) 19
    (g) 20   (h) 24   (i) 100

PROBLEM 31.2. Determine all of the subgroups of the group of order 4 given by the table in Example 31.2.

PROBLEM 31.3. Compute the permutations in the subgroup of S_5 generated by

$$\begin{pmatrix} 1 & 2 & 3 & 4 & 5 \\ 5 & 1 & 2 & 3 & 4 \end{pmatrix}.$$

What is the order of this subgroup? What is the inverse of each element in the subgroup?

PROBLEM 31.4. It can be proved that every subgroup of a cyclic group is cyclic. With this in mind, find all of the permutations in the cyclic group generated by

$$\begin{pmatrix} 1 & 2 & 3 & 4 & 5 & 6 \\ 2 & 3 & 4 & 5 & 6 & 1 \end{pmatrix}$$

and then find all of the subgroups of the group.

PROBLEM 31.5. (a) Taking G to be S_3, given in Example 28.3, and taking H to be the subgroup $\{P_1, P_4\}$, write out possibilities for Rows 1, 2, and 3 as given in Lagrange's Theorem.
(b) Same as (a) with H replaced by $\{P_1, P_2, P_3\}$, so that there are only Rows 1 and 2.

PROBLEM 31.6. (a) Taking G to be the group of symmetries of the square, given in Example 29.2, and H to be the subgroup $\{M_1, M_3\}$, write out possibilities for Rows 1, 2, 3, and 4 as given in Lagrange's Theorem.
(b) Same as (a) with H replaced by $\{M_1, M_3, M_5, M_6\}$, so that there are only Rows 1 and 2.

PROBLEM 31.7. The *order of an element* in a group is defined to be the order of the cyclic subgroup generated by that element. Thus the element P_3 is of order 3 because $\langle P_3 \rangle$ is of order 3 (Example 31.1). Determine the order of each of the following group elements.
(a) Each element of S_3 (Example 28.1).
(b) Each element of the group of symmetries of the square (Example 29.2).
(c) Each element of the group in Example 31.2.
(d) Each element of the group of order 3 given in Example 30.1.
(e) The elements in every group of order 3.
(f) The elements in every group of prime order p.

§32. Isomorphism

We stated earlier that the principal problem of the theory of finite groups is roughly that of determining all Cayley tables that define groups. Because two such tables may be the same except for differences that are inconsequential as far as group theory is concerned, it is useful to have a notion that will filter out such irrelevancies.

If we are interested only in the number of elements in a set, then $\{a, b, c\}$ is the same as $\{x, y, z\}$; in Chapter IV we introduced the notion of equivalence to account for this sameness. We could say that the existence of a one-to-one correspondence between two sets indicates a relationship between the two sets that does not depend on anything other than the number of elements in the sets; for instance, it says nothing about the arrangement of the elements or the names of the elements. Similarly, we want a notion that will reveal when groups are the same with respect to their essential properties as groups; such things as the arrangement of the elements and the names of the elements are again to be ignored. In the case of groups, however, equivalence alone is not sufficient since we must also take operations into account.

The correct notion here is that of *isomorphism*. Before giving the formal definition, let us look at an example.

EXAMPLE 32.1. The groups defined by the following tables are the same except for the names of the elements and symbols used for the operations.

*	e	a	b
e	e	a	b
a	a	b	e
b	b	e	a

#	f	g	h
f	f	g	h
g	g	h	f
h	h	f	g

Given the correspondence $* \leftrightarrow \#$, $e \leftrightarrow f$, $a \leftrightarrow g$, $b \leftrightarrow h$, we could fill in the second table just by knowing the first.

DEFINITION

If G together with $*$ is a group, and H together with $\#$ is a group, then G and H are said to be isomorphic as groups *if there is a one-to-one correspondence between the sets G and H such that if x' denotes the element of H corresponding to the element x of G (for each x in G), then*

$$(y * z)' = y' \# z'$$

for all y and z in G. Such a correspondence between groups is called an isomorphism.

The correspondence indicated in Example 32.1 is an isomorphism. There, $e' = f$, $a' = g$, and $b' = h$. And, for example, $(a * b)' = e' = f$ and also $a' \# b' = g \# h = f$, so that $(a * b)' = a' \# b'$.

EXAMPLE 32.2. Think of the group of integers (with $+$) in two different ways, once in the usual Arabic notation $(\ldots, 1, 2, 3, \ldots)$ and once in Roman numeral notation $(\ldots, I, II, III, \ldots)$. Then the correspondence $1' = I$, $2' = II$, $3' = III, \ldots$ is an isomorphism. For instance, $(2 + 3)' = 5' = V$ and $2' + 3' = II + III = V$. Briefly, it makes no difference whether we add (in Arabic) and then translate (to Roman), or translate (to Roman) and then add (in Roman); we get the same result.

The next theorem states that any group isomorphic with an Abelian group is also Abelian (Abelian groups were defined in Example 31.2). This theorem can be thought of as an illustration that isomorphic groups share essential properties; strictly speaking, however, the theorem simply establishes that the property of being Abelian (or not Abelian) is an essential property of groups, for the essential properties of groups, as groups, are those shared by isomorphic groups—that is what isomorphism is all about.

Theorem 32.1

*If H together with # is a group, and G together with * is an Abelian group, and these two groups are isomorphic, then H is Abelian.*

Proof

Assume that x' denotes the element in H corresponding to x in G with respect to an isomorphism between the two groups. We know that $g_1 * g_2 = g_2 * g_1$ for all g_1, g_2 in G because G is Abelian. Assume that h_1 and h_2 are elements in H. Then by the nature of one-to-one correspondence there are elements g_1, g_2 in G such that $g_1' = h_1$ and $g_2' = h_2$. Therefore

$$
\begin{aligned}
h_1 \; \# \; h_2 &= g_1' \; \# \; g_2' &&(h_1 = g_1' \text{ and } h_2 = g_2') \\
&= (g_1 * g_2)' &&(' \text{ is an isomorphism}) \\
&= (g_2 * g_1)' &&(g_1 * g_2 = g_2 * g_1) \\
&= g_2' \; \# \; g_1' &&(' \text{ is an isomorphism}) \\
&= h_2 \; \# \; h_1 &&(g_2' = h_2 \text{ and } g_1' = h_1)
\end{aligned}
$$

Thus the group H is Abelian. $\square$

Because an isomorphism is, among other things, a one-to-one correspondence, isomorphic groups will necessarily have the same number of elements. The converse statement is false, however. That is, there exist groups having the same order that are not isomorphic. Before giving an example to illustrate this, we prove a useful general fact about isomorphisms.

Theorem 32.2

*If $x \leftrightarrow x'$ (for each x in G) is an isomorphism between groups G (with *) and H (with #), and e and f are the identity elements of G and H, respectively, then $f = e'$. That is, in any isomorphism between groups, identity elements necessarily correspond.*

Similarly, inverse elements correspond in any isomorphism between groups: if $x \leftrightarrow y$ then $x^{-1} \leftrightarrow y^{-1}$.

Proof

Let e and f be the identity elements of G and H, as stated. Then, because e is the identity element of G, $e * x$ for each x in G. If y is in H, then $y = x'$ for some x in G, and then $f \# y = y = x' = (e * x)' = e' \# x' = e' \# y$, that is, $f \# y = e' \# y$, and therefore $f = e'$ by the right cancellation law. This proves the first part of the theorem.

For the second part, we have (for each x in G) $f = e' = (x * x^{-1})' = x' \# (x^{-1})'$, and therefore, since the inverse of x' is unique, it must be the case that $(x^{-1})' = (x')^{-1}$. $\square$

EXAMPLE 32.3. The group of order 4 given by the table in Example 31.2 is not isomorphic with the group of order 4 generated by the permutation

$$\begin{pmatrix} 1 & 2 & 3 & 4 \\ 4 & 1 & 2 & 3 \end{pmatrix}.$$

This can be seen by noticing that $x * x = e$ for each x in the group in Example 31.2; that is, in that group each element is its own inverse. Therefore, if these two groups were isomorphic, then each element in the second group would have to be its own inverse also, by Theorem 32.2. However, this is not the case, since for example

$$\begin{pmatrix} 1 & 2 & 3 & 4 \\ 4 & 1 & 2 & 3 \end{pmatrix}^{-1} = \begin{pmatrix} 1 & 2 & 3 & 4 \\ 2 & 3 & 4 & 1 \end{pmatrix}.$$

The notion of isomorphism permits us to divide groups into classes, called *isomorphism classes*, two groups being in the same class if and only if they are isomorphic. With this definition we can state the principal problem more precisely: determine all isomorphism classes of groups. The number of isomorphism classes of groups of each of the orders 1, 2, . . . , 10 is shown in the following table.

Order	Number of Isomorphism Classes
1	1
2	1
3	1
4	2
5	1
6	2
7	1
8	5
9	2
10	2

This means, for example, that any two groups of order 7 are isomorphic, because there is only one isomorphism class of groups of that order. And it is possible to construct five different Cayley tables for groups of order 8, no two of which represent isomorphic groups. It turns out that there are 14 different isomorphism classes of groups of order 16, 51 different isomorphism classes of groups of order 32, and 267 different isomorphism classes of groups of order 64.

In general, the determination of the number of isomorphism classes of groups of a given order is hopelessly difficult, but there are exceptions. The table above shows that there is just one isomorphism class for each of the orders, 2, 3, 5 and 7. More generally, it can be shown that there is just one isomorphism class of groups of order p for each prime p (Problem 32.8). The converse of this is true, also. That is, if n

is at least 2 and is not a prime, then there are at least two nonisomorphic groups of order n.

The groups of prime order belong to a very special class of groups, known as the class of *simple* groups. The order of the smallest simple group, not a prime, is 60. The word 'simple' is used here in a technical sense, which we shall not define, and does not mean 'uncomplicated'. Although the simple groups of prime order are uncomplicated (we saw in the corollary to Lagrange's Theorem that they each have only two subgroups), other simple groups are, in general, quite complex. The finite simple groups are the groups from which other finite groups can be built, in a sense that we shall not be able to discuss; the problem of determining all (isomorphism classes of) finite simple groups is a very difficult one. In the 1960's two American group theorists, W. Feit and J. G. Thompson, proved that the order of a finite simple group must be even if it is not a prime, and Thompson was awarded a Fields medal at the 1970 International Congress of Mathematicians (Section 33) for his work in this area.

We close with a theorem first published in 1854 by Cayley. Even with the few examples we have given, we have seen that the nature of groups can vary widely—from groups of numbers to groups of permutations to groups defined by tables. Cayley's Theorem asserts that in spite of this broad range of possibilities, each group is isomorphic with some group of permutations. This is an example of what is known as a *representation theorem*: it tells us that any group can be represented as (is isomorphic to) something reasonably concrete. In place of studying the given group, we can just as well study the concrete object (permutation group) representing it, and this can be an advantage. On the other hand it can sometimes be a disadvantage, for recall that part of the power of abstraction comes from the fact that abstraction filters out irrelevancies, and in concentrating on any concrete object we run the risk of being distracted by irrelevancies. Still, Cayley's Theorem has proved to be useful, and proving the theorem will give us a chance to tie together several of the important ideas at which we have looked.

CAYLEY'S THEOREM
  Every group is isomorphic with some group of permutations of its set of elements.

Proof
  Let G be a group with respect to an operation $*$. The theorem states that the group is isomorphic with some group of permutations of the set G. Thus in order to prove the theorem we must first associate with each element of G some permutation of the set G. This association will be given by $g \leftrightarrow T_g$, where T_g is the permutation of the set G defined by

$$xT_g = x * g \qquad \text{for each } x \text{ in } G.$$

(Here we have used the notation introduced following Theorem 29.1. That is, T_g denotes the permutation placing x in correspondence with $x * g$. Notice that in the notation of the definition of isomorphism, we have $g' = T_g$.) That each T_g is a permutation of the set G can be proved as in Problem 30.7.

We must prove that $g \leftrightarrow T_g$ is a one-to-one correspondence and that $T_{g*h} = T_g \circ T_h$ for all g and h in G, the latter being the form of the condition $(g * h)' = g' \# h'$ in the definition of isomorphism in view of $g' = T_g$.

The correspondence $g \leftrightarrow T_g$ is one-to-one, because if $g \neq h$ then in particular $eT_g = e * g = g$ and $eT_h = e * h = h$ and so $T_g \neq T_h$ (recall that permutations, such as T_g and T_h, are equal only if they have the same effect on each element on which they act).

To prove that $T_{g*h} = T_g \circ T_h$, we must show that $xT_{g*h} = x(T_g \circ T_h)$ for every x in G. This is done as follows:

$$
\begin{aligned}
xT_{g*h} &= x * (g * h)   &&\text{(definition of } T_{g*h}) \\
&= (x * g) * h   &&\text{(associative law)} \\
&= (x * g)T_h   &&\text{(definition of } T_h) \\
&= (xT_g)T_h   &&\text{(definition of } T_g) \\
&= x(T_g \circ T_h)   &&\text{(definition of } \circ).
\end{aligned}
$$

The set of all permutations T_g is a subgroup of the group of all permutations of G (Problem 32.9), and so the theorem is proved.   □

PROBLEM SET 32

PROBLEM 32.1. Find two nonisomorphic groups of order 6. (Suggestion: Use Theorem 32.1, Example 28.3, and the group in Problem 31.4.)

PROBLEM 32.2. The subgroup of S_4 generated by the set $\{Q_3, Q_4\}$, where

$$
Q_3 = \begin{pmatrix} 1 & 2 & 3 & 4 \\ 4 & 1 & 2 & 3 \end{pmatrix}, \qquad Q_4 = \begin{pmatrix} 1 & 2 & 3 & 4 \\ 2 & 1 & 4 & 3 \end{pmatrix},
$$

is of order 8. Show that $Q_3^4 = Q_0$ and $Q_4^2 = Q_0$, where Q_0 is the identity element of S_4 (see Problem 28.1). Find the 8 elements of the subgroup. Why is this subgroup not isomorphic with the subgroup of S_8 generated by

$$
\begin{pmatrix} 1 & 2 & 3 & 4 & 5 & 6 & 7 & 8 \\ 8 & 1 & 2 & 3 & 4 & 5 & 6 & 7 \end{pmatrix}?
$$

PROBLEM 32.3. Prove that the group of symmetries of a rectangle (Example 29.2) is isomorphic with the group in Example 31.2.

PROBLEM 32.4. Verify that the group of integers (operation addition) is isomorphic with the group of even integers (operation addition).

PROBLEM 32.5. An isomorphism of a group with itself is called an *automorphism*. For example, the correspondence $x \leftrightarrow x$ always yields an automorphism. Verify that the correspondence $a \leftrightarrow a$, $b \leftrightarrow c$, $c \leftrightarrow b$ yields an automorphism of the group in Example 27.2(g).

PROBLEM 32.6. (a) Verify that $e \leftrightarrow e$, $a \leftrightarrow b$, $b \leftrightarrow c$, $c \leftrightarrow a$ yields an automorphism of the group in Example 31.2. (Automorphism is defined in Problem 32.5.)

(b) Find two more automorphisms of the group in Example 31.2.

(c) Determine all automorphisms of the group in Example 31.2.

PROBLEM 32.7. The subgroup of S_4 generated by the permutation

$$\begin{pmatrix} 1 & 2 & 3 & 4 \\ 2 & 3 & 4 & 1 \end{pmatrix}$$

is of order 4. Determine all automorphisms of this group. (See Problem 32.5.)

PROBLEM 32.8. (a) Prove that if p is a prime then every group of order p is cyclic. (Suggestion: If g is an element of the group, what are the possibilities for $\langle g \rangle$, by Lagrange's Theorem.)

(b) If a group is cyclic of order p and is generated by g, then its set of elements is $\{e, g, g^2, \ldots, g^{p-1}\}$. Use this and (a) to prove that two groups of the same prime order must be isomorphic.

PROBLEM 32.9. (a) Verify that T_e is the identity element of the permutation group in Cayley's Theorem.

(b) Verify that $(T_g)^{-1} = T_{g^{-1}}$ in the permutation group in Cayley's Theorem.

(c) Verify that the set of all permutations T_g in Cayley's Theorem is a group.

PROBLEM 32.10. Prove that if one of two isomorphic groups is cyclic then then the other is also. (Suggestion: If $G = \langle g \rangle$ then $G = \{\ldots, g^{-2}, g^{-1}, e, g, g^2, \ldots\}$. And if $g \leftrightarrow h$ then $g^2 \leftrightarrow h^2$, $g^{-1} \leftrightarrow h^{-1}$, and so on.)

PROBLEM 32.11. If one of two isomorphic groups possesses one of the following properties, then the other group possesses the property as well:

> Abelian (Theorem 32.1).
> Order n (Remark after Theorem 32.1).
> Cyclic (Problem 32.10).
> Each element of the group is its own inverse (Example 32.3).

Using these facts explain why the following pairs of groups are not isomorphic.

(a) S_3 (Example 28.3) and integers (operation addition).

(b) S_3 (Example 28.3) and the group in Example 32.3.

(c) S_3 (Example 28.3) and a cyclic group of order 6.

(d) Group of symmetries of a square (Example 29.2) and a cyclic group of order 8.

(e) Group of order 8 in which each element is its own inverse (there is such a group) and a cyclic group of order 8.

(f) Group of integers (addition) and group of real numbers (addition). (Suggestion: See Chapter IV.)

(g) Group of rational numbers (addition) and group of real numbers (addition). (Suggestion: See Chapter IV.)

(h) Group of integers (addition) and group of rational numbers (addition).

(i) Group of integers (addition) and group II in Example 29.4.

(j) Group of rational numbers (addition) and group II in Example 29.4.

PROBLEM 32.12. Let R denote the group of real numbers with operation addition, and R^+ the group of positive real numbers with operation multiplication. Prove that R is isomorphic with R^+ by making use of the correspondence $x \leftrightarrow \log_{10} x$. (Logarithms are discussed in Section 36.)

REFERENCES

1. ALEKSANDROV, A. D., et al., eds., *Mathematics: Its Content, Methods, and Meaning*, 3 vols., The MIT Press, Cambridge, Mass., 1969. (English translation of 1956 Russian edition.)

2. BELL, E. T., *Men of Mathematics*, Simon and Schuster, New York, 1937.

3. INFELD, LEOPOLD, *Whom the Gods Love, the Story of Evariste Galois*, McGraw-Hill, New York, 1948.

4. JONES, OWEN, *The Grammar of Ornament*, Bernard Quaritch, London, 1910 (reprinted 1928).

5. *The Collected Works of George Abram Miller*, 5 vols., University of Illinois, Urbana, 1935–1959.

6. WEYL, HERMANN, *Symmetry*, Princeton University Press, Princeton, New Jersey, 1952.

CHAPTER VI

Analysis

§33. Mathematics After Euclid

In the previous chapters we have tried wherever possible to illustrate the changing nature of mathematics, and in this chapter the emphasis will be even more in that direction. In concentrating earlier on isolated topics, however, we have ignored a general characteristic of mathematics that is perhaps the most difficult of all to convey, and that is the degree of unity in modern mathematics: the way in which ideas that originated in one area have been seen to have bearing on problems in other areas. There has always been new mathematics, and new applications of old mathematics. Thus what we must do if we are to capture what is different now from two thousand years ago or two hundred years ago, is not merely to give samples of new mathematics in isolation, but attempt to show the extent to which different areas interact, either old or new.

After a brief survey of the history of mathematics, in this section, we shall use one of the central areas of mathematics, analysis, as an example to illustrate both change and unity. This will lead us from several different aspects of Greek mathematics to samples of twentieth century mathematics. We must, of necessity, leave out many proofs and other details in this chapter.

Section 34 explains the ancient origins of some of the later material, Sections 35 through 38 can be thought of as background for calculus, and Sections 39 through 42 contain the heart of the calculus— in a form, we should emphasize, that should be accessible to anyone who has gone through any of the earlier parts of the book. Sections 43 and 44 are mostly expository and contain a minimum of technical mathematics. Sections 45 and 46 on the other hand are more technical, to prepare the way for applications in the last two sections. These sections, 47 and 48, show most clearly the general points to be made in this chapter, and it is suggested that they be read even if there is in-sufficient time for the earlier sections; the first part of Section 48, in particular, can be read without special preparation.

In Chapter I we saw that the ancient Greeks inherited a sub-stantial amount of mathematics, primarily from the Babylonians, and that by the third century B.C. they had added to it and had organized much of what they knew in the deductive form found in Euclid's *Elements*. It is clear that in putting together the mathematics in the *Elements* the Greeks were guided by an outlook that was not chiefly concerned with practicalities. But neither were they doing it simply to amuse themselves. As we indicated, much of their effort was directed toward certain difficult questions that have been of fundamental impor-tance for mathematics ever since, involving motion, area and volume, and the use of numbers to represent physical quantities.

The Greek instinct for asking essential questions continued through the third century A.D. The foremost mathematician of this period was Archimedes of Syracuse (*c.* 287–212 B.C.). As a mathematician, Archimedes was a master in every way: versatile, original, his published work a model of economy and clarity. He developed to its fullest the method of exhaustion, a method for computing areas and volumes which anticipated the invention of the integral calculus by nearly two thousand years (Section 34E). And his role in the history of science was crucial: his use of mathematics in treating physical problems set an example for all who followed, as he laid the foundations for theoretical mechanics and the physics of fluid pressure. At about the same time, Apollonius of Perga introduced one of the earliest rational explanations of the motion of the planets, an explanation that was refined by Ptolemy in the second century A.D. into the system adopted by astronomers until its replacement in the sixteenth century by the heliocentric theory of Copernicus. Of more lasting importance was the work of Apollonius on the theory of conic sections (Section 34D). Apollonius made clear that he felt the properties of these curves were worth understanding for their own sake, but they were later seen to have great practical importance: for example, in the seventeenth century, Galileo's explanation of projectile motion made use of parabolas, and Kepler's explanation of planetary motion made use of ellipses (Section 43). Also of significance in ancient Greece was the beginning of trigonometry by Hipparchus and others (Section 35), and the work of Diophantus on number theory and algebra. The creative period of Greek mathematics had ended by the fourth century A.D., however, although compilations written during the fourth, fifth, and sixth centuries did prove to be of value later.

    The ancient Romans made use of simple mathematics for building and commerce, but they did not appreciate what the Greeks had done, and they added nothing to it: the case for Roman practicality must be made on grounds other than its direct contribution to mathematics and science. Chinese mathematics apparently developed independently of that of the other civilizations we have discussed; while some of their mathematics was by no means trivial, there were no cumulative efforts comparable to that in ancient Greece. Hindu mathematics seems to have been influenced by both the Greeks and the Chinese. The most significant contributions of the Hindus themselves were primarily in elementary trigonometry and the origin of the number system we use today.

    Knowing what was to come later, a mathematician is likely to view the Middle Ages with impatience. Arab mathematicians, such as al-Khowarizmi into the ninth century and Omar Khayyam in the eleventh, did initiate the serious study of algebra; Leonardo of Pisa (thirteenth century), also known as Fibonacci, contributed to algebra, geometry, trigonometry, and number theory; the Frenchman Oresme (fourteenth century) introduced the idea of fractional exponents, worked with infinite series, and anticipated some of the analytic geometry that was to come in the seventeenth century; the German Regiomantanus (fifteenth century) wrote the first modern work on trigonometry; and there were others. In addition, the preservation and translation of mathematical texts during the period was important for mathematicians who followed. But still, the mathematics of the period suffers both in quantity and in quality when compared with what has come since.

    The most striking mathematics of the sixteenth century was the discovery of general solutions for third and fourth degree equations by algebraists in Italy, which we discussed in Chapter V. This was satisfying in itself, but of more importance for the future was the stimulus it gave mathematicians to search for a general method of solving algebraic equations of degree higher than four, which led to the development of Galois theory in the nineteenth century. The French mathematician Vieta brought a valuable new outlook to both algebra and trigonometry in the sixteenth century, realizing the importance of general methods for solving broad problems rather than special methods for solving narrow ones. Vieta, along with the Englishman Robert Recorde and various German mathematicians, also made the first significant attempts to replace words and numbers by algebraic symbols during this period. Computation with Hindu-Arabic numerals became standard, and Simon Stevin of Bruges gave the first systematic treatment of decimal fractions. Thus the sixteenth century saw algebra take on a modern flavor characterized by general methods and also saw the introduction of various technical improvements; but notice that the new mathematics of the period was still elementary by present standards.

Seventeenth century mathematics reached its peak with Newton and Leibniz, as, independently, they clarified the relationship between the derivative and the integral, the two fundamental concepts of the calculus (Sections 40, 41, and 42). But that came late in the century, and much happened before, the only previous period of comparable mathematical progress being the third century B.C. One of the first contributions in the seventeenth century was the publication of the first book on logarithms, an aid in computation, by the Scotsman John Napier (Section 36). Of more significance conceptually were the decisive steps in the invention of analytic geometry, taken by the Frenchmen Descartes and Fermat (Section 37). With analytic geometry one associates numbers with geometrical objects, and thereby obtains, for instance, use of the language of algebra in studying questions about geometry; analytic geometry was essential for the full development of the calculus. In a different direction, Desargues and Pascal began the study of projective geometry, which started from questions about perspective but later led to the most general form of pure geometry. As we saw in Chapter III, it was in the mid-seventeenth century that Fermat, Pascal, and Huygens began the serious study of probability. Finally, with the work of Galileo and Kepler early in the century, and that of Newton late in the century, mathematics became firmly established as the appropriate tool for describing and predicting physical phenomena (Section 43).

Calculus and the branches that have grown from it constitute analysis, the largest area of modern mathematics. Analysis can be characterized as the study of limits, or infinite processes (Section 39), and the most notable achievement of eighteenth century mathematicians was their demonstration of the wide applicability and power of this area of mathematics. Making full use of the ideas they had inherited from Newton and Leibniz and others, they attacked many of the most difficult possible questions about the physical world, and in some cases developed whole branches of mathematics to handle them; a specific example, the calculus of variations, is discussed in Section 44. Euler (Swiss-born) and Lagrange (French) were the foremost mathematicians of the century, the former's book *Introductio in analysin infinitorum*, published in 1748, being the first influential book on analysis.

Three important examples of nineteenth century mathematics have been given earlier in the book: non-Euclidean geometry (Chapter II), groups (Chapter V), and Cantor's theory of infinite sets (Chapter IV).

In analysis, eighteenth century mathematicians had often been more concerned with applying new methods than with understanding logical foundations. Analysis can, however, be developed from axioms in much the same way as geometry or the theory of groups or the theory of sets. When this is done, axioms are formulated, definitions are framed, and theorems are proved in strict logical fashion, just as in any other deductive system. The accomplishment of this for analysis was primarily an achievement of nineteenth century analysts; it was essential that the processes of analysis eventually be examined closely in this way, both to prevent error and, as we can see on looking back, to set the stage for many things that have come since. The depth and the amount of the mathematics done in the nineteenth century is beyond what can be adequately described here, but we shall give other examples of it throughout later sections of this chapter.

The twentieth century opened with a meeting of the International Congress of Mathematicians, at which David Hilbert presented a collection of problems which has given direction and stimulation to a substantial number of twentieth century mathematicians. We met one of these problems in Chapter IV, that connected with the continuum hypothesis; we shall meet others in this chapter. Although mathematical knowledge has expanded enormously since 1900, Hilbert's lecture [11] still remains one of the clearest statements of the nature of twentieth century mathematics. He especially emphasized the importance of purposeful problems in mathematics, and the degree to which an organic unity had begun to emerge in the subject. It would be more difficult to describe the depth and the amount of twentieth century mathematics than to describe that of the nineteenth century. As one symbol that mathematics is very much alive, we have, where appropriate in the book, mentioned winners of Fields medals, awards given by the International Congress of Mathematicians to some of those who have contributed most significantly to the subject.

There are entire areas of twentieth century mathematics that are not discussed in this book: the absence of topology and various areas of contemporary applied mathematics are notable examples. As stated in the Preface, however, surveying mathematics is not our primary goal. Excellent surveys of omitted areas exist in a number of books, some of which are listed at the end of this chapter.

§34. More Greek Mathematics

Throughout this chapter we shall refer to connections between ancient and modern mathematics, and to enable us to do this with a minimum number of interruptions, we collect five topics from ancient Greek mathematics in this section.

A. Three famous problems.
B. Zeno's paradoxes.
C. Archimedes and applied mathematics.
D. Conic sections.
E. The method of exhaustion.

The order here is partly historical, although that is not important. Topic A relates to algebraic and transcendental numbers (Section 47); Topic B to limits (Section 39); Topic C to mathematical physics (Section 43); Topic D to Topic E and a number of later sections; and Topic E to integrals (Section 41).

A. Three Famous Problems Early in the history of Greek geometry three problems began to attract increasing attention.

The duplication of the cube.
The trisection of an arbitrary angle.
The quadrature of the circle.

Each had to do with the construction of one geometrical segment from another, using only unmarked straightedge and compass. With the first the problem was to construct the edge of a cube having twice the volume of a given cube; with the second the problem was to show that any angle could be trisected; and with the third the problem was to construct the side of a square having the same area as a circle of given radius. For comparison we note that the bisection of an angle is a standard construction in elementary geometry, as is also the duplication of a square.

Let it be emphasized that the three famous problems are concerned with theoretical rather than practical constructions. There is no difficulty in carrying out the constructions to any desired degree of accuracy if one is interested only in practicalities: trial and error will suffice if there is nothing better. The three problems are to be thought of in the context of this general question: What geometrical constructions are possible with the use only of unmarked straightedge and compass? With the straightedge a straight line can be drawn through any two distinct points, and with the compass a circle can be drawn with any point as center and passing through any other point. The question is whether, in theory, certain constructions can be carried out using only these two operations applied finitely many times. The three problems became of increasing interest as their difficulty became more apparent, and the Greeks developed a great deal of geometry in attempting to solve them. Although they failed to solve any of the problems, it was not understood until the nineteenth century why failure was inevitable. The reason will be discussed in Section 47.

B. Zeno's Paradoxes. One of the most fundamental questions about quantities such as line segments and time intervals is the following:

Are such quantities infinitely divisible, that is, can they be divided into smaller and smaller parts *ad infinitum*? Or are they made up of parts that are indivisible, that is, parts that cannot themselves be divided into smaller parts? The ancient Greeks considered this question, but they reached no concensus on an answer. In the fifth century B.C. the philosopher Zeno of Elea introduced four paradoxes which can be used to argue that quantities are neither infinitely divisible nor made up of parts that are indivisible. These paradoxes apparently had an unsettling effect on the Greeks, and that is the spirit in which they are given here; we shall make no direct reference to them later.

1. If a distance is infinitely divisible, then in order to travel the distance an object must first travel half of the distance; before doing that it must travel a quarter of the distance; before that an eighth of the distance; and so on *ad infinitum*. Thus the motion can never begin.

2. Achilles, racing to catch a tortoise that has been given a head start, will never be able to catch the tortoise. For by the time Achilles has reached the original position of the tortoise, the tortoise will have moved to a different position; by the time Achilles reaches that position the tortoise will have moved to a still different position; and so on *ad infinitum*.

3. At any instant an object is in a fixed position. If time is made up of indivisible instants, then the object, being in a fixed position at every instant, can never move.

4. Assume that there is a smallest interval of time, an instant. Assume that A_1, A_2, A_3, A_4 are objects of equal size, at rest; that B_1, B_2, B_3, B_4 are objects of the same size as the A's, moving to the right in such a way that each B passes each A in an instant; and that C_1, C_2, C_3, C_4 are objects also of the same size as the A's, moving to the left in such a way that each C passes each A in an instant. If the original positions of the objects are

	A_1	A_2	A_3	A_4	
B_1	B_2	B_3	B_4		
	C_1	C_2	C_3	C_4	

    then an instant later the positions will be

A_1	A_2	A_3	A_4
B_1	B_2	B_3	B_4
C_1	C_2	C_3	C_4 .

But during that instant C_1 will have passed two of the B's, and so the length of time required for C_1 to pass one B will be half of an instant, which contradicts the choice of the instant as the smallest interval of time.

Zeno's paradoxes have come to us only through secondary sources, and there is uncertainty about his reasons for giving them.

But they did contribute to Greek reluctance to attempt quantitative explanations of motion. The questions they raise are intimately related to those arising from the existence of incommensurable lengths and efforts to formulate properly the notions of area and volume. These questions involve ideas of continuity, limit, and the infinite (discussed in Chapter I, in several places to follow, and in Chapter IV, respectively); in each case the Greeks were up against problems that were not settled in a reasonably satisfactory way until late in the nineteenth century. In fact, these problems are of some interest even today.

C. Archimedes: Applied Mathematics. Part of Archimedes' fame rests on his ingenious mechanical inventions, things which he apparently considered only incidental to his real purpose in life. Among these were catapults and other machines of war, a water screw for raising water from one level to another (still used for irrigation in some places), and various devices built using the principles of levers and compound pulleys. Of more importance, both to Archimedes and for us, were his contributions to pure science and mathematics. Two of his surviving books serve to establish him as the founder of mathematical physics: *On the Equilibrium of Planes* (I, II) laid the foundations of theoretical mechanics, and *On Floating Bodies* (I, II) began the science of hydrostatics. In each book Archimedes begins with a few basic assumptions and then derives important consequences from them, in the same manner as Euclid in the *Elements*. The statements of some of the propositions are fairly complex, but here are four from *On Floating Bodies*, Book I, which are examples of science at its most elegant: simple in statement, sweeping in generality.

> Proposition 4. A solid lighter than a fluid will, if immersed in it, not be completely submerged, but part of it will project above the surface.

> Proposition 5. Any solid lighter than a fluid will, if placed in the fluid, be so far immersed that the weight of the solid will be equal to the weight of the fluid displaced.

> Proposition 6. If a solid lighter than a fluid be forcibly immersed in it, the solid will be driven upwards by a force equal to the difference between its weight and the weight of the fluid displaced.

> Proposition 7. A solid heavier than a fluid will, if placed in it, descend to the bottom of the fluid, and the solid will, when weighed in the fluid, be lighter than its true weight by the weight of the fluid displaced.*

D. Conic Sections. In the *Conics* of Apollonius we find Greek geometry at its finest. This work contains Apollonius' contribution to the theory

---

* Based on Heath's edition of *The Works of Archimedes* [9], with permission of Cambridge University Press.

of conic sections, curves which have become fundamental in mathematical descriptions of many events in the physical world. There is a large body of theory relating to conic sections, much of it already in the *Conics*; we shall simply give two different ways of describing conic sections so that they will be available later for examples and applications, in particular in Section 43.

Let a right triangle be rotated about one of its legs. Now let the segments traced out by the hypotenuse be extended infinitely far in both directions; call these extended lines *elements*. The resulting surface is called a *right circular cone*, and the fixed leg of the triangle, extended, is called its *axis* (Figure 34.1). If the right circular cone is cut by a plane,

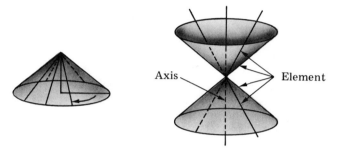

Figure 34.1

the curve formed by the intersection of the cone and plane is called a *conic section*. There are three basic types of conic sections (Figure 34.2): if the plane cuts each element in one nappe (or part), the section is called an *ellipse*; if the plane is parallel to an element of the cone, the section is called a *parabola*; if the plane cuts both parts of the cone, the section is called a *hyperbola*. Notice that a hyperbola consists of two branches,

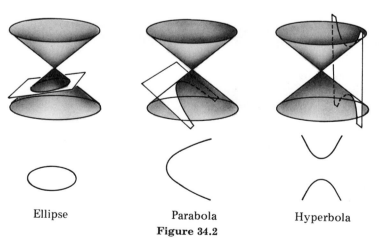

Ellipse   Parabola   Hyperbola

Figure 34.2

and that each of these branches, as well as the single branch of a parabola, is infinite in length. Notice also that an ellipse determined by a plane perpendicular to the axis of the cone will be a circle. And a hyperbola will degenerate into two intersecting lines if the cutting plane contains the axis of the cone.

Here is another way of defining the conic sections; it can be proved that this way is equivalent with that used above.

Ellipse: Given two points F and F' (called *foci*), and a length d greater than the distance between them, the set of all points P in the plane such that $PF + PF' = d$ is an ellipse (Figure 34.3).

Figure 34.3

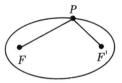

Parabola: Given a point F (*focus*) and a line l (*directrix*), the set of all points P in the plane such that PF is equal to the (perpendicular) distance from P to l is a parabola (Figure 34.4).

Figure 34.4

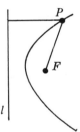

Hyperbola: Given two points F and F' (again called *foci*), and a length d smaller than the distance between them, the set of all points P in the plane such that either $PF - PF' = d$ or $PF' - PF = d$ is a hyperbola (Figure 34.5).

The discovery of conic sections is attributed to Menaechmus in the middle of the fourth century B.C. Aristaeus and Euclid later wrote

Figure 34.5

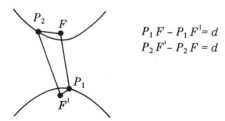

$$P_1 F - P_1 F' = d$$
$$P_2 F' - P_2 F = d$$

works on them that have not survived. But Apollonius' contributions far surpassed that of the others; he is conceded to have been the best of the Greek geometers.

E. The Method of Exhaustion. If a plane figure is bounded by straight lines then the calculation of its area offers little problem: if the figure is a rectangle then the area is simply the product of its dimensions; otherwise the figure can be divided into triangles, the areas of these triangles can be computed (using one-half base times altitude), and then these triangular areas can be added together to get the area of the original figure. If a plane figure is bounded by curves that are not straight lines then the problem of area is much more difficult. For instance, why is πr^2 the area of a circle of radius r? The Greeks developed a method, the method of exhaustion, for attacking such problems. The method evidently was perfected by Eudoxus, who is credited with applications of it found in Book XII of the *Elements*. The method is similar to that of integral calculus, developed in the seventeenth century, but there is a subtle difference—although an important one—in the points of view underlying exhaustion and calculus. The method of exhaustion became most powerful in the hands of Archimedes, and we shall illustrate it by describing his use of it in the *Quadrature of the Parabola*.

If A and B are points on a parabola, then the region enclosed by the parabola and the straight line AB is called a *parabolic segment* (Figure 34.6(a)). By the *height* of such a segment is meant the length of the longest perpendicular, lying in the segment, from the parabola to AB (this height is represented by CD in Figure 34.6(b)). Archimedes

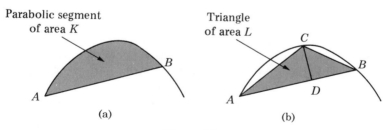

Figure 34.6

proved that if K is the area of such a segment, then $K = \frac{4}{3}L$, where L is the area of the largest triangle, with base AB, that can be inscribed in the segment: this is the triangle with base AB and height the same as that of the segment.

In order to prove this, Archimedes first showed that the area of this largest inscribed triangle ABC is four times the sum of the two largest inscribed triangles having AC and CB as bases. Thus, in Figure

34.7, $L_1 + L_2 = \frac{1}{4}L$, so that $L + L_1 + L_2 = L + \frac{1}{4}L$. This can be repeated to obtain four more triangles (constructed on AD, DC, CE, and EB), and the total area of the polygon made up of all seven of the triangles is then $L + \frac{1}{4}L + (\frac{1}{4})^2 L$. Continuing this process, Archimedes obtained a series of polygons with an ever-increasing number of

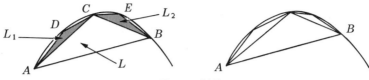

Figure 34.7

sides, and he then showed that the area of the nth such polygon is $L + L/4 + L/4^2 + \cdots + L/4^{n-1}$. As more triangles are added, they 'exhaust' the area of the segment, and in modern terminology (Section 45) we would say that the area K is the sum of the infinite series

$$L + \frac{L}{4} + \frac{L}{4^2} + \cdots + \frac{L}{4^{n-1}} + \cdots,$$

which is $\frac{4}{3}L$. Archimedes did not make use of infinite series—their use would have involved precisely those ideas in these matters that the Greeks had not sorted out—but rather he completed his proof by a different type of argument, showing in any case that the area K could be neither greater than nor less than $\frac{4}{3}L$, so that necessarily $K = \frac{4}{3}L$.

Archimedes also used exhaustion to find, among other things, the area of the surface of a sphere, the volume of a sphere, and the volume of a segment of a sphere, and using related ideas he showed that π is between $3\frac{1}{7}$ and $3\frac{10}{71}$.

One of the most interesting of Archimedes' surviving books is *The Method*, found only in 1906 by a Danish scholar, J. L. Heiberg. To arrive at a theorem two things are required: discovery and proof. Archimedes' other books contain proofs of his theorems: in *The Method* he reveals how, often by using principles of mechanics, many of his theorems were first discovered.

PROBLEM SET 34

PROBLEM 34.1. (Topic A) Describe how to bisect an angle using unmarked straightedge and compass.

PROBLEM 34.2. (Topic A) If S_1 is a square with each edge of length 1 unit, show how to construct a square S_2 whose area is twice that of S_1. (Suggestion: See Problem 47.11.)

PROBLEM 34.3. (Topic A) If C_1 is a cube with each edge of length 1 unit, and C_2 is a cube with twice the volume of C_1, how long is each edge of C_2?

PROBLEM 34.4. (Topic A) If C is a circle with radius 1 unit, and S is a square with area equal to that of C, how long is each edge of S?

PROBLEM 34.5. (Topic B) With the assumption that the set of points on a line can be put in one-to-one correspondence with the set of real numbers, does it follow that a line segment is infinitely divisible or that it is made up of parts that are indivisible?

PROBLEM 34.6. (Topic C) Under typical conditions a piece of ice, such as an iceberg, will float with nine-tenths of its volume submerged. If a piece of ice weighs 10 pounds, how much will the same volume of water weigh?

PROBLEM 34.7. (Topic C) A heavy object is resting on a raft floating in a swimming pool. The object falls off the raft and sinks to the bottom of the pool. Does the water level rise, fall, or remain the same?

PROBLEM 34.8. (Topic D) Let P_1 and P_2 denote points on an ellipse with foci F and F'.
(a) If $P_1F = 5$, $P_1F' = 4$, and $P_2F = 3$, what is P_2F'?
(b) If $P_1F = 10$, $P_2F = 9$, and $P_2F' = 3$, what is P_1F'?

PROBLEM 34.9. (Topic D) Let P denote a point on a parabola with directrix l and focus F.
(a) If P is 20 units from l, what is PF?
(b) If P is 100 units from l, what is PF?
(c) If PF is 10 units, how far is P from l?
(d) If PF is 1 unit, how far is P from l?

PROBLEM 34.10. (Topic D) Let P_1 and P_2 denote points on a hyperbola with foci F and F' such that $FF' = 10$.
(a) If $P_1F = 10$, $P_1F' = 15$, and $P_2F = 14$, what is P_2F'? There are two possible correct answers; give them both.
(b) If $P_1F = 10$, $P_1F' = 15$, and $P_2F = 20$, what is P_2F'? Give both possibilities.

PROBLEM 34.11. (Topic D) Let P_1 and P_2 denote points on a hyperbola with foci F and F' such that $FF' = 9$.
(a) If $P_2F = 9$, $P_2F' = 2$, and $P_1F' = 18$, what is P_1F? Give both possibilities.
(b) If $P_2F = 9$, $P_2F' = 2$, and $P_1F' = 27$, what is P_1F? Give both possibilities.

PROBLEM 34.12. (Topic D) Let P_1 and P_2 denote points on a hyperbola with foci F and F' such that $FF' = 8$.
(a) If $P_1F = 10$, $P_1F' = 13$, and $P_2F = 5$, what is P_2F'? Why is there only one possibility for the length of P_2F' in this case? (Compare Problems 34.10 and 34.11.)
(b) If P_1 is a point on the hyperbola, what can be said about $P_1F + P_1F'$?

PROBLEM 34.13. (Topic D) Let p denote a length greater than the distance between two points A and B. Describe the set of all points C in the plane such that ABC is a triangle with perimeter p.

PROBLEM 34.14. (Topic E) Explain why $0.\bar{9}$ must equal 1, by explaining why both $0.\bar{9} < 1$ and $0.\bar{9} > 1$ are impossible.

PROBLEM 34.15. (Topic E) Justify the following statement from the text, concerning Figure 34.7: '... the total area of the polygon made up of all seven of the triangles is then $L + \frac{1}{4}L + (\frac{1}{4})^2 L$.'

PROBLEM 34.16. (Topic E) Carry out the following steps to justify the final part of the calculation of the area of a parabolic segment.
(a) Let S denote $1 + 1/4 + 1/4^2 + \cdots + 1/4^{n-1}$. What is $4S$?
(b) What is $4S - S$?
(c) Solve the result in part (b) for S.
(d) What is $L + L/4 + L/4^2 + \cdots + L/4^{n-1}$?
(e) Using the answer in part (d), determine what happens to the sum there as n becomes larger and larger.

§35. Trigonometry

As a first approximation we could say that trigonometry is the quantitative study of triangles: using trigonometry we can compute the sizes of various parts of a triangle if certain other parts of the triangle are known. For example if the three sides of a triangle are known then the sizes of the three angles can be computed. Or if two angles and the side between them are known then the size of the remaining angle and the lengths of the remaining sides can be computed. In order to do such things, however, it is necessary to know something about certain numbers that can be associated with angles. These numbers are given by what are called trigonometric functions, and it is these functions that are in fact the heart of the subject. Thus, more accurately, we could say that trigonometry is the study of the properties and applications of trigonometric functions. As is so often the case in mathematics, this takes one far beyond the case of original interest; we shall give several indications of this later. Here, however, we shall look at the trigonometric functions in modern terms, give an elementary application, and then say a few words about how trigonometry began.*

Before defining the trigonometric functions let us introduce the notion of radian. Radians give a method of measuring the sizes of angles that is often more convenient than the method of degrees. Although degrees are preferable for many practical applications, radians are more natural in theoretical mathematics; we shall see support for this claim later on.

To obtain the measure of an angle in radians, first place the angle with its vertex at the center of a circle having radius 1: this has been done with AOB in Figure 35.1. Then the measure of the angle, in radians, is the length of the arc of the circumference cut off by the angle:

---

* Trigonometric functions are particular examples of the functions to be discussed in Section 38. The more general notion of function has been put later because it was recognized later historically.

Figure 35.1

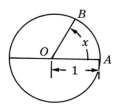

in Figure 35.1, angle AOB has measure x radians. Since the total circumference of the circle is 2π, an angle of $360°$ is the same as an angle of 2π radians. An angle of $180°$ has radian measure π, and an angle of $90°$ has radian measure $\pi/2$. Radian measures greater than 2π correspond to angles determined by more than one complete revolution from OA. Negative radians correspond to angles determined by moving clockwise rather than counter-clockwise from OA. In this way there is an angle corresponding to each real number (that is, to each radian measure). Some examples are shown in Figure 35.2.

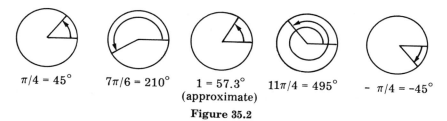

$\pi/4 = 45°$ $7\pi/6 = 210°$ $1 = 57.3°$ $11\pi/4 = 495°$ $-\pi/4 = -45°$

(approximate)

Figure 35.2

Now we are ready for the trigonometric functions. There are six of these in common use, but we shall concentrate on two, the sine and the cosine.

To define the sine of an angle AOB having radian measure x, we first assume the angle placed with its vertex at the center of a circle having radius 1, as before. Then the *sine* of the angle is defined to be the length of the perpendicular BC from B to the line through O and A, with BC taken to be positive if B is above the line through O and A, and negative if it is below. The sine of an angle of radian measure x is denoted by *sin x*. (Figure 35.3.) It is not difficult to convince oneself of the following facts.

$$
\begin{array}{llll}
\sin 0 & = & 0 & (0 \quad \text{radians} = \quad 0°) \\
\sin \pi/2 & = & 1 & (\pi/2 \ \text{radians} = \quad 90°) \\
\sin \pi & = & 0 & (\pi \quad \text{radians} = 180°) \\
\sin 3\pi/2 & = & -1 & (3\pi/2 \ \text{radians} = 270°) \\
\sin 2\pi & = & 0 & (2\pi \quad \text{radians} = 360°)
\end{array}
$$

As x increases from 0 to $\pi/2$, sin x increases continuously from 0 to 1.
As x increases from $\pi/2$ to π, sin x decreases continuously from 1 to 0.

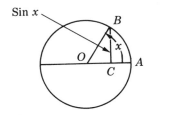 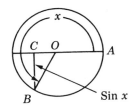

Each circle has radius 1
Figure 35.3

As x increases from π to $3\pi/2$, sin x decreases continuously from 0 to -1. As x increases from $3\pi/2$ to 2π, sin x increases continuously from -1 to 0.

For any angle x greater than 2π radians, sin x will be the same as the sine of a corresponding angle between 0 and 2π: for example, sin $5\pi/2 =$ sin $\pi/2$. Similarly for angles less than 0 radians: for example, sin $-\pi/2 =$ sin $3\pi/2$. In fact, for any x,

$$\cdots = \sin(x - 4\pi) = \sin(x - 2\pi) = \sin x$$
$$= \sin(x + 2\pi) = \sin(x + 4\pi) = \cdots.$$

Although it would be possible to obtain the sine of an angle by physical measurement, from figures such as those above, that is not how sines are actually computed. It turns out that there are strictly arithmetic techniques for computing sin x from any given value of x, and these do not require any kind of geometric construction; we shall encounter such a method when we discuss infinite series (Section 45). These arithmetic techniques have been used to construct extensive tables giving values of sin x corresponding to values of x, and these tables can be consulted for practical applications. Even though we are not primarily concerned with such applications, here is a brief table of

TABLE 35.1

x (degrees)	x (radians)	sin x	cos x	x (degrees)	x (radians)	sin x	cos x
0	0.0	0.0000	1.0000	50	0.8727	0.7660	0.6428
5	0.0873	0.0872	0.9962	55	0.9599	0.8192	0.5736
10	0.1745	0.1736	0.9848	60	1.0472	0.8660	0.5000
15	0.2618	0.2588	0.9659	65	1.1345	0.9063	0.4226
20	0.3491	0.3420	0.9397	70	1.2217	0.9397	0.3420
25	0.4363	0.4226	0.9063	75	1.3090	0.9659	0.2588
30	0.5236	0.5000	0.8660	80	1.3963	0.9848	0.1736
35	0.6109	0.5736	0.8192	85	1.4835	0.9962	0.0872
40	0.6981	0.6428	0.7660	90	1.5701	1.0000	0.0000
45	0.7854	0.7071	0.7071				

that kind. It gives values of x in degrees and radians, and the corresponding values of sin x and cos x (cos x will be defined shortly). The values in all except the degrees column have been rounded off.

An instructive picture of the behavior of sine can be obtained by plotting its graph.* To do this, we construct a horizontal 'axis' for indicating the different possible values of x, and then use a vertical 'axis' for indicating corresponding values of sin x. The resulting graph is shown in Figure 35.4.

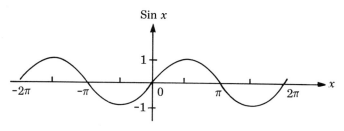

Figure 35.4

The cosine is defined in a manner similar to that of the sine. Explicitly, the *cosine* of an angle of measure x, abbreviated *cos x*, is defined to be the length of OC in Figure 35.5, with OC taken to be positive when C is in the same direction as A and negative if in the opposite direction.

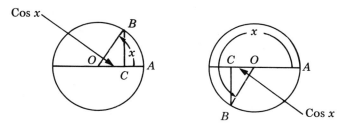

Each circle has radius 1

Figure 35.5

Figure 35.6 shows the graph of the cosine; as with the sine, it is the graph of the cosine that will be most useful later.

We shall have no need for the remaining trigonometric functions, but let us give the definitions of the four that are most common. They can be defined in terms of sine and cosine, as follows: the *tangent* is defined by tan x = sin x/cos x, the *cotangent* by cot x = cos x/sin x, the *secant* by sec x = 1/cos x, and the *cosecant* by csc x = 1/sin x.

---

* Graphs will be discussed more formally in Section 37.

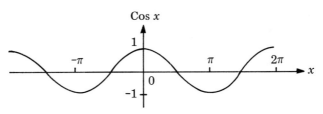

Figure 35.6

We turn now to an application of trigonometry; others will come later. One of the theorems of trigonometry is the Law of Cosines, which states that for any triangle PQR with sides of lengths p, q, and r, the following relation holds true (Figure 35.7):

$$r^2 = p^2 + q^2 - 2pq \cos R$$

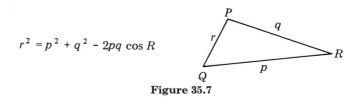

Figure 35.7

The Pythagorean Theorem is a special case of the Law of Cosines, obtained by taking R to be a right angle; for if R is a right angle, that is, $\pi/2$ radians, then $\cos R = \cos \pi/2 = 0$, and so the equation above reduces to $r^2 = p^2 + q^2$.

If any three of p, q, r, or R are known, then the fourth can be obtained using the equation in the Law of Cosines. For example, if $p = 5$, $q = 5$, $r = 3$, then $\cos R = 41/50 = 0.82$. To get R from this we refer to a table giving correspondences between angles and their cosines, such as Table 35.1. In this case we find that $\cos R = 0.82$ implies that R is approximately 35°, or 0.61 radian. With a more extensive table a more accurate value could be obtained for R. Applications of such methods to surveying and engineering should be apparent.

The first notable use of trigonometry is believed to have been by Hipparchus in the second century B.C., although the oldest extant book containing trigonometry is the *Sphaerica* of Menelaus, from around A.D. 100. Spherical trigonometry is concerned with problems in three-dimensional space analogous to those of two-dimensional space studied in plane trigonometry, and the *Sphaerica*, dealing as it does with spherical trigonometry, illustrates the historical fact that spherical trigonometry for use in astronomy was developed before plane trigonometry for use in such things as surveying. The most influential writing on trigonometry from the classical Greek period is contained in the *Almagest* of Ptolemy, which appeared in the middle of the second century A.D. The *Almagest* is devoted primarily to Ptolemy's system for explaining the apparent motions of the planets, but it also contains important contributions to trigonometry. Trigonometry continued to be studied mainly in relation to astronomy until the thirteenth century. At that time the Persian Nasir Eddin wrote the first book treating trigonometry as a subject of separate interest.

PROBLEM SET 35

PROBLEM 35.1. Determine the degree measure of an angle having the following radian measure.

(a) $\pi/9$
(b) 6π
(c) $-\pi/2$
(d) $\pi/18$
(e) $13\pi/18$
(f) 340π
(g) $-71\pi/2$
(h) 2
(i) π^2

PROBLEM 35.2. Determine the radian measure of an angle having the following degree measure.

(a) $30°$
(b) $60°$
(c) $-15°$
(d) $-180°$
(e) $225°$
(f) $765°$
(g) $2°$
(h) $1'\ (= 1/60°)$
(i) $1''\ (=1/60')$

PROBLEM 35.3. Using the value 3.1416 in place of π, determine the degree measure of an angle of 1 radian, accurate to within 0.01 of a degree.

PROBLEM 35.4. Determine the numerical value of each of the following.

(a) $\cos 0$
(b) $\cos \pi/2$
(c) $\cos -\pi/2$
(d) $\cos 3\pi$
(e) $\cos 26\pi$
(f) $\cos -251\pi$
(g) $\sin 7\pi/2$
(h) $\sin 251\pi$
(i) $\sin -237\pi/2$

PROBLEM 35.5. (a) For which values of x is $\sin x = 0$?
(b) For which values of x is $\sin x = 1$?
(c) For which values of x is $\sin x = -1$?
(d) For which values of x is $\sin x = \frac{1}{2}$?
(e) For which values of x is $\sin x = 2$?

PROBLEM 35.6. Same as Problem 35.5 with sine replaced by cosine.

PROBLEM 35.7. Determine the values of x between 0 and 2π for which each of the following conditions is satisfied.

(a) $\sin x > 0$
(b) $\sin x \geq 0$
(c) $\sin x < 0$
(d) $\cos x > 0$
(e) $\cos x \leq 0$
(f) $\sin x = \cos x$
(g) $\sin x > \cos x$
(h) $\sin x = -\cos x$
(i) $\sin x + \cos x > 0$

PROBLEM 35.8. (a) Verify that $\sin \pi/4 = \cos \pi/4$, using the figures used to define sine and cosine.
(b) The value 0.7071 for $\sin 45°$ and $\cos 45°$, given in Table 35.1, is approximate. What is the exact value?

PROBLEM 35.9. (a) Explain why $\cos x = \sin (\pi/2 - x)$ for $0 \leq x \leq \pi/2$, using elementary properties of triangles and the figures used to define sine and cosine.
(b) Explain why $\cos x = \sin (\pi/2 - x)$ for each x, using the graphs of sine and cosine.

PROBLEM 35.10. Prove that $(\sin x)^2 + (\cos x)^2 = 1$ for each x.

PROBLEM 35.11. If the two equal sides of an isosceles triangle are each 5 units, and the angle between them is 60°, what is the length of the third side of the triangle?

PROBLEM 35.12. If the three sides of a triangle are 4, 5, and 6 units, respectively, what is the size of the angle opposite the side of length 4?

PROBLEM 35.13. (a) Using the definition of sine and the fact that corresponding pairs of sides of similar triangles have their lengths in the same ratio, explain why $b/c = \sin B$ for the right triangle shown in Figure 35.8. (b) Explain why $a/c = \cos B$.

Figure 35.8

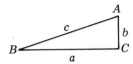

PROBLEM 35.14. In the third century B.C. Aristarchus of Samos used ideas like those of trigonometry to deduce that the sun (S) is between 18 and 20 times as far from the earth (E) as is the moon (M). With the moon half-full, so that the angle at M was a right angle, Aristarchus measured the angle at E and obtained (in our notation) 87°. This would give angle ESM the value 3° (Figure 35.9). Therefore $EM/ES = \sin 3°$ (Problem 35.13(a)).

Figure 35.9

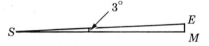

(a) Using the approximate value $\sin 3° = 0.052$, how many times greater would this imply ES than EM?

(b) Aristarchus' measurement was incorrect. Angle ESM is approximately 10' (=1/6°) when angle EMS is a right angle. Using $\sin 10' = 0.0029$, how many times greater does this imply ES than EM?

PROBLEM 35.15. (a) Aristarchus thought the distance from the earth to the moon to be approximately 19 times the radius of the earth, and Hipparchus thought the distance to be approximately 67 times the radius of the earth [6]. Measurement shows the angle subtended at the center of the moon by a radius of the earth to be approximately 1° (see Figure 35.10). Using this value and the approximate value $\sin 1° = 0.017$, what do you obtain in place of the values 19 and 67?

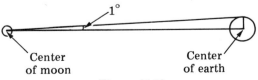

Figure 35.10

(b) Using the approximate value 4,000 miles for the radius of the earth, and the value computed in (a), what do you obtain for the distance from the earth to the moon? (The accepted value is about 239,000 miles.)

§36. Logarithms

When first invented in the early seventeenth century, logarithms were used to shorten calculations arising in such fields as astronomy. These calculations can now be made by electronic computers, and the importance of logarithms has shifted to the theoretical significance of the logarithmic function, which did not fully evolve until the mid-nineteenth century. We shall define logarithms in a way that will make clear how they can be useful for calculations; but it is the logarithmic function that will be of use to us later.

To grasp the idea behind logarithms, first consider the correspondence between powers of 2 and their exponents:

$$\cdots \tfrac{1}{32} \quad \tfrac{1}{16} \quad \tfrac{1}{8} \quad \tfrac{1}{4} \quad \tfrac{1}{2} \quad 1 \quad 2 \quad 4 \quad 8 \quad 16 \quad 32 \cdots$$
$$\cdots 2^{-5} \quad 2^{-4} \quad 2^{-3} \quad 2^{-2} \quad 2^{-1} \quad 2^{0} \quad 2^{1} \quad 2^{2} \quad 2^{3} \quad 2^{4} \quad 2^{5} \cdots \Big\} \text{ powers of 2}$$
$$\cdots -5 \quad -4 \quad -3 \quad -2 \quad -1 \quad 0 \quad 1 \quad 2 \quad 3 \quad 4 \quad 5 \cdots \} \text{ exponents.}$$

Figure 36.1

Now observe that if we multiply any two numbers in the first row (say $2 = 2^1$ and $16 = 2^4$), then the product will also be a power of 2 ($2 \cdot 16 = 32 = 2^5$). Furthermore, the exponent in the product will be the sum of the exponents in the two factors ($1 + 4 = 5$). This is nothing more than a law of exponents: $2^m \cdot 2^n = 2^{m+n}$ for all integers m and n. The significant point is that a *product* in the first row corresponds to a *sum* in the third row—and addition is easier than multiplication. If we are concerned only with positive numbers of the form 2^m, with m denoting an integer, then the table above (extended to the right and left if necessary) will permit us to carry out any multiplication by performing a corresponding addition.

The key to logarithms is this: fill in the table so that the first row contains *all* positive real numbers.* This introduces immediate problems. For instance, what number q would appear in the last row corresponding to 3 in the first row? In other words, for what q is $2^q = 3$? Because $2^1 = 2$ and $2^2 = 4$, it is apparent that such a q, if it exists at all, must be between 1 and 2. Thus to find such a q we must be willing to admit exponents that are not integers; in fact, we must admit all real numbers as exponents. Let us postpone the question of how this can be done. The point now is that it can be done, and when it has, then for each

---

* This statement is meant to be suggestive, and is not to be taken literally. We cannot actually write out all real numbers.

positive real number x (in the first row) there will be a real number y (in the third row) such that $2^y = x$. Moreover, the whole process can be carried out in such a way that multiplication in the first row still corresponds to addition in the third row: $2^a \cdot 2^b = 2^{a+b}$ for all real numbers a and b. Then by the logarithm of a positive real number x in the first row is simply meant the number y that would correspond with it in the third row. This number y is called the *logarithm to the base 2 of x*, and it is written $\log_2 x$. Thus $\log_2 x = y$ means $2^y = x$.

With this specific example based on 2 behind us, we are ready for the general definition of logarithm. If b is any positive real number other than 1, then the process described above can be carried out with b in place of 2. This yields, for each positive real number x (first row), a real number y (third row) such that $b^y = x$. This number y is called the *logarithm to the base b of x*, and it is written $\log_b x$. Thus $\log_b x = y$ means $b^y = x$. Notice once more that a logarithm is simply an exponent: $\log_b x$ is the power to which b must be raised to produce x.

Here are some examples:

$$\log_2 8 = 3 \qquad \text{because} \quad 2^3 = 8$$
$$\log_{10} 10000 = 4 \qquad \text{because} \quad 10^4 = 10000$$
$$\log_3 (1/9) = -2 \qquad \text{because} \quad 3^{-2} = \frac{1}{3^2} = \frac{1}{9}$$
$$\log_4 2 = \tfrac{1}{2} \qquad \text{because} \quad 4^{\frac{1}{2}} = \sqrt{4} = 2.$$

The last example uses the fact that $4^{\frac{1}{2}} = \sqrt{4}$. That is the meaning of $\frac{1}{2}$ as an exponent: $b^{\frac{1}{2}} = \sqrt{b}$ by definition. This brings us back to the question we postponed: Can we, in a consistent and useful way, give meaning to exponents that are not integers? In algebra this question is answered for rational (fractional) exponents, by first defining $b^{1/n}$ to be the nth root of b. That is, $b^{1/n}$ is the positive real number whose nth power is b: $(b^{1/n})^n = b$. Thus $8^{1/3} = 2$ because $2^3 = 8$; and $625^{\frac{1}{4}} = 5$ because $5^4 = 625$. Then $b^{m/n}$ is defined to be $(b^{1/n})^m$. So $8^{2/3} = (8^{1/3})^2 = 2^2 = 4$; and $625^{3/4} = (625^{\frac{1}{4}})^3 = 5^3 = 125$. These definitions, together with $b^{-r} = 1/b^r$, do extend the meaning of exponents to all rational numbers. The extension to all real numbers is more difficult, but once again, it can be done; more will be said about this in the discussion of infinite series (Section 45).

The important property from our initial illustration, that multiplication can be replaced by addition, translates into the language of logarithms as the following law:

$$\log_b (x \cdot y) = \log_b x + \log_b y.$$

The left-hand side corresponds with multiplication (in the first row) followed by passage to the third row, while the right-hand side corresponds with passage to the third row (from each of x and y) followed by addition (in the third row); the point is that we arrive at the same number either way. Although we are not primarily concerned with proficiency with exponents and logarithms, let us write out a formal proof of this fact; it is a useful exercise for understanding the definition of logarithm.

Let r denote $\log_b x$ and s denote $\log_b y$.
Then $b^r = x$ and $b^s = y$. Therefore

$$b^{r+s} = b^r b^s = xy,$$

and so

$$\log_b xy = r + s.$$

That is,

$$\log_b xy = \log_b x + \log_b y.$$

We have made use of the exponent law $b^{r+s} = b^r b^s$, which is established for fractional exponents in algebra; it is valid for other exponents as well.

Let us say something about the choice of b, the base, in the definition of logarithm. We specified that b cannot be 1. The reason for this is simple: if $\log_1 2 = a$, then $1^a = 2$, an absurdity because $1^a = 1$ for every possible a; in fact $\log_1 x$ will always lead to an absurdity unless $x = 1$. With the exception of 1, however, any other positive real number is acceptable as a base. When a particular base b has been chosen we get what is called a 'system' of logarithms, consisting of all values of $\log_b x$ for different values of x. If the base were chosen to be 10 then a partial table giving values for the logarithms would look like this:

x	$\log_{10} x$
0.001	-3
0.01	-2
0.1	-1
1.0	0
10.0	1
100.0	2

The system of logarithms based on 10 is, in fact, the one used for calculations. It is called the system of *common* or *Briggsian* logarithms (Briggs improved Napier's ideas shortly after Napier first introduced logarithms). This system based on 10 is most suitable for calculations because our number system is based on 10. Here is an illustration of why this is so; notice that we use the key fact that the logarithm of a product of two numbers is the sum of the logarithms of the two numbers.

$$\log_{10} 981 = \log_{10} (100 \cdot 9.81)$$
$$= \log_{10} 100 + \log_{10} 9.81$$
$$= 2 + \log_{10} 9.81.$$

Thus if we were to know $\log_{10} 9.81$ then we could easily get $\log_{10} 981$. In general, it is a routine matter to get the base 10 logarithm of any positive real number, if the base 10 logarithms of numbers between 1 and 10 are available: one need only add an appropriate integer to a logarithm already known.

Extensive tables of base 10 logarithms are available, the earliest having been compiled already in the seventeenth century. Here is an abbreviated sample.

TABLE 36.1

x	$\log_{10} x$	x	$\log_{10} x$
1.0	0.00000	5.5	0.74036
1.5	0.17609	6.0	0.77815
2.0	0.30103	6.5	0.81291
2.5	0.39794	7.0	0.84510
3.0	0.47712	7.5	0.87506
3.5	0.54407	8.0	0.90309
4.0	0.60206	8.5	0.92942
4.5	0.65321	9.0	0.95424
5.0	0.69897	9.5	0.97772

It is natural to wonder how tables of logarithms are prepared. From the point of view taken above, it is a question of determining exponents, and it then becomes a paradox of history that logarithms were in use before exponents were fully understood. One convenient method of computing logarithms, that is based on calculus, will be given when we discuss infinite series (Section 45). Logarithms are in general irrational, and thus can be given only approximately using finitely many decimal places. But approximations are sufficient for numerical applications.

We shall eventually see that for theoretical purposes, and for many applications other than direct numerical calculation, the appropriate system of logarithms is based on the number e, which we encountered in connection with the normal probability curve (Section 21) and which will be discussed more fully later on (Sections 39 and 45). The points to be stressed now are that logarithms can be thought of as kinds of exponents, and that from the early seventeenth century until the invention of desk calculators and electronic computers they were a tremendous aid in performing lengthy computations.

PROBLEM SET 36

PROBLEM 36.1. Construct a table like that in Figure 36.1, using powers of 3 in place of powers of 2.

PROBLEM 36.2. Construct a table like that in Figure 36.1, using powers of $\frac{1}{2}$ in place of powers of 2.

PROBLEM 36.3. Simplify each of the following.

(a) $9^{1/2}$ (b) $27^{1/3}$ (c) $27^{2/3}$
(d) $36^{3/2}$ (e) $(\frac{1}{8})^{1/3}$ (f) $64^{2/3}$
(g) $(\frac{1}{125})^{2/3}$ (h) $4^{-1/2}$ (i) $32^{-1/5}$
(j) $32^{-3/5}$ (k) $16^{-3/4}$ (l) $64^{-2/3}$
(m) $49^{-3/2}$ (n) $(\frac{1}{121})^{-3/2}$

PROBLEM 36.4. Determine each of the following.

(a) $\log_2 2$ (b) $\log_2 16$ (c) $\log_2 (\frac{1}{32})$
(d) $\log_{10} 100000$ (e) $\log_{10} 0.0001$ (f) $\log_3 9$
(g) $\log_3 (\frac{1}{27})$ (h) $\log_4 2$ (i) $\log_{27} 3$
(j) $\log_{100} 10$ (k) $\log_{10} \sqrt{10}$ (l) $\log_{1/2} 8$
(m) $\log_{1/8} 2$ (n) $\log_{125} 25$

PROBLEM 36.5. Using Table 36.1, and the law $\log_{10} (xy) = \log_{10} x + \log_{10} y$, compute each of the following.

(a) $\log_{10} 15$ (b) $\log_{10} 18$ (c) $\log_{10} 32$
(d) $\log_{10} 81$ (e) $\log_{10} 17.5$ (f) $\log_{10} 125$

PROBLEM 36.6. Prove that $\log_b x/y = \log_b x - \log_b y$. (Suggestion: $b^{r-s} = b^r/b^s$.)

PROBLEM 36.7. Using Table 36.1, and the law in Problem 36.6, compute each of the following.

(a) $\log_{10} (\frac{1}{2})$ (b) $\log_{10} (\frac{2}{3})$ (c) $\log_{10} (\frac{1}{9})$
(d) $\log_{10} (\frac{7}{8})$ (e) $\log_{10} 3.25$ (f) $\log_{10} 0.2$

PROBLEM 36.8. Prove that $\log_b (x^s) = s(\log_b x)$. (Suggestion: $(b^r)^s = b^{rs}$.)

PROBLEM 36.9. Using Table 36.1, and the law in Problem 36.8, compute each of the following.

(a) $\log_{10} (2^{10})$ (b) $\log_{10} 256$ (c) $\log_{10} 3^5$
(d) $\log_{10} (2^{1/2})$ (e) $\log_{10} \sqrt{5}$ (f) $\log_{10} \sqrt[3]{49}$

PROBLEM 36.10. If you have read Section 32, do Problem 32.12.

PROBLEM 36.11. (a) Studying Figure 36.1, and noting that 12 is halfway between 8 and 16, which of the following seems most likely: $2^{3.5} < 12$, $2^{3.5} = 12$, or $2^{3.5} > 12$?

(b) Because $2^{1/2} = \sqrt{2}$, it follows that $2^{0.5} = 1.414$, approximately. Note that 1.5 is halfway between 1 and 2, and $1.414 < 1.5$. Using this and part (a) as guides, which of the following seems most likely:

$$2^{(m+n)/2} < (2^m + 2^n)/2, \quad 2^{(m+n)/2} = (2^m + 2^n)/2, \quad 2^{(m+n)/2} > (2^m + 2^n)/2$$

(m and n unequal positive integers)?

(c) Prove that your choice in (b) is the correct one. (Suggestion: Use Problem 6.5(e).)

PROBLEM 36.12. In the Cayley-Klein consistency proof of the non-Euclidean geometry of Chapter II, the 'line' through two points P and Q consisted of the portion of the (Euclidean) line through P and Q, and within the given circle; this 'line' is indicated by AB in Figure 36.2. (See Figure 14.1, also.) The 'length' of the 'segment' PQ is defined to be

$$\text{length } PQ = \log \frac{AQ/AP}{BQ/BP},$$

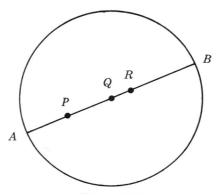

Figure 36.2

where the absence of a subscript on log indicates $\log_e$ (Example 45.10). Notice that length PQ, defined in this way, depends on the two ratios AQ/AP and BQ/BP, which are independent of any units for measuring the Euclidean segments AQ, AP, BQ, and BP.

(a) Write the expressions giving length PR and length QR.

(b) Using the laws $\log (xy) = \log x + \log y$ (text), and $\log (x/y) = \log x - \log y$ (Problem 36.6), verify that

$$\text{length } PQ + \text{length } QR = \text{length } PR.$$

(c) Using the fact that $\log x$ increases without limit as x becomes large, explain why it is true that if one of two points (say P) remains fixed and the other (Q) moves toward the boundary (B), the 'distance' between P and Q increases without limit.

§37. Analytic Geometry

In Section 5 we discussed the use of real numbers for representing the points on a straight line. The basic idea of plane analytic geometry is to extend this notion from lines to planes, using pairs of real numbers in place of single real numbers; the basic idea of solid analytic geometry is to extend the notion still further, using triples of real numbers. Possible uses of these extensions, for representing positions of objects in the physical world, for example, should be apparent. The principle is familiar in the form of parallels of latitude and longitude for representing positions on the earth's surface. Mathematically, however, the idea of associating numbers with points opens up possibilities that go far beyond mere numerical descriptions of positions in space, for it serves as a bridge between geometry and algebra, the two most fundamental branches of mathematics. This makes the tools of algebra available when solving problems in geometry, and it makes the use of geometric intuition available when solving problems in algebra. It has done a great deal more than that, in fact, furnishing the language for much of modern mathematics and science. Although we shall make no use of solid analytic geometry, the language of plane analytic geometry will be used in nearly every one of the topics to follow.

Assume that two perpendicular lines are given in a plane, and assume further that a unit of length has been chosen. Then using this unit of length we can put the points on each of the lines in correspondence with the real numbers (Figure 37.1). This is conventionally done

Figure 37.1

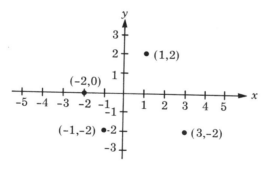

by taking one of the lines to be vertical with numbers increasing upward, and the other line to be horizontal with numbers increasing to the right, 0 on each line corresponding with the intersection of the two lines. The two given lines are referred to as *axes*. The position of any point in the plane can be specified by giving the pair of real numbers that describes its distances from the two axes; these two numbers are called the *co-ordinates* of the point. In doing this, the distance from the vertical axis is always given first, and the signs determine direction: a point with positive first coordinate is to the right of the vertical axis, and a point with negative first coordinate is to the left of the vertical axis; similarly for distances from the horizontal axis. This establishes a one-to-one correspondence between the set of all points in the plane and the set of all pairs of real numbers. For example, the point 3 units to the right of the vertical axis and 2 units below the horizontal axis is specified by the pair (3, −2). This point, together with the points corresponding to (1, 2), (−2, 0), and (−1, −2), is shown in Figure 37.1. The point with coordinates (0, 0) is called the *origin*. (It is sometimes convenient to use one unit along one axis, and a different unit along the other axis; our units will always be assumed equal, however.)

One is normally interested more in collections of points than in individual points. For instance, a single position of a planet relative to the sun is of less interest than the collection of all points swept out by the planet on its orbit around the sun; it is knowledge of the latter which allows one to deduce physical laws and thereby predict future behavior. Translated into the language of analytic geometry, as all such problems eventually must be, this leads to the algebraic description of sets of points in the plane. We now look at how this is done.

First consider sets of points that are determined by forcing their coordinates to satisfy some particular condition. For example, consider the set l_1 determined by the condition: a point is in l_1 if and only if its two coordinates are equal. It is easy to see that l_1 is precisely the set of points on the line shown in Figure 37.2. And the line l_2 in the figure

Figure 37.2

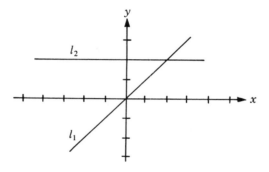

consists of those points having first coordinate arbitrary and second coordinate equal to 2. To make it easier to exploit this idea we introduce two variables to represent the two coordinates: x will represent the first coordinate, y the second. The horizontal axis will be called the *x-axis*, the vertical axis will be called the *y-axis*. Any equation involving x and y, or just one of them, will now determine a set of points in the plane: the set of those points whose coordinates satisfy the given equation. This set of points is called the *graph* of the equation. Thus the graph of $x = y$ is the line l_1 in the figure, and the graph of $y = 2$ is the line l_2. The two primary concerns of analytic geometry are with analyzing the graphs of equations involving the two variables x and y, and with finding equations that will have given geometric configurations (such as ellipses) as their graphs. We have already illustrated the first of these in our discussion of trigonometry, the two graphs there being those of $y = \sin x$ and $y = \cos x$. Let us give another specific example involving the construction of a graph, and then we shall put conic sections in this context.

Consider the equation $y = x^3 - 3x^2 + 2$. A point will be on the graph of this equation if the coordinates of the point satisfy the equation, otherwise the point will not be on the graph. Thus $(2, -2)$ is on the graph because $-2 = 2^3 - 3 \cdot 2^2 + 2$, but $(1, -1)$ is not on the graph because $-1 \neq 1^3 - 3 \cdot 1^2 + 2$. For this particular equation there is one point on the graph for each value of x, and the coordinates of that point can be determined by substituting x into the equation and computing the corresponding value of y. For example, if $x = 1$, then $y = 1^3 - 3 \cdot 1^2 + 2 = 0$, and so $(1, 0)$ is on the graph.* Other such points can be obtained in the same way and these can be arranged in a table and then plotted in the plane. After plotting sufficiently many points, they can be connected with a smooth curve and this will give us the graph of the equation. Just how many points should be plotted will depend on the particular equation. We shall see later that calculus can be of some assistance in these constructions. Finally, we should mention that not all graphs are smooth like the one in Figure 37.3; see the two graphs in the next section, for instance.

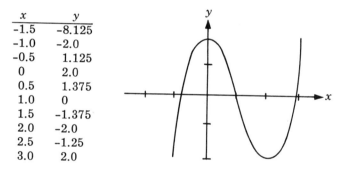

x	y
-1.5	-8.125
-1.0	-2.0
-0.5	1.125
0	2.0
0.5	1.375
1.0	0
1.5	-1.375
2.0	-2.0
2.5	-1.25
3.0	2.0

Graph of $y = x^3 - 3x^2 + 2$

Figure 37.3

Now let us look at the problem of finding equations that will have given geometric configurations as their graphs. First consider the case of a circle, which is a special kind of ellipse (Figure 37.4). Can we write an equation in x and y that will have as its graph the circle with center at the origin and with radius 1, for instance? The answer is Yes, and in order to write the equation, we notice first that by the Pythagorean Theorem the distance r from the origin to the point representing (x, y) satisfies $x^2 + y^2 = r^2$. Thus the distance from the origin to this point will be 1 if and only if $x^2 + y^2 = 1$, and so this is the equation we are

* Strictly speaking we should distinguish between a point and its coordinates, but it is more convenient to treat them as the same thing.

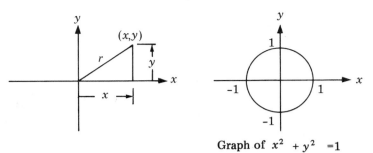

Graph of $x^2 + y^2 = 1$

Figure 37.4

looking for. It can be seen that for any positive number r the graph of $x^2 + y^2 = r^2$ will be the circle with center at the origin and with radius r.

With more work, but no new essential ideas, it can be shown that an ellipse with foci on the x-axis will have equation $(x/a)^2 + (y/b)^2 = 1$, where a and b are nonzero real numbers determined by the shape of the particular ellipse (which is determined in turn, in the language of Section 34D, by the distance between the foci and the distance d used to define the ellipse). Figure 37.5 shows such an ellipse having $a = 4$ and

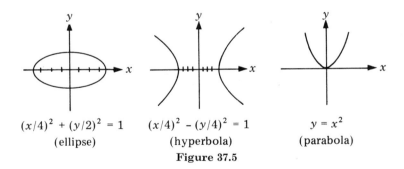

$(x/4)^2 + (y/2)^2 = 1$ $(x/4)^2 - (y/4)^2 = 1$ $y = x^2$
(ellipse)   (hyperbola)   (parabola)
Figure 37.5

$b = 2$. Notice that for each x between -4 and 4 there are two values of y giving points on the graph: for example, $(0, 2)$ and $(0, -2)$ are on the graph, and $(1, \sqrt{15}/2)$ and $(1, -\sqrt{15}/2)$ are on the graph.

Similarly, a hyperbola with foci on the x-axis will have equation $(x/a)^2 - (y/a)^2 = 1$, where a and b are nonzero real numbers determined by the shape of the particular hyperbola. And a parabola passing through the origin, with focus on the y-axis, will have equation $y = ax^2$, for a an appropriate nonzero real number. Samples are shown in Figure 37.5.

Notice that the equation for each of these conic sections is second-degree, that is, it can be put in the form

$$Ax^2 + Bxy + Cy^2 + Dx + Ey + F = 0$$

for appropriate constants A, B, C, D, E, and F (some perhaps 0). For example, $(x/4)^2 + (y/2)^2 = 1$ corresponds to $A = (1/4)^2$, $B = 0$, $C = (1/2)^2$, $D = 0$, $E = 0$, and $F = -1$. It can be shown, with allowance for some peculiar exceptions (such as $x^2 + y^2 = -1$, whose graph contains no points), that the graph of any second-degree equation is a conic section. The effect of having D or E nonzero is to shift the conic section away from the origin; the effect of having B nonzero is to rotate the conic section. Figure 37.6 gives an example of an ellipse that has been shifted and rotated. If A, B, and C are all zero the equation is first-degree and its graph is a straight line. Notice that the graph of $y = x^3 - 3x^2 + 2$, which we constructed earlier, is not a conic section.

Figure 37.6

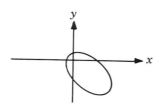

$$5x^2 + 6xy + 5y^2 - 4x + 4y - 4 = 0$$

The notion from analytic geometry that is necessary for what follows is only the general one of the relationship between curves in the plane and equations involving x and y; we shall not require detailed knowledge of equations for conic sections, for example. But the discussion above does illustrate the type of problems with which analytic geometry is concerned, namely, the classification of equations corresponding to particular types of curves, and the classification of curves corresponding to particular types of equations.

The first book on analytic geometry was Descartes' *La géométrie*, published as an appendix to his *Discours de la méthode*, which appeared in 1637.

PROBLEM SET 37

PROBLEM 37.1. Plot the following points relative to a set of coordinate axes.

(a) $(0, 1)$ (b) $(1, 3)$ (c) $(-1, 3)$

(d) $(4, -4)$ (e) $(-4, -4)$ (f) $(0, -5)$

(g) $(-\frac{5}{2}, -\frac{1}{3})$ (h) $(0.2, -0.7)$ (i) $(-\pi, -2\pi)$

PROBLEM 37.2. Which of the following points are on the graph of $y = x^3 + x + 1$?

(a) $(0, 0)$ (b) $(0, 1)$ (c) $(1, 0)$

(d) $(1, 3)$ (e) $(-\frac{1}{2}, \frac{3}{8})$ (f) $(1011, 10)$

PROBLEM 37.3. (a) Give the coordinates of two points on the graph of $y = \sin x$.

(b) Give the coordinates of two points not on the graph of $y = \sin x$.

PROBLEM 37.4. The graph of $x^2 + y^2 = -1$ contains no points. Why?

PROBLEM 37.5. It can be shown that the graph of any equation of the form $Ax + By + C = 0$ is a straight line (A, B, and C constants with at least one of A and B not zero); for this reason such equations are called *linear* equations. Draw the graph of each of the following linear equations.

(a) $x + y = 0$ (b) $x + y + 1 = 0$ (c) $2y + 1 = 0$
(d) $x + 2y + 2 = 0$ (e) $x - y = 1$ (f) $x - y = -1$
(g) $5x - 5y = 1$ (h) $x - y = 5$ (i) $\pi x - \sqrt{2} = 0$

PROBLEM 37.6. Determine the equations having the following curves for their graphs.

(a) Straight line 2 units to the right of the y-axis.
(b) Straight line 30 units below the x-axis.
(c) Circle with center at the origin and radius 3.
(d) Circle with center at the origin and radius $\sqrt{5}$.
(e) Straight line through $(-1, 1)$ and $(1, -1)$.
(f) Circle with center at the origin and passing through the point $(2, 2)$.
(g) Circle with center at $(1, 1)$ and radius 1.
(h) Straight line through (a, b) and (c, d).
(i) Circle with center at (a, b) and radius r.
(j) Square with vertices at $(1, 1)$, $(-1, 1)$, $(-1, -1)$, and $(1, -1)$. (Suggestion: This will require four equations with restrictions on each, one being $x = 1$ for $-1 \le y \le 1$.)

PROBLEM 37.7. Draw a graph of each of the following equations.

(a) $y = -x^2$ (b) $x = y^2$ (c) $y = x^2 + 1$
(d) $y = (x + 1)^2$ (e) $y = x^3$ (f) $y = x^4$
(g) $y = x^3 + x^2$ (h) $x^2 + y^2 = 4$ (i) $\left(\dfrac{x}{2}\right)^2 + \left(\dfrac{y}{3}\right)^2 = 1$
(j) $\left(\dfrac{x}{3}\right)^2 + \left(\dfrac{y}{2}\right)^2 = 1$ (k) $\left(\dfrac{x}{2}\right)^2 - \left(\dfrac{y}{3}\right)^2 = 1$ (l) $\left(\dfrac{y}{3}\right)^2 - \left(\dfrac{x}{2}\right)^2 = 1$

PROBLEM 37.8. Assume a and b to be positive real numbers, and discuss the relative positions of each of the following pairs of points. The language of symmetry (Section 29) can be helpful here, although it is not essential.

(a) (a, b) and $(-a, b)$ (b) (a, b) and $(a, -b)$
(c) (a, b) and $(-a, -b)$ (d) (a, b) and (b, a)
(e) (a, b) and $(b, -a)$ (f) (a, b) and $(-b, a)$
(g) (a, b) and $(-b, -a)$ (h) (a, b) and $(a + b, a + b)$

PROBLEM 37.9. (This problem assumes familiarity with some of the terminology concerning symmetry, from Section 29.) Consider three types of symmetry:

symmetry with respect to the origin;
symmetry with respect to the x-axis;
symmetry with respect to the y-axis.

State which of these types of symmetry is possessed by the graph of each of the following equations.

(a) $x^2 + y^2 = 1$ (b) $y = 3$ (c) $x = -2$
(d) $y = x^2$ (e) $y = x$ (f) $y = -x$
(g) $y = x + 1$ (h) $\left(\dfrac{x}{4}\right)^2 + \left(\dfrac{y}{2}\right)^2 = 1$ (i) $\left(\dfrac{x}{4}\right)^2 - \left(\dfrac{y}{4}\right)^2 = 1$
(j) $y = x^3 - 3x^2 + 2$

§38. Functions

The notions of set and function are the most basic in modern mathematics. In earlier parts of the book we have often used the language of sets, and it will be clear from the examples below that we have made implicit use of functions. We have chosen not to introduce functions explicitly until it became necessary and natural to do so: that is the way they first entered mathematics. We are now nearing calculus, and as functions are the objects on which the processes of calculus operate, we have reached an appropriate place for discussing them.

In the broadest sense, a *function* is simply a relationship that assigns to each object in one set a uniquely determined object in another set. We say in such a case that we have a function from the first set to the second; we use the notation $x \mapsto y$ to denote that x in the first set is assigned to y in the second. For example, if we assign to each word the total number of letters it contains (counting a letter twice if it appears twice, and so on), then we have a function from the set of all words to the set of natural numbers: number $\mapsto$ 6, of $\mapsto$ 2, letters $\mapsto$ 7. If we assign to each word the number of *different* letters it contains, then we have another function from the set of all words to the set of natural numbers: number $\mapsto$ 6, of $\mapsto$ 2, different $\mapsto$ 7, letters $\mapsto$ 5. The important thing is that each object in the first set has only one object in the second set assigned to it by any particular function. It is quite possible that a single object in the second set will be associated with many objects in the first set: of $\mapsto$ 2, to $\mapsto$ 2, it $\mapsto$ 2, . . . , in each of the examples. It is also possible that an object in the second set will have no object in the first set assigned to it: there is no standard word associated with 1,000,000 by the functions above, for instance.

As we have said, we have encountered functions throughout the book without calling them that. Here are a few:

The assignment   line segment $AB \mapsto$ length of AB gives a function from the set of line segments to the set of real numbers (which depends on a unit of length, such as meter, having been chosen).

The assignment $x \mapsto x^2$ gives a function from the set of real numbers to the set of real numbers. Or, if we restrict the possibilities for x to natural numbers, $x \mapsto x^2$ gives a function from the set of natural numbers to the set of natural numbers.

The assignment   angle $\mapsto$ radian measure of the angle   gives a function from the set of plane angles to the set of real numbers (Section 35).

The assignment $x \mapsto \sin x$ gives a function from the set of real numbers (radian measures of angles) to the set of real numbers (Section 35).

The assignment $x \mapsto \log_{10} x$ gives a function from the set of positive real numbers to the set of real numbers (Section 36).

Any one-to-one correspondence between two sets gives a function from either of the two sets to the other (Section 22).

The assignment $n \mapsto n!$ gives another function from the set of natural numbers to the set of natural numbers (Section 18).

The assignment $(n, k) \mapsto C(n, k)$ gives a function from the set of *pairs* of natural numbers to the set of natural numbers (Section 18).

The notion of function originated with the development of analytic geometry and calculus in the seventeenth century, in the narrow sense of functions from the set of real numbers (or some subset of real numbers) to the set of real numbers. In fact, the only functions considered then were those that could be given by formulas, such as $x \mapsto x^2$ or $x \mapsto \sin x$ or $x \mapsto \log_{10} x$. It was not until the nineteenth century that it was realized that even for the purposes of calculus it is necessary to take into account the existence of functions that cannot be given by formulas. An example of such a function is the *Dirichlet function*: for x a real number, let $x \mapsto 0$ if x is rational and $x \mapsto 1$ if x is irrational. (Dirichlet (1805–1859) was responsible for the spirit of the broad definition of function with which we began.) Most of the functions considered in elementary calculus can be given by formulas, however, and further, they can be viewed geometrically in the form of a graph, as we shall illustrate after introducing one convenient bit of notation.

Just as the use of letters to denote numbers is necessary for expressing general statements concisely in algebra, the use of letters to denote functions is necessary for expressing general statements concisely in calculus. Especially when a function can be given by a formula, such as $x \mapsto x^2$, it is useful to express the relationship symbolically by writing $f(x)$ (or $g(x)$ or $F(x)$ or something similar) to denote the value assigned to x. Thus we might write $f(x) = x^2$ to represent the function given by $x \mapsto x^2$. Or we might write $g(x) = \sin x$ to represent the function given by $x \mapsto \sin x$. With f and g as in these two examples, we would then write $f(2) = 2^2 = 4$, $g(\pi/2) = \sin \pi/2 = 1$, and so forth. In general, if f denotes any function (relationship) from one set to another and a is an element of the first set, then $f(a)$ is the element in the second set that is assigned to a by f. The use of these symbols simply permits us to write about functions in general, and thus to refer to 'the function f' just as we might refer to 'the number x' in algebra.

In discussing analytic geometry we pointed out that any equation involving x and y has a graph associated with it. If we are given a function f from some set of real numbers to the set of real numbers, then by the *graph* of that function we mean the graph of $y = f(x)$. The graphs of the sine and cosine functions are shown in Figure 35.4 and Figure 35.6, respectively. The graphs of $y = x^3 - 3x^2 + 2$ and $y = x^2$ are shown in Figure 37.3 and Figure 37.5, respectively. Figure 38.1 shows the graph of $y = 1/x$. Notice that the function $1/x$ is not defined when $x = 0$, and so there is no point corresponding to $x = 0$ on its graph.

For later reference we give two further examples. The first is that of a sequence of real numbers. A sequence can commonly be thought

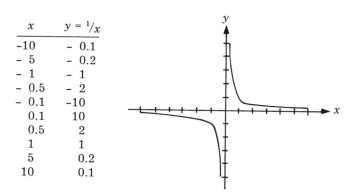

x	$y = \frac{1}{x}$
-10	- 0.1
- 5	- 0.2
- 1	- 1
- 0.5	- 2
- 0.1	-10
0.1	10
0.5	2
1	1
5	0.2
10	0.1

Graph of $y = \frac{1}{x}$

Figure 38.1

of as a set of things arranged in order, so that there is a first, a second, a third, and so on. In particular, then, a sequence of real numbers is some set of real numbers arranged so that there is a first, a second, a third, and so on. This can be expressed in the language of functions by saying that a sequence of real numbers is a function from the set of natural numbers to the set of real numbers. Thus if f is a sequence of real numbers then $f(1), f(2), f(3), \ldots$ are all real numbers. One normally writes f_n rather than $f(n)$ to denote the value assigned to n by such a function, and, when convenient, sequences are given just by indicating the values assigned to the first few natural numbers, as $f_1, f_2, f_3, \ldots$. For example 1, 1/2, 1/3, 1/4, $\ldots$ is the sequence (function) given by $f_n = 1/n$ for each natural number n. (Example 23.1 shows that if f is any particular sequence, then not every real number can be an f_n.)

Our final example is important in the theory of numbers. For each positive real number x, let $\pi(x)$ denote the number of primes that do not exceed x.* Since the primes are 2, 3, 5, 7, 11, 13, $\ldots$, we see that $\pi(1) = 0$, $\pi(2) = 1$, $\pi(2.5) = 1$, $\pi(3) = 2$, $\pi(10) = 4$, and so on. Figure 38.2. shows the graph of $y = \pi(x)$. Notice that it consists of horizontal straight line segments, with a 'jump' of one unit at each prime. We shall say more about this function when we discuss the distribution of primes in Section 48.

PROBLEM SET 38

PROBLEM 38.1. Let the function f be defined by $f(x) = x^2 + 2$ for each x, and determine each of the following.

    (a) $f(0)$ (b) $f(3)$ (c) $f(-3)$

---

* Primes are defined and discussed in Section 48. The use of π to denote the function in this example has become standard. We used Π to denote the function giving the angle of parallelism in Chapter II; there is no connection between these or with the real number π.

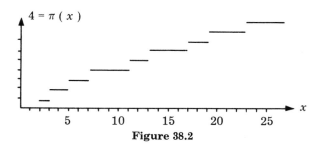

Figure 38.2

(d) $f(9)$ (e) $f(0) + f(1)$ (f) $2 \cdot f(2)$
(g) $f(t)$ (h) $f(t^2)$ (i) $f(x^2)$

PROBLEM 38.2. Let the functions g and h be defined by $g(x) = x^2$ and $h(x) = \cos x$, and determine each of the following.

(a) $h(0)$ (b) $g(0)$ (c) $g(0) + h(0)$

(d) $g(1) + h(\pi)$ (e) $g(\pi) + h(\pi)$ (f) $g(0) - h\left(\dfrac{\pi}{2}\right)$

(g) $2 \cdot g(1) + 3 \cdot h(0)$ (h) $g(h(0))$ (i) $h(g(0))$

PROBLEM 38.3. Draw the graph of each of the functions given by the following relations.

(a) $f(x) = x$ (b) $f(x) = x^2$ (c) $f(x) = -1/x$
(d) $f(x) = \log_{10} x$ (e) $f(x) = \log_2 x$ (f) $f(x) = 1 + \sin x$
(g) $f(x) = x + \sin x$ (h) $f(x) = \sin x + \cos x$ (i) $f(x) = 2 \sin x$
(j) $f(x) = \sin 2x$ (k) $f(x) = 1 + \pi(x)$ (l) $f(x) = x + \pi(x)$

PROBLEM 38.4. The *absolute value* of a real number x, denoted $|x|$, is defined by

$$|x| = x \quad \text{if} \quad x \geq 0$$

and

$$|x| = -x \quad \text{if} \quad x < 0.$$

Geometrically, $|x|$ is the distance from the point corresponding to 0 to the point corresponding to x, when the real numbers have been made to correspond to the points on a line. Thus $|0| = 0$, $|3| = 3$, $|-3| = 3$.

(a) Draw the graph of $y = |x|$.   (b) Draw the graph of $y = |x| + x$.
(c) Draw the graph of $y = |x| - x$.   (d) Draw the graph of $y = |x| + 1$.

(e) Draw the graph of $y = |x + 1|$.   (f) Draw the graph of $y = \dfrac{|x|}{x}$.

PROBLEM 38.5. With π denoting the function defined on page 225, determine each of the following.

(a) $\pi(0.5)$ (b) $\pi(8)$ (c) $\pi(16.9)$
(d) $\pi(17)$ (e) $\pi(18)$ (f) $\pi(20)$
(g) $\pi(21)$ (h) $\pi(30)$ (i) $\pi(\pi)$

PROBLEM 38.6. How would the graph of the function π on page 225 change if the definition of the function were changed to:

let $\pi(x)$ denote the number of primes less than x?

PROBLEM 38.7. Write the first five terms of the sequences having nth term f_n as follows.

(a) $f_n = n^2$ (b) $f_n = n - 1$ (c) $f_n = 3$

(d) $f_n = 1/n^2$ (e) $f_n = 1/2^n$ (f) $f_n = 1/(2n)$

(g) $f_n = (-1)^n$ (h) $f_n = (-1)^n + (-1)^{n+1}$ (i) $f_n = 10^n$

(j) $f_n = \dfrac{n-1}{n+1}$ (k) $f_n = \sin(n\pi)$ (l) $f_n = \sin(n\pi/2)$

(m) $f_n = n \sin(n\pi/2)$ (n) $f_n = \dfrac{1}{2n}\left[1 + (-1)^n\right]$ (o) $f_n = 1 - \dfrac{(-1)^n}{n}$

PROBLEM 38.8. (a) If you have read Section 22, state the definition of *one-to-one correspondence* using the language and notation of this section.
(b) If you have read Section 27, state the definition of *operation on a set* using the language and notation of this section.
(c) If you have read Section 32, state the definition of *isomorphism* using the language and notation of this section.

§39. Limits

The fundamental processes of calculus are based on the concept of limit. This concept proved difficult for mathematicians, being part of the circle of ideas related to continuity and the infinite, which we have referred to often. Even in the refined form in which the concept is now used, it is not easy to acquire the facility necessary for proving theorems about limits; as we remarked about continuity in Section 5, the idea is not a superficial one. In spite of this, it is relatively easy to grasp the basic notion of limit, and, with it, that of calculus. And that is our goal. We shall rely as much as possible on specific examples in the text and in the problems, and it is safe to move on from this section when these examples seem convincing.

EXAMPLE 39.1. Consider the sequence given by $f_n = \dfrac{1}{n}$ for each n:

$$1, \frac{1}{2}, \frac{1}{3}, \frac{1}{4}, \ldots, \frac{1}{n}, \ldots$$

Geometrically, the set of numbers in the sequence looks like Figure 39.1:

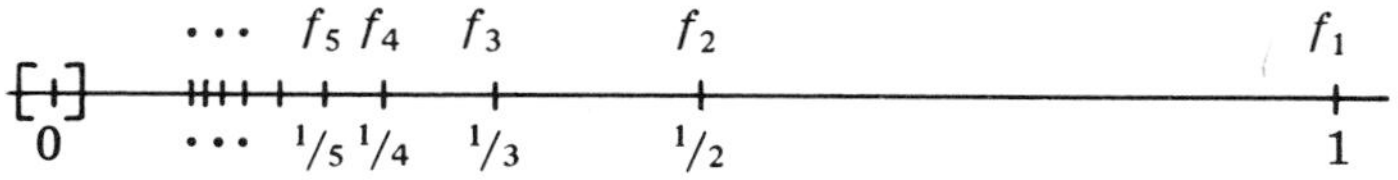

Figure 39.1

The successive terms of the sequence approach nearer and nearer to 0. Moreover, if we are given any preassigned segment containing 0, such as that indicated by [ ] in the figure, then by continuing sufficiently far in the sequence, we can arrive at a term such that all later terms are within the given segment. For example, suppose the preassigned segment were to extend from -0.001 to $+0.001$. Then all terms later than the 1000th would be within that segment: $-0.001 < f_n < +0.001$ for all $n > 1000$. In a situation such as this we say that the sequence has 'limit' 0.

It is helpful to think of such examples in terms of approximations. The limit of the sequence is 0, and each term of the sequence can be thought of as an approximation to that limit. The first term, 1, does not seem a very good approximation; the second term, $\frac{1}{2}$, is certainly better; the third term, $\frac{1}{3}$, is better still; and so on. The crucial point is that no matter how closely we wish to approximate the limit, all terms sufficiently far along in the sequence will give an acceptable approximation. We shall not insist that the successive terms of the sequence give consistently better approximations, as happened in the example, but simply that after a certain term in the sequence none of the terms falls outside our acceptable standard of approximation. Let us now move to a careful definition.

Notice that there are four things involved in the example: the sequence (f), the limit (0), the preassigned segment (-0.001 to $+0.001$), and the natural number (1000) such that for all larger n the terms f_n are within the preassigned segment. It is conventional to use ε (Greek letter epsilon) to denote the distance from the limit to the ends of the preassigned segment in such cases: thus $\varepsilon = 0.001$ in the example. In the language of the preceding paragraph, ε is the standard of approximation: we insist on knowing that all terms after a certain one fall within distance ε of the limit.

DEFINITION

If $f_1, f_2, f_3, \ldots$ is a sequence of real numbers, then a real number L is the limit *of the sequence if for each preassigned positive number ε, no matter how small, there is a natural number m such that*

$$L - \varepsilon < f_n < L + \varepsilon$$

for all $n > m$.

We indicate this by writing

$$f_1, f_2, f_3, \ldots \to L$$

$f_{m+1}, f_{m+2}, \ldots$
are all in here

or

$$\lim f_n = L \quad \text{as} \quad n \to \infty.$$

In the first example, $f_n = 1/n$, $L = 0$, $\varepsilon = 0.001$, $m = 1000$, and

$$1, \frac{1}{2}, \frac{1}{3}, \frac{1}{4}, \ldots \to 0,$$

or

$$\lim \frac{1}{n} = 0 \quad \text{as} \quad n \to \infty.$$

The notation $n \to \infty$ is read 'as n approaches infinity', and simply means 'as n becomes large', in the sense made precise by the definition.

Here are some further examples. The third of these arose in Problem 5.2.

$$\frac{1}{2}, \frac{3}{4}, \frac{7}{8}, \frac{15}{16}, \cdots \qquad\qquad \to 1$$

$$1, -\frac{1}{2}, \frac{1}{3}, -\frac{1}{4}, \ldots \qquad\qquad \to 0$$

$$0.9,\ 0.99,\ 0.999,\ 0.9999, \ldots \qquad \to 1$$

$$1, 1, \frac{1}{2}, \frac{1}{2}, \frac{1}{4}, \frac{1}{3}, \frac{1}{8}, \frac{1}{4}, \frac{1}{16}, \frac{1}{5}, \cdots \to 0$$

The last sequence is constructed by intertwining successive terms of

$$1, \frac{1}{2}, \frac{1}{4}, \frac{1}{8}, \frac{1}{16}, \cdots \quad \text{and} \quad 1, \frac{1}{2}, \frac{1}{3}, \frac{1}{4}, \cdots;$$

the terms in the resulting sequence do not get consistently nearer 0, but the condition in the definition of limit is fulfilled just the same.

Here are two sequences without limits. The first oscillates between 0 and 1, and as a result does not stay near either one. The second clearly does not approach any real number.

$$1, 0, 1, 0, 1, 0, \ldots$$

$$1, 2, 3, 4, 5, 6, \ldots$$

Some of the remaining examples are less obvious. They are given as illustrations, without proofs, and it is not necessary to see why they are valid. The first is a sequence from Problems 4.8 and 4.9; each denominator is the sum of the preceding numerator and denominator, and each numerator is the preceding numerator plus twice the preceding denominator.

$$1, \frac{3}{2}, \frac{7}{5}, \frac{17}{12}, \frac{41}{29}, \cdots \to \sqrt{2}$$

The following example arose in Section 21. The point here is that the sequence given does have a limit, but the limit does not arise in ways that seem quite as apparent as that of the rational numbers or numbers like $\sqrt{2}$ and π. The limit of this particular sequence is of such fundamental importance in mathematics, however, that it is denoted by a special symbol, the letter e. The number e is irrational and is approximately 2.71828; it was discussed in Problem 21.10, and we shall return to it in Section 45.

$$1, \ 1 + \frac{1}{1!}, \ 1 + \frac{1}{1!} + \frac{1}{2!}, \ 1 + \frac{1}{1!} + \frac{1}{2!} + \frac{1}{3!}, \ \ldots \to e.$$

Here is a different sequence that can be proved to have the same limit:

$$\left(1 + \frac{1}{1}\right)^{1}, \left(1 + \frac{1}{2}\right)^{2}, \left(1 + \frac{1}{3}\right)^{3}, \left(1 + \frac{1}{4}\right)^{4}, \ \ldots \to e.$$

Figure 39.2 shows some examples using geometrical figures in place of numbers. The concept behind these examples is similar to that used above, and will be of more concern when we discuss integrals. The first is taken from Section 34E, the second from Problem 4.11, and the third from Section 21.

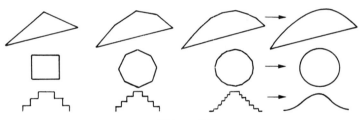

Figure 39.2

Recall that a sequence of real numbers is a function from the set of *natural* numbers to the set of real numbers. We now shift our attention from limit of sequence to limit of a different kind of function, namely, function from the set of *real* numbers to the set of real numbers. When we are ready for a careful definition of this second kind of limit, we shall point out how the two kinds of limits are similar. Once more, we begin with an example. (It may be helpful at this point to read the first part of Section 40, until the notion of limit appears. That will motivate the present discussion.)

EXAMPLE 39.2. Consider the function given by

$$f(x) = \frac{x^2 + x}{x} \text{ for each real number } x \neq 0.$$

Because we are not allowing x to be 0, it might seem preferable to cancel x and write $f(x) = x + 1$. But we want to insist that x not be 0, and the first form will help remind us of that. Even though we are not allowed to consider $x = 0$, however, we can consider values of x approximating 0. The question we ask is this: As x is made to approximate 0 more and more closely, do the corresponding values of $f(x)$ approximate anything more and more closely? If so, then the value approximated by the values of $f(x)$ is called the limit of the function f as x approaches 0. And in this particular example, using that $f(x) = x + 1$ for $x \neq 0$, we see that the values of $f(x)$ approximate 1 as x is made to approximate 0, and so 1 is the limit. The graph of the function is shown in Figure 39.3, with a small circle in the figure at $x = 0$ to show that the function is not defined there. In terms of this graph, we are simply asking whether the y-values on the graph are all near any particular value when the corresponding x-values are all near 0. And they are near 1.

Figure 39.3

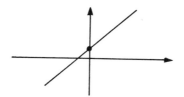

        Although it may seem artificial at the moment to avoid $x = 0$, we shall see in the next section that there is a good reason for doing so.

        In general we shall be given a function f and a real number c, and we shall want to know whether the values $f(x)$ are necessarily close to some particular value when the values x are close to c but different from c. In the cases we consider, this will invariably be most easily determined from a graph.

        We shall now give a definition of this kind of limit that is free of geometry. For our purposes the geometric interpretation will be sufficient, however, and it will not be a handicap to skip this definition. We prepare the way for the definition by rewriting the definition of limit of a sequence in a form slightly different from that given before:

$$\lim f_n = L \quad \text{as} \quad n \to \infty$$

means

for each positive number ε, we have

$$L - \varepsilon < f_n < L + \varepsilon$$

if n is sufficiently near ∞

(the last phrase being a corruption of 'if n is sufficiently large'). For later purposes notice that $n = \infty$ is not considered; f_∞ has no meaning, in fact, since ∞ is not a natural number.

        Now make two changes: in place of ∞ consider some real number c; and in place of a sequence f (a function from the set of natural numbers to the set of real numbers), consider a function f from the set of real numbers other than c to the set of real numbers.

DEFINITION

The real number L is said to be the limit *of the function f as x approaches c, if, for each positive number ε, we have L − ε < f(x) < L + ε if x is different from c but sufficiently near c. We indicate this by writing*

$$\lim f(x) = L \quad \text{as} \quad x \to c.$$

Thus $\lim f(x) = L$ as $x \to c$ means that we can guarantee $f(x)$ close to L by restricting x to be close to c but different from c. Just as we did not consider f_∞ in the definition of limit of a sequence, we do not consider $f(c)$ here, even though $f(c)$ may have meaning; the reason for this will become clear in the next section. In geometric terms, $\lim f(x) = L$ as $x \to c$ means that for each segment $L - \varepsilon$ to $L + \varepsilon$ on the y-axis, there is a corresponding segment on the x-axis (indicated by ( ) in Figure 39.4) such that if x is in that segment, and $x \neq c$, then the corresponding y-value on the graph of f is necessarily between $L - \varepsilon$ and $L + \varepsilon$.

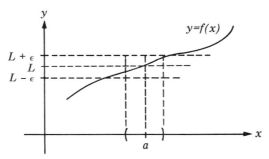

Figure 39.4

EXAMPLE 39.3. Consider the function f given by $f(x) = x^2$ for each real number x. What is $\lim f(x)$ as $x \to 3$? Answer: 9. For any preassigned ε, x^2 will be between $9 - \varepsilon$ and $9 + \varepsilon$ if x is sufficiently near 3. In this case it is also true that $f(3) = 9$, but that is irrelevant for saying that the limit is 9.

EXAMPLE 39.4. Consider the function π, which was considered along with its graph in Section 38. What is $\lim \pi(x)$ as $x \to 2.5$? Answer: 1. For $\pi(x) = 1$ if x is any value sufficiently close to 2.5, say between 2.4 and 2.6, and so certainly $\pi(x)$ is between $1 - \varepsilon$ and $1 + \varepsilon$ for x between 2.4 and 2.6, no matter what ε is.

What is $\lim \pi(x)$ as $x \to 7$? Answer: $\pi(x)$ has no limit as $x \to 7$. For $\pi(x)$ will be at most 3 if x is anything less than 7, while $\pi(x)$ will be at least 4 if x is anything more than 7. Thus the values of $\pi(x)$ are not all near any one number regardless of how close to 7 we restrict x. We say in such a case that the limit fails to exist. The failure for $\pi(x)$ to have a limit as $x \to 7$ manifests itself in the graph of $\pi(x)$ as a 'jump' at $x = 7$.

EXAMPLE 39.5. Consider the function given by $f(x) = \sin(1/x)$ for each $x \neq 0$ (Figure 39.5). We ask for $\lim \sin(1/x)$ as $x \to 0$. Because $\sin \pi = \sin 2\pi = \cdots =$

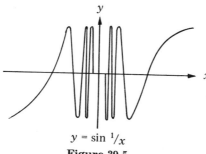

$$y = \sin \frac{1}{x}$$
Figure 39.5

0 and $\sin(-\pi) = \sin(-2\pi) = \cdots = 0$, the graph of the function $f(x) = \sin(1/x)$ will intersect the x-axis at $1/\pi$, $1/2\pi$, ... and at $-1/\pi$, $-1/2\pi$, ... Between these values it will oscillate alternately to $+1$ and -1. Regardless of how close to 0 we restrict x, the values of $\sin(1/x)$ will not all be near any one value; they will always include all values between $+1$ and -1. Thus $\lim \sin(1/x)$ as $x \to 0$ fails to exist.

Once more, the statements we make about limits can be proved, but it would take us too far afield to do it. It is enough if the statements seem convincing based on graphs and intuition.

PROBLEM SET 39

PROBLEM 39.1. State whether each of the following sequences has a limit. If Yes give its value; if No give a reason.

(a) $0, \dfrac{1}{2}, 0, \dfrac{1}{3}, 0, \dfrac{1}{4}, \ldots$

(b) $0, 1, -1, 2, -2, 3, -3, \ldots$

(c) $1 + \dfrac{1}{1}, 1 + \dfrac{1}{2}, 1 + \dfrac{1}{3}, 1 + \dfrac{1}{4}, \ldots, 1 + \dfrac{1}{n}, \ldots$

(d) $7, 7, 7, 7, \ldots, 7, \ldots$ 　　　　　　　(e) $1, \dfrac{1}{2}, 1, \dfrac{1}{3}, 1, \dfrac{1}{4}, \ldots$

(f) $\dfrac{1}{3}, \dfrac{2}{4}, \dfrac{3}{5}, \dfrac{4}{6}, \ldots, \dfrac{n}{n+2}, \ldots$ 　　(g) $-1, \dfrac{1}{2}, -1, \dfrac{1}{3}, -1, \dfrac{1}{4}, \ldots$

(h) $0, \dfrac{1}{2}, \dfrac{4}{3}, \dfrac{3}{4}, \dfrac{6}{5}, \ldots, 1 - \dfrac{(-1)^n}{n}, \ldots$ 　(i) $\dfrac{2}{1}, \dfrac{3}{4}, \dfrac{4}{9}, \dfrac{5}{16}, \ldots, \dfrac{n+1}{n^2}, \ldots$

(j) $\dfrac{1}{2}, \dfrac{4}{3}, \dfrac{9}{4}, \dfrac{16}{5}, \ldots, \dfrac{n^2}{n+1}, \ldots$ 　(k) $0.9, 0.99, 0.999, 0.9999, \ldots$

(l) $-\dfrac{1}{2}, \dfrac{1}{4}, -\dfrac{1}{8}, \dfrac{1}{16}, \ldots, \left(-\dfrac{1}{2}\right)^n, \ldots$ 　(m) $\dfrac{4}{3}, \dfrac{9}{8}, \dfrac{16}{15}, \dfrac{25}{24}, \ldots, \dfrac{(n+1)^2}{n(n+2)}, \ldots$

(n) $\sqrt{1}, \sqrt{2}, \sqrt{3}, \sqrt{4}, \ldots, \sqrt{n}, \ldots$ 　(o) $\pi(1), \pi(2), \pi(3), \pi(4), \ldots, \pi(n), \ldots$

(p) $1 + \dfrac{1}{2}, 1 + \dfrac{1}{2} + \dfrac{1}{4}, 1 + \dfrac{1}{2} + \dfrac{1}{4} + \dfrac{1}{8}, \ldots, 1 + \dfrac{1}{2} + \dfrac{1}{4} + \dfrac{1}{8} + \cdots + \dfrac{1}{2^n}, \ldots$

(q) $\cos \pi, \cos 2\pi, \cos 3\pi, \ldots, \cos n\pi, \ldots$

(r) $\cos \dfrac{\pi}{2}$, $\cos \pi$, $\cos \dfrac{3\pi}{2}$, ..., $\cos \dfrac{n\pi}{2}$, ...

(s) $\sin \dfrac{\pi}{2}$, $\dfrac{1}{2} \sin \pi$, $\dfrac{1}{3} \sin \dfrac{3\pi}{2}$, ..., $\dfrac{1}{n} \sin \dfrac{n\pi}{2}$, ...

(t) $\cos 2\pi$, $\cos 4\pi$, $\cos 6\pi$, ..., $\cos 2n\pi$, ...

(u) $\sin 1$, $\sin \dfrac{1}{10}$, $\sin \dfrac{1}{100}$, $\sin \dfrac{1}{1000}$, ..., $\sin \dfrac{1}{10^{n-1}}$, ...

(v) $\log_{10} 2$, $\log_{10} 3$, $\log_{10} 4$, $\log_{10} 5$, ..., $\log_{10} n$, ...

(w) $\log_2 2$, $\log_3 2$, $\log_4 2$, $\log_5 2$, ..., $\log_{n+1} 2$, ...

PROBLEM 39.2. (a) through (o). State whether each of the sequences in Problem 38.7 has a limit. If Yes give its value; if No give a reason.

PROBLEM 39.3. State whether each of the following limits exists. If Yes give its value; if No give a reason.

(a) $\lim x^2$ as $x \to 5$ (b) $\lim (x^2 + 1)$ as $x \to 5$

(c) $\lim 2$ as $x \to 5$ (d) $\lim 2x$ as $x \to \pi$

(e) $\lim x^2$ as $x \to \sqrt{3}$ (f) $\lim \dfrac{x^2 - 4}{x - 2}$ as $x \to 2$

(g) $\lim \dfrac{x^2 - 16}{x - 4}$ as $x \to 4$ (h) $\lim \dfrac{x^2 - 16}{x - 4}$ as $x \to -2$

(i) $\lim \dfrac{x^3 - 1}{x - 1}$ as $x \to 1$ (j) $\lim \dfrac{x^2 - 2x + 1}{x - 1}$ as $x \to 1$

(k) $\lim \dfrac{x^3 + x^2 + 1}{x}$ as $x \to 1$ (l) $\lim \sin x$ as $x \to 2\pi$

(m) $\lim \cos x$ as $x \to 0$ (n) $\lim \cos 2x$ as $x \to 0$

(o) $\lim 2 \sin x$ as $x \to \pi/2$

(p) $\lim [(\sin x)^2 + (\cos x)^2]$ as $x \to \pi/2$

(q) $\lim 2 \cos 2x$ as $x \to 0$

(r) $\lim \cos \dfrac{1}{x}$ as $x \to 0$

(s) $\lim [\sin x + \sin 2x]$ as $x \to \pi/2$

(t) $\lim \sin \dfrac{1}{x}$ as $x \to \dfrac{1}{20\pi}$

(u) $\lim \log_{10} x$ as $x \to 1$

(v) $\lim D(x)$ as $x \to 1$, where D is the Dirichlet function (page 224).

(w) $\lim D(x)$ as $x \to \sqrt{2}$, where D is the Dirichlet function (page 224).

PROBLEM 39.4. State whether each of the following limits exists. If Yes give its value; if No give a reason.

(a) $\lim \pi(x)$ as $x \to 11$

(b) $\lim \pi(x)$ as $x \to 2.1$

(c) $\lim \pi(2x)$ as $x \to 3$

(d) $\lim \pi(x)$ as $x \to p$, p a prime

(e) $\lim \pi(2x)$ as $x \to p$, p a prime.

PROBLEM 39.5. (a) Construct a sequence with limit 3 and with each of its terms after the first larger than the term before it.

(b) Construct a sequence with limit 3 and with each of its terms after the first smaller than the term before it.

(c) Construct a sequence with limit 3 and with its terms alternately larger and smaller than 3.

PROBLEM 39.6. (a) Is there a sequence with its terms alternately positive and negative and having limit 0? If Yes give an example; if No give a reason.

(b) Is there a sequence with its terms alternately positive and negative and having limit 1? If Yes give an example; if No give a reason.

PROBLEM 39.7. Compute the first six terms of the sequence with nth term $(1 + 1/n)^n$, and compare with the approximation 2.71828 for the number e. (See page 230 and Problem 21.10.)

PROBLEM 39.8. For each of the following sequences, find the smallest natural number m such that

$$L - 0.01 < f_n < L + 0.01$$

for all $n > m$, where L is the limit of the sequence.

(a) $1, -\dfrac{1}{2}, \dfrac{1}{3}, -\dfrac{1}{4}, \ldots, \dfrac{(-1)^{n+1}}{n}, \ldots \to 0$

(b) $1, \dfrac{1}{4}, \dfrac{1}{8}, \dfrac{1}{16}, \ldots, \dfrac{1}{n^2}, \ldots \to 0$

(c) $0.9, 0.99, 0.999, 0.9999, \ldots \to 1$

(d) $1, 1, \dfrac{1}{2}, \dfrac{1}{2}, \dfrac{1}{4}, \dfrac{1}{3}, \dfrac{1}{8}, \dfrac{1}{4}, \dfrac{1}{16}, \dfrac{1}{5}, \ldots \to 0$ (see page 229).

(e) $\cos \dfrac{\pi}{2}, \cos \dfrac{3\pi}{2}, \cos \dfrac{5\pi}{2}, \cos \dfrac{7\pi}{2}, \ldots \to 0$

(f) $10 - \dfrac{10}{1}, 10 + \dfrac{10}{2}, 10 - \dfrac{10}{3}, 10 + \dfrac{10}{4}, \ldots, 10 + \dfrac{(-1)^n 10}{n}, \ldots \to 10$

§40. Derivatives

The two fundamental processes of calculus are differentiation, that of obtaining derivatives, and integration, that of obtaining integrals. We shall study integration in the next section. We begin now with a specific example of a derivative.

Assume that an object falls from rest near the earth's surface, and that it is free of air resistance and acted on only by the force of gravity. It can be established that during the first t seconds the distance d traveled by the object will be given by $d = \frac{1}{2}gt^2$, where g is a constant that depends on the units used to measure distance and time (approximately, g is 32.2 if feet and seconds are used, and 9.81 if meters and seconds are used).* We consider the question: How fast will the object be falling at the end of t seconds? With the concept of derivative we can give this question a precise meaning, and then answer it. The constant factor $\frac{1}{2}g$ would enter our discussion only as a distraction, so let us

---

* We shall see later why $\frac{1}{2}(32.2)$ or $\frac{1}{2}(9.81)$ (that is, $\frac{1}{2}g$) is used rather than 16.1 or 4.905.

ignore it for the present and consider the more simple looking formula $d = t^2$. Further, let us choose a particular instant, say $t = 3$. Thus we assume an object to be moving according to the law $d = t^2$, and we are asking how fast it will be moving when $t = 3$ (Figure 40.1).

Figure 40.1

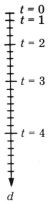

The notion we are after is that of instantaneous velocity, or instantaneous rate of change. If an object travels D units along a straight line in T seconds, then its average velocity during that time is D/T. If, for example, it moves 10 meters in 5 seconds, then its average velocity during that 5 seconds is 2 meters per second. Letting f denote the function given by $d = f(t) = t^2$, we see that $f(0) = 0$ and $f(3) = 9$, so that an object moving according to our particular law will travel $f(3) - f(0) = 9$ units during the first 3 seconds after it is dropped, or 3 units per second on the average. The table shows the average velocity for the object over various intervals of time either terminating or beginning at $t = 3$. The average velocity 'from $t = 3$ to $t = 3$' would make no sense, for it would be $[f(3) - f(3)]/(3 - 3) = 0/0$. But notice from the table that as we consider shorter and shorter intervals of time on either side of $t = 3$, the average velocity approaches nearer and nearer to 6 units per second. To make this statement more precise, we

Time Interval			Distance Traveled	Average Velocity
$t = 0$	to	$t = 3$	9 units	3 units per second
$t = 2$	to	$t = 3$	5 units	5 units per second
$t = 2.5$	to	$t = 3$	2.75 units	5.5 units per second
$t = 2.9$	to	$t = 3$	0.59 units	5.9 units per second
$t = 3$	to	$t = 3.1$	0.61 units	6.1 units per second
$t = 3$	to	$t = 3.5$	3.25 units	6.5 units per second
$t = 3$	to	$t = 3.9$	6.21 units	6.9 units per second
$t = 3$	to	$t = 6$	27 units	9 units per second

observe that if $t = 3 + h$ (Figure 40.2) is any time other than $t = 3$, then the average velocity over the interval $t = 3$ to $t = 3 + h$ will be

$$\frac{f(3 + h) - f(3)}{(3 + h) - 3} = \frac{(3 + h)^2 - 3^2}{h}$$

$$= \frac{9 + 6h + h^2 - 9}{h}$$

$$= 6 + h$$

(with h positive if $3 + h$ is after 3, and negative if it is before). This average velocity $6 + h$ does indeed approach 6 as $3 + h$ approaches 3, that is, as h approaches 0. The instantaneous velocity of the object

Figure 40.2

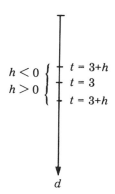

$h < 0$ { $t = 3+h$
$h > 0$ { $t = 3$
              $t = 3+h$

d

when $t = 3$ is therefore *defined* to be 6 units per second. This is nothing more than a limit. In other words, the instantaneous velocity at $t = 3$ of an object moving according to the law $d = t^2$ is defined to be

$$\lim \frac{(3 + h)^2 - 3^2}{h} \quad \text{as} \quad h \to 0.$$

If we apply the same reasoning to a motion given by a general function f rather than the particular one $f(t) = t^2$, and consider an arbitrary time t in place of 3, then we are led to the following definition.

DEFINITION

The instantaneous velocity at time t *of an object moving along a straight line according to the law* $d = f(t)$ *is defined to be*

$$\lim \frac{f(t + h) - f(t)}{h} \quad \text{as} \quad h \to 0,$$

*if the limit exists.**

---

* The qualification 'if the limit exists' is necessary because of cases such as those in Examples 39.4 and 39.5, where limits fail to exist. We shall avoid such problems in what follows.

Computing this limit for the law $d = f(t) = \frac{1}{2}gt^2$ would yield that the instantaneous velocity of a freely falling object t seconds after it is dropped will be gt. For instance, 2 seconds after it is dropped the instantaneous velocity will be $(32.2)(2) = 64.4$ feet per second (or 19.62 meters per second).

Notice that with $h = 0$ the expression $[f(t + h) - f(t)]/h$ always reduces to 0/0. This illustrates why, in defining the limit of a function as $x \rightarrow c$, we do not consider $x = c$.

The essential feature of what we have just discussed is as follows. We have one quantity (distance, or position) which is dependent upon another quantity (time); as the second changes the first will change. Such relationships are common: whenever we have a function f from one set to another, changing x in the first set will tend to change $f(x)$ in the second. The appropriate concept for describing rates of change in many such circumstances is that of derivative, whose definition is obtained from that of instantaneous velocity simply by freeing the two variable quantities to be things other than distance and time.

DEFINITION

Assume that f is a function from the set of real numbers to the set of real numbers, and that x is a real number. Then the derivative of f, at x, is defined to be

$$\lim \frac{f(x + h) - f(x)}{h} \quad as \quad h \rightarrow 0,$$

if the limit exists.

If the limit defining the derivative of the function f does exist for each real number x, then we can think of the derivative itself as giving a function from the set of real numbers to the set of real numbers. This function, the derivative of f, is denoted by f'. Thus for each real number x, the real number $f'(x)$ is the derivative of f at x. If f is the function given by $f(x) = x^2$ for each x, then essentially the same calculation as that used to compute instantaneous velocity at $t = 3$ in the first example above will show that $f'(x) = 2x$ for each x. Similarly, if $f(x) = x^3$, then

$$f'(x) = \lim \frac{(x + h)^3 - x^3}{h} \qquad as \quad h \rightarrow 0$$

$$= \lim \frac{x^3 + 3x^2h + 3xh^2 + h^3 - x^3}{h} \qquad as \quad h \rightarrow 0$$

$$= \lim (3x^2 + 3xh + h^2) \qquad as \quad h \rightarrow 0$$

$$= 3x^2.$$

Computing derivatives of various important functions is one of the goals in any extensive treatment of calculus. It will be useful for us to have some of these formulas available. We shall not prove them. The example just given illustrates what is involved, although the details are sometimes more difficult.

FORMULA FOR DERIVATIVE OF A POLYNOMIAL

If

$$f(x) = a_0 + a_1 x + a_2 x^2 + \cdots + a_n x^n,$$

where the subscripted a's are constant real numbers, then

$$f'(x) = a_1 + 2a_2 x + \cdots + na_n x^{n-1}.$$

EXAMPLE 40.1.
If $f(x) = x^3$, then $f'(x) = 3x^2$.
If $f(x) = x^{15}$, then $f'(x) = 15x^{14}$.
If $f(x) = x^n$, then $f'(x) = nx^{n-1}$ (n any natural number).
If $f(x) = x^6 - 4x^2 + 2$, then $f'(x) = 6x^5 - 8x$.
If $f(x) = 10$, then $f'(x) = 0$.
The last example illustrates the general fact that if a function of x is constant, that is, does not change as x changes, then its derivative is 0 at each x; this should be expected, since the derivative is a measure of rate of change.

FORMULAS FOR DERIVATIVES OF SINE AND COSINE

If $f(x) = \sin x$, then $f'(x) = \cos x$.

If $f(x) = \cos x$, then $f'(x) = -\sin x$.

EXAMPLE 40.2.
The derivative of the cosine function at $\pi/2$ is $-\sin (\pi/2) = -1$.
The derivative of the sine function at $3\pi/2$ is $\cos (3\pi/2) = 0$.

Let us mention two general principles that can be established concerning derivatives. The first applies to any function that is a sum of other functions, such as $f(x) = \sin x + \cos x$. The principle asserts that the derivative of such a function is the sum of derivatives of these separate functions. Thus if $f(x) = \sin x + \cos x$ then $f'(x) = \cos x - \sin x$. In general,

if $f(x) = g(x) + h(x)$, then $f'(x) = g'(x) + h'(x)$.

The second principle applies to any function that is a constant times some other function, such as $f(x) = 3 \sin x$. This principle asserts that the derivative of such a function is the constant times the derivative of the other function. Thus if $f(x) = 3 \sin x$ then $f'(x) = 3 \cos x$. In general,

$$\text{if } f(x) = cg(x), \quad \text{then} \quad f'(x) = cg'(x),$$

when c is any real number.

One of the important applications of derivatives is in determining maximum and minimum values of functions. Here is how this comes about. Consider a function f with graph as shown in Figure 40.3. The

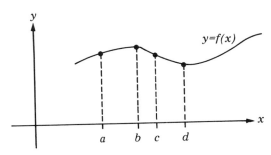

Figure 40.3

derivative of f at x, $f'(x)$, gives a measure of the way $f(x)$ changes as x changes. It can be shown by studying the definition of derivative that an increase in x causes an increase in $f(x)$ at any value such as a where $f'(a) > 0$. Similarly, an increase in x causes a decrease in $f(x)$ at any value such as c where $f'(c) < 0$. On the other hand, at a value such as b, where the function reaches a maximum (relative to other values nearby), it is the case that $f'(b) = 0$; and at a value such as d, where the function reaches a minimum (again relative to other values nearby), it is also the case that $f'(d) = 0$. Briefly: derivative positive implies function increasing, derivative negative implies function decreasing, function either maximum or minimum implies derivative zero.* Problems 40.12, 40.13, 40.15, and 40.16 suggest why this is so.

EXAMPLE 40.3. Let us apply this to the function $f(x) = x^3 - 3x^2 + 2$, whose graph was given in Figure 37.3. By the formula for derivative of a polynomial, the derivative of this function is $f'(x) = 3x^2 - 6x$. And $3x^2 - 6x = 0$ for $x = 0$ and $x = 2$. Looking at the graph of the function, we see that $x = 0$ corresponds to a (relative) maximum and $x = 2$ to a (relative) minimum. It can be shown that for many functions, including this one, the following simple test will reveal whether or not there is a relative maximum or minimum where $f'(x) = 0$: if f'' denotes the derivative of f', then $f''(x) < 0$ corresponds to a maximum and $f''(x) > 0$ corresponds to a minimum. In the present example, $f''(x) = 6x - 6$, and $f''(0) = -6 < 0$ (maximum) while $f''(2) = 6 > 0$

---

* This assumes that the function has a derivative for each value of x. We shall always assume this, unless stated otherwise.

(minimum). Such facts are often helpful in constructing graphs of functions such as the one just considered.

EXAMPLE 40.4. Assume that we are given 200 feet of fence, and that we wish to enclose a rectangular field with the fence in such a way as to get the maximum area. What dimensions should we use? If one dimension is denoted by x, as in Figure 40.4, then the other will be $100 - x$. The area will be $A(x) = (100 - x)x = 100x - x^2$, and we want the x that will make this maximum.

Figure 40.4

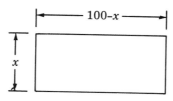

We find that $A'(x) = 100 - 2x$, and so $A'(x) = 0$ for $x = 50$. And $A''(x) = -2$ for all x, so in particular $A''(50) = -2 < 0$. Thus $x = 50$ is the value giving maximum area. In other words we get maximum area by making the field square. This particular problem can be solved without calculus (such as in Problem 6.5), but it does illustrate a technique that is very useful in applications.

Applications of derivatives to maximum and minimum problems extend throughout pure and applied science, as well as to many areas of mathematics. We shall give more examples in Section 44.

PROBLEM SET 40

PROBLEM 40.1. Assume an object to be moving along a straight line according to the law $d = t^2 + t + 1$.

(a) Compute the average velocity of the object over each of the following time intervals:

$t = 0$	to	$t = 2$	$t = 1.5$	to	$t = 2$
$t = 1$	to	$t = 2$	$t = 1.9$	to	$t = 2.$

(b) What is the instantaneous velocity of the object at $t = 2$?

PROBLEM 40.2. Same as Problem 40.1 with the law $d = t^2 + t + 1$ replaced by the law $d = t^2 - t$.

PROBLEM 40.3. Assume that an object is dropped from the top of a 300 foot building, acted on only by the force of gravity.

(a) Determine its position and instantaneous velocity 1 second after it is dropped.

(b) Determine its position and instantaneous velocity 2 seconds after it is dropped.

(c) Determine its position and instantaneous velocity 3 seconds after it is dropped.

(d) Determine how long it will take the object to reach the ground.

PROBLEM 40.4. Using appropriate formulas given in the text, compute f' and f'' for each of the following functions.

(a) $f(x) = x^{10}$ (b) $f(x) = 3$

(c) $f(x) = x^4 + x^3 + x^2 + x + 1$

(d) $f(x) = \frac{1}{5}x^5 + \frac{1}{4}x^4 + \frac{1}{3}x^3 + \frac{1}{2}x^2 + x + 1$

(e) $f(x) = x^{100} - 2x^{20} + 7x^5$ (f) $f(x) = x + \sin x$

(g) $f(x) = \sin x + \cos x$ (h) $f(x) = 2 \sin x$

(i) $f(x) = -3 \cos x$ (j) $f(x) = 2x - 3 \sin x + 5 \cos x$

PROBLEM 40.5. Assume $g(x) = x^2 + 1$ and $h(x) = \cos x$. Compute each of the following.

(a) $g'(1)$ (b) $g'(0)$

(c) $h'(\pi)$ (d) $h'(3\pi/2)$

(e) $g'(1) + h'(\pi)$ (f) $g'(0) + h'(3\pi/2)$

PROBLEM 40.6. Assume $g(x) = x^3 - 1$ and $h(x) = \sin x$. Compute each of the following.

(a) $g'(0)$ (b) $g'(4)$

(c) $h'(\pi)$ (d) $h'(\pi/2)$

(e) $g''(0) + h''(\pi)$ (f) $g''(4) + h''(\pi/2)$

PROBLEM 40.7. Compute each of the following derivatives directly from the definition of derivative, that is, using the method carried out for x^3 on page 238, and not the formula for derivative of a polynomial.

(a) If $f(x) = x^2$,   then $f'(x) = 2x$.

(b) If $f(x) = 4x$,   then $f'(x) = 4$.

(c) If $f(x) = x^4$,   then $f'(x) = 4x^3$.

(d) If $f(x) = 6$,   then $f'(x) = 0$.

(e) If $f(x) = x^2 + 1$,   then $f'(x) = 2x$.

PROBLEM 40.8. Compute the relative maximum and minimum values of each of the following functions, making use of both first and second derivatives to justify each answer.

(a) $x^2 - 6x + 1$ (b) $x^3 - 3x + 1$

(c) $x^3 - 3x^2 - 9x$ (d) $2x^3 + 3x^2 - 12x$

(e) $x^4 - 4x^3 + 4x^2 + 1$ (f) $\sin x$

(g) $2 \sin x$ (h) $-\cos x$

PROBLEM 40.9. Assume that 200 feet of fence is given, and that it is required to enclose three sides of a rectangular field with the fence, the fourth side to be bounded by an already existing fence. What dimensions should be used to obtain the field of greatest area?

PROBLEM 40.10. Let $f(x) = |x|$ for each x, where $|x|$ denotes the absolute value of x, defined in Problem 38.4. Verify that this function does not have a derivative at $x = 0$, by carrying out the following steps.

(a) Explain why $f(0 + h) - f(0) = h$ for $h > 0$.

(b) Explain why $[f(0 + h) - f(0)]/h = 1$ for $h > 0$.

(c) Explain why $f(0 + h) - f(0) = -h$ for $h < 0$.

(d) Explain why $[f(0 + h) - f(0)]/h = -1$ for $h < 0$.

(e) Why does $\lim [f(0 + h) - f(0)]/h$ as $h \to 0$ fail to exist?

PROBLEM 40.11. Consider this statement from the text: 'derivative positive implies function increasing, derivative negative implies function decreasing, function either maximum or minimum implies derivative zero.'

(a) Verify the statement for the sine function by sketching the sine function together with its derivative, the cosine function.

(b) Verify the statement for the cosine function by sketching the cosine function together with its derivative, the negative of the sine function.

PROBLEM 40.12. Consider the function f shown in Figure 40.3. Verify that $f'(x) = 0$ at a value such as b where the function reaches a relative maximum, by carrying out the following steps.

(a) Explain why $f(b + h) - f(b) < 0$ for $h > 0$ and h close to 0.
(b) Explain why $[f(b + h) - f(b)]/h < 0$ for $h > 0$ and h close to 0.
(c) Explain why $\lim [f(b + h) - f(b)]/h > 0$ as $h \to 0$ is impossible.
(d) Explain why $f(b + h) - f(b) < 0$ for $h < 0$ and h close to 0.
(e) Explain why $[f(b + h) - f(b)]/h > 0$ for $h < 0$ and h close to 0.
(f) Explain why $\lim [f(b + h) - f(b)]/h < 0$ as $h \to 0$ is impossible.
(g) Using parts (c) and (f), explain why necessarily $f'(b) = 0$ if $f'(b)$ exists and the function f reaches a relative maximum at b.

PROBLEM 40.13. Consider the function f shown in Figure 40.3. Verify that $f'(x) = 0$ at a value such as d where the function reaches a relative minimum, by carrying out steps similar to those in Problem 40.12.

PROBLEM 40.14. (a) Verify that if $f(x) = x^3$ then $f'(0) = 0$.
(b) Draw the graph of $y = x^3$.
(c) Note that the function f has neither a maximum nor a minimum at $x = 0$. What does this imply about the converses of the statements proved in Problems 40.12 and 40.13?

PROBLEM 40.15. Consider the function f shown in Figure 40.3. Verify that at a value such as a where $f'(x) > 0$, it is the case that an increase in x causes an increase in $f(x)$, by carrying out the following steps. (Assume $f'(a) > 0$ throughout.)

(a) Explain why $[f(a + h) - f(a)]/h > 0$ for $h > 0$ and h close to 0.
(b) Explain why $f(a + h) - f(a) > 0$ for $h > 0$ and h close to 0.
(c) Explain why $[f(a + h) - f(a)]/h > 0$ for $h < 0$ and h close to 0.
(d) Explain why $f(a + h) - f(a) < 0$ for $h < 0$ and h close to 0.
(e) Using parts (b) and (d), explain why $f'(a) > 0$ implies that an increase in x causes an increase in $f(x)$.

PROBLEM 40.16. Consider the function f shown in Figure 40.3. Verify that at a value c where $f'(x) < 0$, it is the case that an increase in x causes a decrease in $f(x)$, by carrying out steps similar to those in Problem 40.15.

§41. Integrals

In discussing the method of exhaustion (Section 34E), we described how to compute the area of a region bounded partially by something other than straight lines. But the region considered was of a very special kind, that of a parabolic segment, and the computations depended on some very special properties of that region. In order to handle more general problems of area, mathematicians developed the concept of the integral.

The basic idea of the integral is much like that of the method of exhaustion: compute approximations for the area by using simpler figures whose areas can be arrived at easily, choosing these approximations in such a way that they become successively closer to the area of the original figure. With the integral, however, systematic use is made of analytic geometry and the concept of limit, and as a result we gain enormously. We begin with a specific example to illustrate the general idea.

EXAMPLE 41.1. What is the area A of the region above the x-axis, below the graph of $y = x^2$, and between $x = 0$ and $x = 2$? (Figure 41.1(a).) We can obtain

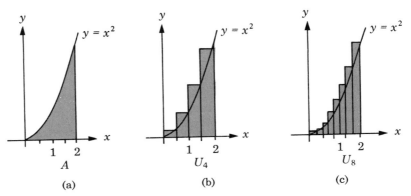

Figure 41.1

an approximation for this area by recognizing that the region can be approximated by rectangles and that we know how to compute areas of rectangles. Figure 41.1(b) shows such an approximation using four rectangles of equal widths. Denote the sum of the areas of the four rectangles by U_4, where the subscript 4 is used to suggest that there are four rectangles and U is used to suggest that the rectangles chosen will give an *upper* bound for the area, that is, an area at least as great as the area A. Each rectangle has width $\frac{1}{2}$, and the heights are the y-values $(1/2)^2$, $(2/2)^2$, $(3/2)^2$, and $(4/2)^2$, corresponding to the x-values $1/2$, $2/2$, $3/2$, and $4/2$, respectively. Thus

$$U_4 = \frac{1}{2}\left(\frac{1}{2}\right)^2 + \frac{1}{2}\left(\frac{2}{2}\right)^2 + \frac{1}{2}\left(\frac{3}{2}\right)^2 + \frac{1}{2}\left(\frac{4}{2}\right)^2$$

$$= \frac{1}{2}\left(\frac{1}{2}\right)^2 [1^2 + 2^2 + 3^2 + 4^2] = \frac{30}{8} = \frac{15}{4}.$$

We can get a better approximation by using more rectangles. Figure 41.1(c) shows an approximation using eight rectangles of equal widths. Their total area, which we denote by U_8, is

$$U_8 = \frac{1}{4}\left(\frac{1}{4}\right)^2 + \frac{1}{4}\left(\frac{2}{4}\right)^2 + \cdots + \frac{1}{4}\left(\frac{8}{4}\right)^2 = \frac{51}{16}.$$

We could continue, looking at special cases with more and more rectangles, but the key is rather in the following:
(i) attempt to get a general formula for U_n, and
(ii) realize that $A = \lim U_n$ as $n \to \infty$.
In truth, $\lim U_n$ as $n \to \infty$ is taken as the definition of the area A; the figures make it seem a reasonable definition.

Let us carry out (i) and (ii). In computing U_n in this case we will have n rectangles each of width $2/n$. The right-hand edges of the rectangles will then be at $2/n$, $2(2/n) = 4/n$, $3(2/n) = 6/n$, and so forth. If we take their heights as before so that the upper right-hand edge of each rectangle is on $y = x^2$, then their heights will be $(2/n)^2$, $(4/n)^2$, ..., $(2n/n)^2$. Thus

$$U_n = \frac{2}{n}\left(\frac{2}{n}\right)^2 + \frac{2}{n}\left(\frac{4}{n}\right)^2 + \cdots + \frac{2}{n}\left(\frac{2n}{n}\right)^2$$

$$= \frac{2}{n^3}[2^2 + 4^2 + \cdots + (2n)^2]$$

$$= \frac{2^3}{n^3}[1^2 + 2^2 + \cdots + n^2].$$

We must now use the formula (see Problem 41.7)

$$1^2 + 2^2 + \cdots + n^2 = \frac{1}{6}n(n+1)(2n+1).$$

Therefore

$$U_n = \frac{2^3}{n^3} \cdot \frac{1}{6}n\,(n+1)\,(2n+1)$$

$$= \frac{4}{3} \cdot \frac{2n^3 + 3n^2 + n}{n^3}$$

$$= \frac{4}{3}\left(2 + \frac{3}{n} + \frac{1}{n^2}\right).$$

Now we are ready for (ii). Because $3/n \to 0$ and $1/n^2 \to 0$ as $n \to \infty$, we see that

$$A = \lim U_n = \lim \frac{4}{3}\left(2 + \frac{3}{n} + \frac{1}{n^2}\right) = \frac{8}{3} \quad \text{as } n \to \infty.$$

That is, the area A is 8/3.

Had we used rectangles having their upper left-hand corners rather than their upper right-hand corners on $y = x^2$, then we would have gotten approximating areas smaller than A; Figure 41.2 shows this for L_8, with L meant to suggest *lower* bound. With details differing little from those for the case of upper limits, it can be shown that

$$L_n = \frac{4}{3}\left(2 - \frac{3}{n} + \frac{1}{n^2}\right).$$

Thus we see that $\lim L_n = 8/3$ as $n \to \infty$. So, as we would expect, $\lim U_n = \lim L_n$. The common limit then is taken to be A. The separate U_n and L_n give only approximations, which become more accurate with larger n.

Figure 41.2

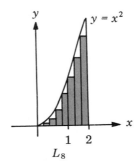

L_8

Passing now from our specific example to the general question of area, we assume that we are given a function f and two real numbers a and b, with $a < b$. We also assume, in order to avoid technical distractions, that the graph of $y = f(x)$ lies entirely above the x-axis for values of x between a and b (Figure 41.3). Finally, we assume the

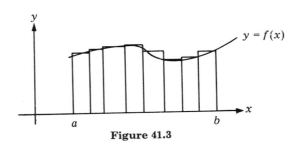

Figure 41.3

function f to be continuous: this is a condition which means, roughly, that the graph of $y = f(x)$ is uninterrupted, or that it can be traced without lifting one's pencil from the paper; the function given by $x \mapsto \pi(x)$, discussed on page 225, is not continuous; the function given by $x \mapsto x^2$ is continuous. (The concept of continuous function, which is very important in calculus, can be defined more precisely, but the description just given will suffice for our purposes. Most of the functions we have considered are continuous.) Can we find, or even give a meaning to, the area of the region R above the x-axis, below the graph of $y = f(x)$, and between $x = a$ and $x = b$? To answer this we simply extend what we did in the specific example, as follows.

In place of considering only rectangles of equal widths, we allow the bases of the rectangles to be determined in any way subject to the condition that they cover the segment from a to b with no overlap. Second, in place of considering just those rectangles with upper edges wholly outside or wholly inside the region (as in U_n and L_n, respectively), we require only that the upper edge of each rectangle be intersected by the graph of $y = f(x)$. The basis for the integral calculus is that the values obtained from approximations by any such system of rectangles will tend to a definite limit (real number) as the number of rectangles in the system is increased in such a way that the widths of the rectangles approach 0. Moreover, the limits obtained from different systems (such as those using upper limits or those using lower limits in the example) will be equal. This unique limiting value (8/3 in the example) is then defined to be the area of the region R.

Several remarks are in order. First, the statements above, as well as the others we shall make, require proof. And before they can be proved they must be formulated in terms that are independent of the geometry involved. The geometry is important for guiding intuition, of course, and the discussion we have given does rely heavily on it. But intuition can be misleading, and when the ideas are formulated carefully the results involve only the function f and the numbers a and b; that is, they involve only things expressible in terms of real numbers. The limiting value obtained by this process (represented above by the area of the region R) is therefore denoted by a symbol which reflects that it is completely determined by f, a, and b. The symbols used are

$$\int_a^b f \quad \text{or} \quad \int_a^b f(x)\,dx$$

(the latter having certain technical advantages that need not concern us). With this notation the example amounted to $\int_0^2 x^2\,dx = 8/3$. The real number represented by these symbols is called the *definite integral* of the function f between the values a and b. An important advantage of freeing $\int_a^b f$ from its geometric interpretation, in addition to permitting one to prove statements about it, is that it can now be reinterpreted for uses other than that of computing areas.

If the graph of f lies partially below the x-axis, then one simply proceeds as above but attaches a negative sign to the areas of those regions below the x-axis (because the function f takes on negative values there); of course the value of an integral must be interpreted accordingly for any applications. If $b < a$, then $\int_a^b f$ is defined by $\int_a^b f = -\int_b^a f$. Further, as we have said, not all functions are continuous, while we required f to be continuous in discussing $\int_a^b f$; it is possible to talk about definite integrals for many functions that are not continuous, with the adjustments required being sometimes easy, sometimes not. A closely related problem is that some functions arising in applications of integrals are given by formulas that are not easy to work with, and some of the functions that arise are not given by formulas of any kind. Such problems are dealt with in calculus and its extensions, and we mention them primarily to show that the description we have given for $\int_a^b f$, while giving the basic idea, does not tell the full story.

Definite integrals would be of limited use if they could be computed only by direct methods, such as that used above to show that $\int_0^2 x^2\,dx = 8/3$. The function given by $x \mapsto x^2$ is, after all, fairly simple, but even working with it was not trivial; other functions, such as trigonometric and logarithmic functions, are much more difficult. Fortunately it is not necessary to rely on such direct methods; this is perhaps the most important single fact about calculus, and we shall discuss it in the next section.

Let us mention two other examples. The first is from Chapter III, where, in Section 21, we discussed the functions h and A. Examination will show that for $t > 0$ these functions are connected by the relation $A(t) = \int_0^t h$, for $A(t)$ denotes the area under the graph of $y = h(t)$ from 0 to t.

A second example involves the number e, which arose naturally in Chapter III as part of the formula defining the function h just referred to. In Section 39 we gave two different ways of characterizing e; here is yet another. Question: For what value $x_0 > 1$ is the area above the x-axis, below $= 1/x$, and between 1 and x_0, equal to 1? Answer: $x_0 = e$. (Figure 41.4.) The answer should seem interesting, even if, at this point, the question does not. We shall return to this in Example 45.10.

Figure 41.4

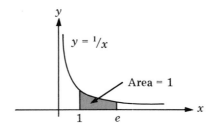

In addition to computations of areas and probabilities, integrals are used to compute volumes and lengths of curves; they are also used to compute such things as mass, force, and energy in mechanics; they are, in fact, used throughout physics and engineering. To survey all of the applications based on the concept of the integral would be to survey much of modern mathematics and science and technology.

PROBLEM SET 41

PROBLEM 41.1. Use the method of Example 41.1 to compute the following things for the area of the region above the x-axis, below the graph of $y = x^2$, and between $x = 0$ and $x = 3$.

(a) U_3 (b) U_6

(c) U_n (d) $\lim U_n$ as $n \to \infty$

(e) L_3 (f) L_6

(g) L_n (h) $\lim L_n$ as $n \to \infty$

(i) $U_n - L_n$ (j) $\lim (U_n - L_n)$ as $n \to \infty$

PROBLEM 41.2. Same as Problem 41.1 with $x = 3$ replaced by $x = 6$.

PROBLEM 41.3. Same as Problem 41.1 with $x = 0$ replaced by $x = 1$, and $x = 3$ replaced by $x = 4$.

PROBLEM 41.4. Use the method of Example 41.1 and the identity

$$1^3 + 2^3 + 3^3 + \cdots + n^3 = \left[\frac{n(n + 1)}{2}\right]^2$$

to compute the following things for the area of the region above the x-axis, below the graph of $y = x^3$, and between $x = 0$ and $x = 2$.
(a) U_4
(b) U_8
(c) U_n
(d) $\lim U_n$ as $n \to \infty$
(e) L_4
(f) L_8
(g) L_n
(h) $\lim L_n$ as $n \to \infty$
(i) $U_n - L_n$
(j) $\lim (U_n - L_n)$ as $n \to \infty$

PROBLEM 41.5. Same as Problem 41.4 with $x = 2$ replaced by $x = 4$.

PROBLEM 41.6. Write integrals to represent the areas of the following regions. Do not attempt to evaluate the integrals.
(a) Region below $y = \cos x$, above the x-axis, and between $x = -\pi/4$ and $x = 0$.
(b) Region below $y = \sin x$, above the x-axis, and between $x = 3\pi/4$ and $x = \pi$.
(c) Region below $y = x^4$, above the x-axis, and between $x = 1$ and $x = 5$.
(d) Region below $y = 4$ and above $y = x^2$.
(e) Region below $y = 1$, above $y = \sin x$, and between $x = 0$ and $x = \pi/2$.

PROBLEM 41.7. Let $S_2 = 1^2 + 2^2 + 3^2 + \cdots + n^2$. Verify that $S_2 = \frac{1}{6} n(n + 1)(2n + 1)$ by carrying out the following steps.
(a) Verify that $(k + 1)^3 - k^3 = 3k^2 + 3k + 1$ for every number k.
(b) Write the relation in (a) for $k = 0, 1, 2, \ldots$, and n, and add the results.
(c) Show that the result in (b) is

$$(n + 1)^3 = 3S_2 + 3S_1 + n + 1,$$

where $S_1 = 1 + 2 + 3 + \cdots + n$.
(d) Using $S_1 = \frac{1}{2}n(n + 1)$ (Problem 2.11), solve the equation in (c) for S_2 to obtain the desired formula.

PROBLEM 41.8. The following example shows why care is required when working with geometry and limits.
(a) Let P_1 denote the perimeter and A_1 the area of the large triangle in Figure 41.5. The base and height are each 1 unit. What is A_1?

Figure 41.5

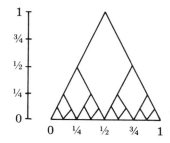

(b) Let P_2 denote the sum of the perimeters and A_2 the sum of the areas of the two triangles of height $\frac{1}{2}$ in the figure. What is A_2? Explain why $P_2 = P_1$.

(c) Let P_3 denote the sum of the perimeters and A_3 the sum of the areas of the four triangles of height $\frac{1}{4}$ in the figure. What is A_3? Explain why $P_3 = P_1$.

(d) Continuing, at the nth stage there will be 2^{n-1} triangles each of height $(1/2)^{n-1}$ (the case $n = 4$ is shown). What is A_n? Explain why $P_n = P_1$.

(e) Using the results in part (d), verify that $\lim A_n = 0$ as $n \to \infty$, while $\lim P_n = P_1$ as $n \to \infty$. Thus a fixed perimeter can enclose an arbitrarily small area. Furthermore, for sufficiently large n the perimeter will be visually indistinguishable from a straight line segment.

§42. The Fundamental Theorem of Calculus

The full power of the calculus comes from the fact that the concepts of derivative and integral are not independent but are instead closely related. The discovery of this relationship is generally credited to Newton and Leibniz; more accurately, they played the decisive roles in an evolutionary process that began in ancient Greece and accelerated during the seventeenth century through the work of Cavalieri, Fermat, Huygens, Kepler, Barrow, and others.

It was pointed out in Section 40 that each function f having a derivative gives rise to a new function f', defined by using $f'(x)$ to denote the derivative of f at x. It is also possible to use the definite integral to obtain a new function from each function f. We do this by first choosing a specific real number a, and then defining a function F by

$$F(t) = \int_a^t f$$

for each t. Thus, geometrically, $F(t)$ denotes the area above the x-axis, below the graph of $y = f(x)$, and between $x = a$ and $x = t$ (Figure 42.1).

EXAMPLE 42.1. Let f be the function given by $f(x) = x$ for each real number x. Then the graph of f is as shown in Figure 42.2, and with $a = 0$, $F(t)$ will be

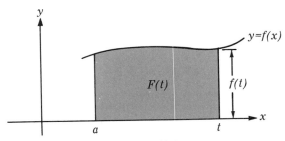

Figure 42.1

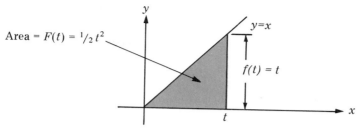

Figure 42.2

the area of a triangle with base and height both equal to t. Thus $F(t) = \frac{1}{2}t^2$ for each t.

Notice also that this was the idea used to obtain the function A from the function h in Section 21: $A(t) = \int_0^t h$.

The function F obtained from f in the manner described is called an *indefinite integral* of f. The function F is obtained from f through the integral; Newton and Leibniz showed that, conversely, the function f can be obtained from F through the derivative. This is summarized in the following important theorem.

FUNDAMENTAL THEOREM OF CALCULUS

If

$$F(t) = \int_a^t f,$$

then F has a derivative for each value of t, and

$$F'(t) = f(t).$$

In other words, if we begin with f, form an indefinite integral to get F, then form the derivative of F to get F', we will be back where we started, with the function f. This is sometimes described by saying that the operations of differentiation (forming derivatives) and integration (forming indefinite integrals) are *inverse* operations.

We can check this for Example 42.1. There $f(x) = x$ for each x and so $f(t) = t$. And we showed that $F(t) = \frac{1}{2}t^2$, so that by the formula for derivative of a polynomial $F'(t) = 2(\frac{1}{2})t = t$ for each t. Thus $F'(t) = f(t)$, as the Fundamental Theorem tells us to expect.

Now we shall explain a remark made in the discussion of integrals, namely, that in computing definite integrals it is not necessary to rely on the direct method suggested by the definition of integral. For this purpose, define an *antiderivative* of a function f to be any function having derivative f. Thus if $g(x) = \frac{1}{2}x^2$ for each x, then g is an antiderivative of the function f given by $f(x) = x$ for each x, because $g' = f$. A much more general example is given by the Fundamental Theorem, for it tells us that an indefinite integral F of any function f is an antiderivative of f. The fact we are after is the following, which can be proved from the Fundamental Theorem.

COROLLARY

If F is any antiderivative of f, then

$$\int_a^b f = F(b) - F(a).$$

EXAMPLE 42.2.   Let us again calculate the area in Example 41.1, which amounted to computing $\int_0^2 x^2\, dx$. We first note that F given by $F(x) = \dfrac{x^3}{3}$ is a function having derivative f, where $f(x) = x^2$. That is, F is an antiderivative of f. Therefore

$$\int_0^2 x^2\, dx = F(2) - F(0) = \frac{2^3}{3} - \frac{0^3}{3} = \frac{8}{3},$$

as we found before.

Notice that we computed this *integral* by using a *derivative* formula. That is the power of the corollary above: limits arising in the computation of definite integrals are much harder to handle than limits arising in the computation of derivatives, and we now know that any formula giving a derivative also gives an antiderivative, which in turn can be used to compute definite integrals.

EXAMPLE 42.3.   What is the area under the portion of the cosine curve shown in Figure 42.3? The area is given by $\int_{-\pi/2}^{\pi/2} \cos x\, dx$. And we saw in Section 40

Figure 42.3

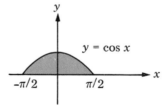

that the derivative of the sine function is the cosine function, so that sine is an antiderivative of cosine. Therefore

$$\int_{-\pi/2}^{\pi/2} \cos x\, dx = \sin\left(\pi/2\right) - \sin\left(-\pi/2\right) = 1 - (-1) = 1 + 1 = 2,$$

that is, the area is 2. Another example will be given in the next section.

The elements of calculus were put in the form in which they are discussed today during the early nineteenth century, through the work of the Frenchman Augustin-Louis Cauchy (1789–1867) and others. An excellent history of the calculus can be found in Boyer's book *History of the Calculus* [3].

PROBLEM SET 42

PROBLEM 42.1. Find an antiderivative for each of the following functions.
(a) 1
(b) x
(c) x^2
(d) x^3
(e) x^n, n a natural number
(f) $a_n x^n + a_{n-1} x^{n-1} + \cdots + a_1 x + a_0$, where the subscripted a's denote constants.
(g) $\sin x$
(h) $\cos x$

PROBLEM 42.2. Use the method of Examples 42.2 and 42.3 to evaluate each of the following definite integrals.
(a) $\int_0^2 x^3 \, dx$
(b) $\int_{+1}^2 x^3 \, dx$
(c) $\int_{-1}^1 x^3 \, dx$
(d) $\int_1^2 x^4 \, dx$
(e) $\int_0^1 x^{99} \, dx$
(f) $\int_0^3 2 \, dx$
(g) $\int_{-1}^1 (x^6 + x^4) \, dx$
(h) $\int_{-1}^1 (x^4 + x^2 + 1) \, dx$
(i) $\int_1^2 (4x^3 + 3x^2 + 2x + 1) \, dx$
(j) $\int_0^{\pi/2} \sin x \, dx$
(k) $\int_\pi^{2\pi} \sin x \, dx$
(l) $\int_\pi^{2\pi} \cos x \, dx$

PROBLEM 42.3. Compute each of the following areas.
(a) Above the x-axis, below $y = x + 2$, and between $x = 0$ and $x = 3$.
(b) Above the x-axis, below $y = x^4$, and between $x = 1$ and $x = 2$.
(c) Above the line $y = (2/\pi)x$, below $y = \sin x$, and between $x = 0$ and $x = \pi/2$. (Draw a sketch and consider the difference of two areas.)
(d) Above $y = x^3$, below $y = x^2$, and between $x = 0$ and $x = 1$. (Draw a sketch and consider the difference of two areas.)

PROBLEM 42.4. (a) Draw the graph of $y = 4 - x^2$, for x between -2 and $+2$.
(b) Use the result found by the method of exhaustion in Section 34E to calculate the area above the x-axis, below the graph of $y = 4 - x^2$, and between $x = -2$ and $x = +2$.
(c) Write a definite integral that will yield the area in part (b).
(d) Evaluate the integral in (c) by the method of Examples 42.2 and 42.3, and compare with the result found in part (b).

PROBLEM 42.5. Assume $f(x) = 2x$ for each x.
(a) What is $F(t) = \int_0^t f$?
(b) What if $F'(t)$?
(c) Does the result in part (b) agree with the Fundamental Theorem of Calculus?

PROBLEM 42.6. (a) If $F(t) = \int_1^t \log_{10} x \, dx$, what is $F'(100)$?
(b) If $G(u) = \int_0^u (\sin x)^2 \, dx$, what is $G'(\pi/2)$?

PROBLEM 42.7. Notice that if $f(x) = x^2$ and $g(x) = x^2 + 3$, then $f' = g'$, that is, $f'(x) = g'(x)$ for each x.
(a) Find a function h different from both f and g such that $f' = h'$.
(b) Describe an infinite number of different functions each having derivative equal to f'.
(c) If C is a constant real number and $h(x) = f(x) + C$ for each x, then $h' = f'$. Why?

PROBLEM 42.8. (a) Let f be a function such that $f'(x) = 0$ for each x. Explain why f should be a constant function, that is, why there should be a constant real number C such that $f(x) = C$ for each x. (Recall that a derivative is a measure of rate of change of a function. For instance, what if x were time and $f(x)$ were the position of an object at time x?)

(b) Use part (a) to show that if g and h are functions such that $g' = h'$, then $g - h$ is a constant function, that is, there is a constant real number C such that $g(x) - h(x) = C$ for each real number x. (The principles following Example 40.2 should be helpful.)

(c) How is part (b) here related to part (c) of Problem 42.7?

PROBLEM 42.9. Carry out the following steps to obtain a sketch of the proof of the Corollary of the Fundamental Theorem of Calculus. Assume f, a, b, and F as in the statement of the Corollary (page 252).

(a) Let $G(t) = \int_a^t f$. What is G'?

(b) By (a), $G' = F'$. Why?

(c) By (b), $G(t) - F(t)$ is a constant, that is, there is a constant real number C such that $G(t) - F(t) = C$ for all t. Why? (Suggestion: Use Problem 42.8.)

(d) Use part (c) with $t = a$ to show that $C = -F(a)$.

(e) Use parts (c) and (d) with $t = b$ to show that $G(b) = F(b) - F(a)$.

(f) Explain why the Corollary follows from part (e).

§43. Laws of Motion

We saw earlier that the first significant use of mathematics to explain physical phenomena can be credited to Archimedes, in the third century B.C. His work dealt with objects at rest, however, and the study of objects in motion did not become an exact science until the seventeenth century. Much of this latter development was the work of three men, Galileo (Italian), Kepler (German), and Newton (English), and we now look at their contributions.

In discussing instantaneous velocity, in Section 40, we stated that if an object falls freely near the earth's surface then it will move according to the law $d = \frac{1}{2}gt^2$. This law was discovered by Galileo, early in the seventeenth century, and it represents the first substantial example of the power of experiment combined with theory. In outlining how Galileo arrived at the law, and later on as well, we shall need to refer to the notion of acceleration; so let us first briefly examine that.

To say that a vehicle is accelerating is simply to say that it is changing its velocity—its instantaneous velocity. If the vehicle is moving at a constant velocity of 60 miles per hour, it is not accelerating. In order to change from a velocity of 30 miles per hour to a velocity of 60 miles per hour, however, acceleration will be required. Similarly, acceleration will be required in order to change from 60 miles per hour to 30 miles per hour; this would sometimes be called deceleration, but mathematically it is more convenient to think of it as negative acceleration. Thus, to repeat, acceleration relates to change in velocity. And just as instantaneous velocity means instantaneous rate of change of distance with respect to time (a limiting concept), *instantaneous acceleration* means instantaneous rate of change of velocity with respect to time (also a limiting concept). Mathematically, if an object is moving according to the law $d = f(t)$, then its instantaneous velocity at time t will be given by $f'(t)$ (derivative); and its instantaneous acceleration at time t will be given by $f''(t)$ (derivative of the derivative). If an object is moving at constant velocity, then its *position* is changing at a constant rate; if an object is moving at constant acceleration, then its *velocity* is changing at a constant rate. Now let us return to Galileo.

On the basis of observation, Galileo conjectured that an object falling freely would move in such a way that its acceleration would remain constant. From this conjecture Galileo was able to deduce, mathematically, that the distance traveled by the object by any time t would be of the general form we have given, namely, a constant times t^2. Finally, Galileo was able to verify through experiment that the result he had deduced did indeed describe the motion of falling objects; that is, he was able to verify that he had found a law that could be used to predict the behavior of falling objects. Galileo's experiments were actually with objects rolling down inclined planes, but it turns out that for these purposes there is no essential difference between the two kinds of motion. We shall discuss the mathematics behind Galileo's deduction at the end of this section, using ideas that were not available to him. The point to be made now is that on the basis of observation Galileo was able to reach a conjecture, on the basis of that conjecture he was able to deduce a law, and then, on the basis of experiment, he was able to verify that this law was reliable for making predictions. Now we shall look at another example, this one involving Kepler and efforts to give a rational explanation for the motion of the planets.

The Egyptians and the Babylonians had made observations of the motions of planets and stars, and they had been aware of many of the regularities in these motions. The Greeks attempted to give geometrical descriptions of the observed motions of the planets, and, as we pointed out in discussing history, the most refined of these descriptions was that of Ptolemy. Ptolemy was able to draw on observational data collected by Hipparchus in the second century B.C., and constructed a theory of planetary motion based on three assumptions: (1) the earth was assumed stationary at the center of the universe, (2) the planets and the sun were assumed to move in orbits made up of circles, and (3) the planets and the sun were assumed to move in their orbits with constant speed. The most complicated part of the Ptolemaic system came in the details of (2). It could not be assumed that the planets and sun moved in simple circular orbits around the earth, because that would not have been consistent with observation. Thus it was assumed that there were two circles corresponding to each of the planets and to the sun: a small one, called the *epicycle*, around which the planet moved with constant speed, and a larger one, called the *deferent*, around which the center of the epicycle moved with constant speed. This is illustrated in Figure 43.1. The full

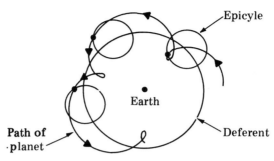

Figure 43.1

details of the Ptolemaic system were more involved than the figure suggests, however, for in order to obtain complete agreement with the observed motions it was necessary to assume, among other things, that the centers of the deferents were to one side of the earth, in a way that varied with each deferent. As more accurate observational data became available it was necessary to make refinements in the theory, which resulted in making the descriptions still more involved. No real improvements were made in the explanation until the sixteenth century, when the Polish astronomer Nicolaus Copernicus was able to simplify the theory by assuming the sun rather than the earth to be stationary at the center of the universe, a thought which had occurred to the Greek astronomer Aristarchus long before. Copernicus retained the idea of circles moving around circles, however, because simple circular motion at constant speed still did not give agreement with observation.

But the Copernican system proved to be unsatisfactory also. The criticism from the Church, whose leaders objected to the assumption that man was not at the center of the universe, is well known. But a more serious problem from a scientific point of view arose when improved data showed that the explanation of Copernicus still did not agree with observation. These improved data became available in the latter part of the sixteenth century through extensive observations made by Tycho Brahe, a native of Denmark. If these data revealed the Copernican system to be inadequate, however, they also opened the way for an explanation that was more satisfactory than that of the Copernican system. This explanation was given by Kepler, who had worked with Tycho Brahe in Tycho's later years. Kepler's description of planetary motion was summarized in three laws, the first two given in 1609, the third in 1619. Kepler's first law offered a new description of the orbits of the planets, the second replaced the assumption that they move with constant speed, and the third established a uniformity about the motions of the different planets. Here are Kepler's three laws:

I.   The planets move in elliptical orbits with the sun at one focus.
II.   The imaginary line connecting the sun to a planet sweeps out equal areas in equal intervals of time.
III.   The ratio of the cube of the semimajor axis to the square of the period is a constant, which is the same for all planets.

While the orbits described by the first law are elliptical, they do not differ greatly from circular orbits; but they differ enough to account for the observed facts. As to the second law, with the areas ASB, CSD, and ESF all equal in the figure it follows that the planet will move from A to B, C to D, and E to F in equal intervals of time (Figure 43.2). The

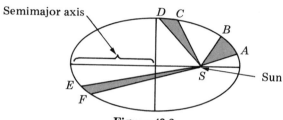

Figure 43.2

period of a planet is the time required for one complete orbital revolution around the sun (one year for the earth), and thus if T_1 denotes the period of a planet and R_1 the length of its semimajor axis, with T_2 and R_2 the corresponding values for a second planet, then the third law can be expressed by the formula

$$\frac{R_1^3}{T_1^2} = \frac{R_2^3}{T_2^2}.$$

We now have two examples of the use of mathematics for describing motion: Galileo's law for objects falling freely near the earth's surface, and Kepler's laws for the motions of the planets. The discoveries of these laws were remarkable achievements, and they show why the early seventeenth century was one of the most dramatic periods in the history of science. The next step was just as remarkable, however. In 1687 Newton published *Philosophiae naturalis principia mathematica*, probably the most influential scientific book ever written. In this book Newton was able to derive a single mathematical law explaining both the motion of objects near the earth's surface and the motion of the planets. Even though our primary interest is in mathematics, we shall sketch Newton's arguments keeping mathematical details to a minimum. A full understanding of Newton's work, and certainly the work that was built upon it by others who came later, requires all of the methods of calculus; in fact, efforts to widen the applicability of Newton's methods were responsible for the creation of a great deal of eighteenth-century mathematics extending the calculus.

Newton had at his disposal two important ideas that Galileo had discovered in analyzing the motion of projectiles (such as balls fired from a cannon). The first involved rejection of an idea going back to Aristotle, who had maintained that the natural state for many objects was to be at rest: for Aristotle, continued motion for such objects was considered to be impossible without a cause. Galileo claimed that while it is true that an object at rest will tend to remain at rest, it is also true that an object in motion will tend to remain in motion. In other words, the natural state is not resistance to motion, but resistance to *change* in motion. This is the first of Newton's famous three laws of motion.

Newton's First Law. An object will continue in a state of rest, or of motion in a straight line with constant speed, unless it is acted upon by a net (unbalanced) force.

Thus a thrown baseball would travel indefinitely in a straight line if it were not for forces such as gravity and air resistance acting upon it.

A second idea Galileo discovered in analyzing the motion of projectiles was that the motion could be studied as a combination of two separate motions occurring simultaneously, one vertical and affected by gravity, the other horizontal and due to whatever initial force had acted on the object in a horizontal direction. One could put together information known or deduced about these motions considered separately and thereby obtain a description of the net resultant motion of the object. This idea could easily be extended to apply to any net motion made up of simpler motions.

Now let us see how Newton applied these ideas to motions such as that of the planets. He first deduced, using Galileo's two ideas together with the idea of limit, that a planet moving under a so-called *central force*, that is, a force constantly pulling it toward a fixed point (such as the sun), will move according to Kepler's second law. Referring to Figure 43.3, we can see that this will be a result of the planet's natural tendency to travel in a straight line (Newton's first law) combined with the force pulling it toward the sun (the central force). Newton then

Figure 43.3

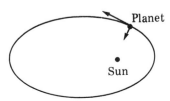
Planet

Sun

showed that, conversely, an object moving in an elliptical orbit according to Kepler's second law must be continuously acted on by some force toward a focus of the elliptical orbit. There remained the question of what the magnitude of such a force must be in order to account for the motion. Newton's first step in the resolution of this question was the derivation of the law that if an object moves along a path that is a conic section (in particular an ellipse), under a force always directed toward a focus of the conic section, then the force acting on the object must be inversely proportional to the square of the distance of the object from the focus: in symbols,

$$f = \frac{c}{r^2},$$

where f denotes force, r distance from object to focus, and c is a constant. This is known as the *inverse square law*. Now the question was reduced to determination of the constant c, and for this Newton adopted the assumption that any two objects in the universe are attracted by a force that is directly proportional to the product of their masses. (The mass of an object can be thought of as a measure of the object's resistance to change in motion.) This assumption led to Newton's *law of universal gravitation*, assumed by Newton to pertain to the force of attraction between any two objects in the universe:

$$f = G\frac{m_1 m_2}{r^2}$$

where m_1, m_2 denote the masses of the objects, r the distance between them, and G is a universal constant whose value—which was not determined by Newton—depends on the units chosen to measure mass, distance, and force.

The usefulness of the law of universal gravitation was quickly established. It was verified for the motion of the moon around the earth, and it was used to derive all three of Kepler's laws, already known to be consistent with observed data. What is more—and this brings us back to our original claim that Newton was able to give a single mathematical law accounting for the discoveries of both Galileo and Kepler—it was possible to derive Galileo's results on freely falling objects and projectile motion from the law of universal gravitation.

This concludes our discussion of the seventeenth century development of laws of motion. The connections between mathematics and motion that were established during this period, in particular the results from Newton's *Principia*, were the starting point for some of the most important work in mathematics and physics throughout the eighteenth and nineteenth centuries. Vital and spectacular products of modern technology such as energy and rockets all have their origin in seventeenth century mathematics and what has grown from it.

To close this section let us show how Galileo's law of motion for freely falling objects can be deduced from the assumption that such objects fall with constant acceleration. To do this we must pass from information about acceleration to information about velocity, and then to information about position. The order here is inverse to that corresponding to the taking of derivatives: with a derivative we pass from position to velocity, and with another derivative we pass from velocity to acceleration. In the present case we exploit the Fundamental Theorem of Calculus: integration is the inverse of taking derivatives.

Each of acceleration, velocity, and distance (position) is a function of time, t; let us choose the suggestive symbols a, v, and d to denote these functions. Then we know that $d'(t) = v(t)$ for each t, and $d''(t) = v'(t) = a(t)$ for each t. We begin with Galileo's assumption that $a(t)$ is a constant: specifically, $a(t) = g$ for each time t. Then v must be a function such that $v'(t) = g$ for each t, that is, v must be an antiderivative of the function having constant value g. Clearly $v(t) = gt$ is such a function. If C_1 is any constant, then $v(t) = gt + C_1$ is another such function (see Problem 42.7); but if we assume the object falls from rest then $v(0) = 0$, forcing $C_1 = 0$.

We now have $v(t) = gt$, and d must be a function such that $d'(t) = gt$ for each t, that is, d must be an antiderivative of the function v. Clearly $d(t) = \frac{1}{2}gt^2$ is such a function. Again, if C_2 is any constant, then $d(t) = \frac{1}{2}gt^2 + C_2$ is another such function; but if we measure position from where the object is dropped then $d(0) = 0$, forcing $C_2 = 0$. Thus $d(t) = \frac{1}{2}gt^2$ is the law we were seeking.

The process just carried out was that of solving a differential equation: we began with an equation involving a derivative of an unknown function, and determined the function from that equation. In general, a differential equation may involve an unknown function f as well as one or more of its derivatives f', f'', and so on, and it is required to determine the function f from the equation. In the example, it was required to determine $d(t)$ from the equation $d''(t) = g$; this is one of the easiest types of differential equations to solve. The study of differential equations outgrew such elementary equations and techniques in the eighteenth century, however, and it has been a major branch of analysis and applicable mathematics ever since.

PROBLEM SET 43

PROBLEM 43.1. Assume that each function d below describes the position of an object at time t. Determine the velocity, $v(t)$, and the acceleration, $a(t)$, for each object at time t.

(a) $d(t) = t^2 + t$ (b) $d(t) = 3t^2 - t + 2$

(c) $d(t) = t^3 + 1$ (d) $d(t) = \sin t$

(e) $d(t) = 2 \cos t$ (f) $d(t) = t + \sin t$

PROBLEM 43.2. Assume that the velocity of a moving object is given by the law $v(t) = 2t + 1$. Which of the following are possibilities for the law describing its position?

(a) $d(t) = t^2 + 1$ (b) $d(t) = 2$

(c) $d(t) = t^2 + t$ (d) $d(t) = t^2 + t + 1$

(e) $d(t) = 2t + 1$ (f) $d(t) = t^2 + t - 1$

PROBLEM 43.3. Assume that the acceleration of a moving object is given by the law $a(t) = 4$. Which of the following are possibilities for the law describing its position?

(a) $4t$ (b) $2t^2 + t$

(c) 0 (d) $2t^2 + 2t + 2$

(e) $4t^2 + 4t + 4$ (f) $2t^2 + 4t - 1$

PROBLEM 43.4. Follow the procedure used to derive the law $d(t) = \frac{1}{2}gt^2$, at the end of the section, to show that if an object moves with constant acceleration g, has velocity v_0 at time $t = 0$, and has position d_0 at time $t = 0$, then the law describing its motion is $d(t) = \frac{1}{2}gt^2 + v_0 t + d_0$. (Suggestion: Explain why $C_1 = v_0$ and $C_2 = d_0$.)

PROBLEM 43.5. If an object is thrown down from the top of a building with an initial velocity of 24 feet per second, then the law describing its motion is $d(t) = 16t^2 + 24t$. (We use $g = 32$ for simplicity. See Problem 43.4 for the derivation of the law given here.) Answer the following questions about the motion of such an object.

(a) Where is the object 1 second after it is thrown?

(b) What is its instantaneous velocity t seconds after it is thrown?

(c) What is its instantaneous velocity 1 second after it is thrown?

(d) What is its average velocity during the first second after it is thrown?

(e) Where is the object 3 seconds after it is thrown?

(f) What is its instantaneous velocity 3 seconds after it is thrown?

(g) What is its average velocity during the first 3 seconds after it is thrown?

(h) How long will be required for the object to travel the first 16 feet?

(i) How long will be required for the object to attain an instantaneous velocity of 88 feet per second?

PROBLEM 43.6. (a) through (i). Same as Problem 43.5 with the law $d(t) = 16t^2 + 24t$ replaced by the law $d(t) = 16t^2 + 40t$, which corresponds to an instantaneous velocity of 40 feet per second.

PROBLEM 43.7. (a) The period of Jupiter is approximately 12 earth years. Show that Jupiter is approximately 5.2 times as far as the earth from the sun. (Use Kepler's third law with $T_1 = 1$, $T_2 = 12$, and solve for R_2 in terms of R_1.)

(b) The mean (average) distance from a planet to the sun is the same as the length of the semimajor axis of its orbit. The mean distance from the earth to the sun is approximately 93 million miles. Show that the mean distance from Jupiter to the sun is approximately 484 million miles.

PROBLEM 43.8. (a) through (k). Use Kepler's third law, as in Problem 43.7, to complete the blanks in the following table. Estimate any cube roots that arise by trial and error.

Planet	Mean Distance from Sun Astronomical Units*	Mean Distance from Sun Millions of Miles	Period of Revolution around the Sun†
Mercury	0.39	(a)	0.24
Venus	(b)	(c)	0.62
Earth	1.00	93	1.00
Mars	1.52	142	(d)
Jupiter	5.20	484	(e)
Saturn	(f)	(g)	29.46
Uranus	(h)	1784	84.01
Neptune	30.06	2795	(i)
Pluto	(j)	(k)	248.43

* The mean distance from the earth to the sun is 1 astronomical unit.
† Periods are expressed as multiples of the earth's period.

PROBLEM 43.9. Kepler's third law also applies to the motion of satellites around planets, but the constant R^3/T^2 is different from what it is for the motion of the planets around the sun.

(a) Using the approximate value 239,000 miles for the mean distance between the center of the moon and the center of the earth (which is the same as the length of the semimajor axis of the moon's orbit), and 27.3 days for the moon's period, compute R^3/T^2 for objects orbiting the earth.

(b) Using the value in part (a), compute the period for an artificial satellite orbiting the earth at a mean distance of 1,000 miles above the earth's surface. (Take the value of R to be 5,000 miles.)

PROBLEM 43.10. Verify that $f(t) = \sin t$ is a solution of the differential equation $f''(t) = -f(t)$. (This type of differential equation arises in the study of the motion of an object subject to an elastic force, such as an object bobbing at the end of a suspended spring. The motion of the object will be periodic, just as the sine function.)

§44. Maxima and Minima

Applications of mathematics to problems of maxima and minima have a long and important history, going back at least to Heron of Alexandria around the first century A.D. These applications range from questions about simple geometric figures to questions about the design of spaceships, and the mathematics involved varies from the most elementary to the most advanced. While we cannot convey the depth of much of this mathematics, we can discuss the extent of the applications; particularly some of the historically important ones. And we can also indicate the influence these applications have had on the development of mathematics itself.

EXAMPLE 44.1. The law of reflection for light states that if light is reflected by a smooth surface, then the angle of incidence is equal to the angle of reflection (Figure 44.1). A rational explanation for this law was given by Heron of Alexandria in his *Catoptics* (reflection), and it is the first known application of what later came to be a basic hypothesis in geometrical optics and dynamics: nature acts in the most economical way possible. Heron argued that light travels in a straight line, and if reflected will do so in such a way as to make the total distance from source to reflecting surface to eye as small as possible. On the basis of this argument he was able to deduce the law of reflection in the following way.

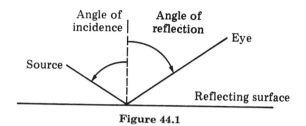

Figure 44.1

Assume that RR' denotes the reflecting surface, and that S and E denote the source and the eye, respectively. Let P denote the point on RR' such that angle RPS = angle $R'PE$. Then it is to be shown that the shortest path from S to reflecting surface to E is the path SPE (this is clearly equivalent with equality of the angles of incidence and reflection). (Figure 44.2.)

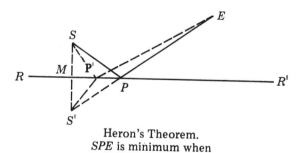

Heron's Theorem.
SPE is minimum when
angle RPS = angle $R'PE$.
Figure 44.2

It suffices to show that if P' is any point other than P on RR', then $SP' + P'E > SP + PE$. Draw SMS' perpendicular to RR' with $SM = S'M$. Then $S'PE$ is a straight line. And $S'P = SP$, so that $S'P + PE = SP + PE$. But if P' is any point other than P on RR', then $S'P' + P'E$ represents the sum of two sides of a triangle $(S'P'E)$ of which $S'PE$ is the third side. Therefore, $S'P' + P'E > S'P + PE$, and so $SP' + P'E > SP + PE$. This establishes the result.

We shall give another application of Heron's Theorem in Example 44.2 and return to optics in Example 44.4.

EXAMPLE 44.2. Among all triangles with given area and given base, the isosceles has smallest perimeter.

Assume the length of the base RS to be b, and the area to be A. Then the height is determined from $A = \frac{1}{2}bh$, namely, $h = 2A/b$. The specific value of h is not important, however. What is important is that the possibilities for the third vertex of the triangle will be those points on a line parallel to the base and h units from it, such as P and P' in Figure 44.3. Among all such

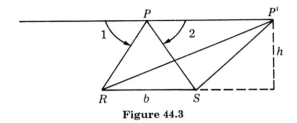

Figure 44.3

points, we require the one having the sum of its distances from R and S a minimum. By Heron's Theorem this is the point P with angle 1 = angle 2, which does give an isosceles triangle.

The next example shows the converse of this to be true also.

EXAMPLE 44.3. Among all triangles with given perimeter and given base, the isosceles has greatest area.

Assume the length of the base to be b, and the perimeter to be p. Then the total length of the remaining two sides must be $p - b$. If we label the ends of the base with F and F', then the possibilities for the third vertex of the triangle will be those points P such that $PF + PF' = p - b$, that is, the points on an ellipse with foci at F and F' (with d as in Figure 34.3, $d = p - b$). The area of any such triangle will be $\frac{1}{2}bh$ (see Figure 44.4). This area will clearly be greatest when P is at M, that is, when $PF = PF'$, because that will give the greatest possible value for h. This does give an isosceles triangle.

Figure 44.4

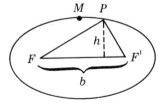

The proofs in the preceding examples show what can be done with cleverness and elementary geometry, but they are much too special to be of wide applicability. We now discuss two general techniques for solving more difficult problems of maxima and minima. The first involves derivatives, and the second involves what is known as the calculus of variations. We illustrated the use of derivatives for this purpose in Examples 40.3 and 40.4, and next give another such example; the examples above could have been handled with derivatives as well. The calculus of variations will be discussed after Example 44.5.

EXAMPLE 44.4. Heron's derivation of the law of reflection for light (Example 44.1) rested on the argument that the path followed by the light will be such as to make the total *distance* traveled as small as possible. This argument amounted to the assumption that the path followed will be such as to make the total *time* required as small as possible, if the experiment is assumed to take place in a homogeneous medium (such as in air or in water, but not a combination of the two). By centering attention on time, rather than distance, Fermat was able to obtain a considerable improvement over the result of Heron.

Heron had sought to explain the experimentally-arrived-at law of reflection. Fermat was interested in explaining the law of refraction, obtained experimentally by Snell in 1621. There had been many attempts to arrive at a precise description of the way in which light rays bend in passing from one medium to another (such as air to water, or glass to air), a phenomenon observed when a straight object is partially submerged in water. The law of refraction (Snell's law) does this by asserting that if light passes from one homogeneous medium to another, then the path followed will be made up of two straight line segments, meeting at the boundary between the media in such a way that

$$\frac{\sin \alpha_1}{\sin \alpha_2} = \frac{c_1}{c_2},$$

where α_1 is the angle of incidence, α_2 is the angle of refraction, c_1 is the velocity of light in the first medium, and c_2 is the velocity of light in the second medium (Figure 44.5). Fermat was able to show that Snell's law is a

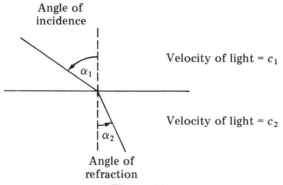

Figure 44.5

consequence of the assumption that the path followed by the light will be such as to make the total time required as small as possible. In other words, the law of reflection and the law of refraction are consequences of a common underlying principle. Fermat then extended this result so as to apply when the velocity of light is assumed to vary from point to point, such as in passing through different levels of the atmosphere surrounding the earth. He obtained what has come to be known as Fermat's *principle of least time*: Of all possible paths connecting two points, light will travel from one of the points to the other along the path requiring the least time. Fermat's derivation of Snell's law made use of calculus; it was in fact one of the earliest applications of calculus.

EXAMPLE 44.5. Among all rectangles with given perimeter, the square has greatest area (Example 40.4 is a special case of this). This can be extended: among all quadrilaterals with given perimeter, the square has greatest area. And moving from 4-sided polygons to polygons with n sides, it can be shown that of all n-sided polygons with given perimeter, the regular n-gon has greatest area (a regular polygon is one having equal sides and equal angles). Removing all such restrictions on the shape of the boundary, we ask for the closed curve with given perimeter that will enclose the greatest area: the answer is a circle. The analogous problem in three dimensions is to find the shape of the surface with given area that will enclose the greatest volume: the answer is a sphere.

These are examples of *isoperimetric problems*, so-called because curves having equal perimeters are said to be *isoperimetric*. For a masterly discussion of these problems, Chapter X of Polya's book *Induction and Analogy in Mathematics* (Volume I of *Mathematics and Plausible Reasoning* [19]) is recommended warmly. Chapters VIII and IX of the same book contain discussions of other maximum and minimum problems.

We turn now to one of the most applicable of the advanced branches of mathematics, the calculus of variations. Its methods are not elementary, by any means. In fact we shall see that even though many of its problems can be stated in very simple terms, the precise mathematical formulation of these problems requires the language of calculus—and their solution requires much more. The start of the calculus of variations is generally taken to be the late seventeenth century, with the problem that we shall discuss in the next example. During the eighteenth century it grew into one of the main branches of analysis, and the mathematicians involved in that early development were the best the eighteenth century had to offer: James and John Bernoulli, Euler, Lagrange. The applications of the calculus of variations to physics and engineering are profound. And the origin of functional analysis, one of the most active areas of mathematical research in the twentieth century, can be traced in part to the calculus of variations. We shall have to be content with the statement of several problems and a description of what their solutions turn out to be, with only the slightest hint of what is involved in those solutions. Fortunately, these things are of enough interest in their own right to make this worthwhile.

EXAMPLE 44.6. In June of 1696 the Swiss mathematician John Bernoulli posed the following problem: Among all paths connecting two points A and B, determine the one along which a particle will slide from A to B in the shortest time. It is assumed that the particle starts from rest and is acted on only by the force of gravity, that the path is frictionless, and that B is lower than A but not directly beneath it. Two of the possible paths, a straight line segment and a circular arc, are shown in Figure 44.6. Neither of these gives the correct answer. This problem is known as the *brachistochrone problem* (from *brachistos* and *chronos*, Greek for shortest and time, respectively).

Figure 44.6

Bernoulli, and his older brother James (after whom the Bernoulli experiments discussed in Section 20 were named), were members of a family that produced at least a half dozen other successful mathematicians or scientists over a span of three generations. John and James both found solutions to the brachistochrone problem, which were published in May of 1697. John's solution was especially elegant, and involved an analogy of this problem with optical problems solvable by use of Fermat's principle of least time. (A discussion of this solution can be found in Chapter IX of Polya's book [19] referred to earlier.) James' solution, on the other hand, used a method that was later extended to more general problems. We shall give some indication of what is involved in the solution of this and other problems in the calculus of variations in the next example. We first describe the answer to the brachistochrone problem.

If a circle rolls along a straight line without slipping, the path traced by a fixed point on the circumference of the circle is called a *cycloid*; Figure 44.7 shows points on a cycloid determined by three different positions of the

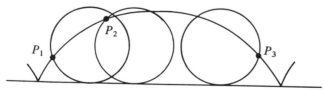

Figure 44.7

circle. The curve giving the solution to the brachistochrone problem consists of a portion of an inverted cycloid, that is, a cycloid determined by a circle rolling below rather than above a horizontal straight line. There is only one cycloid that will give a path yielding the minimum time; it is the only cycloid passing through B and determined by a circle rolling below and along a horizontal line through the initial point A.

Galileo had considered the brachistochrone problem earlier in the seventeenth century, and seems to have thought the solution to be an arc of a circle. Also related, and of more interest, is a property of cycloids that had been discovered by Huygens and applied by him to the theory of pendulum clocks: The amount of time required for a particle to slide along an inverted cycloid to the lowest point of the cycloid is the same regardless of the initial starting point of the particle on the cycloid.

EXAMPLE 44.7. Given two points (x_1, y_1) and (x_2, y_2) in the plane (Figure 44.8), and any arc connecting them, we can revolve the arc about the x-axis and thereby generate what is known as a *surface of revolution*. This basic idea was used to describe cones in Section 34D. The given arc will be part of the graph of some function f, and the problem we want to consider is the following: Among all curves $y = f(x)$ connecting the two given points, determine the one that will generate the surface of revolution having least area.

Figure 44.8

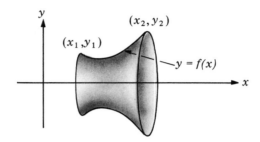

Because of the elastic properties of soap films, this problem can be restated in physical terms as follows. Assume a wire circle to be dipped in a soap solution and then withdrawn, thereby obtaining a circular disk of soap film bounded by the wire circle. Now let a smaller wire circle touch the soap film concentrically, and then move it directly away keeping the planes of the wire circles parallel. The problem we have asked above is equivalent with asking for the shape of the soap film so obtained. This equivalence rests on the tendency of soap films to assume the shape having least surface area—another example of the principle of nature acting in the most economical way possible. (A discussion of soap-film experiments is given in the book *What is Mathematics?* by Courant and Robbins [7], and is reproduced in *The World of Mathematics* [18], edited by James R. Newman, under the title 'Plateau's Problem'.)

Let us return to the formulation of this problem in terms of graphs of functions in the plane, and use it to point out the difference between the maximum and minimum problems treated by calculus and those treated by the calculus of variations. In a problem treated by calculus we are given a single function (such as in Figure 40.3), and we seek those real numbers for which that function will assume maximum or minimum values (such as b and d in Figure 40.3). In other words, we seek one or more *real numbers* from among the set of all possible x-values. In contrast, in a problem such as the one we are now considering, we seek one or more *functions* from among the set of all possible functions whose graphs pass through the given points. The present problem can be put in more explicit mathematical form by making use of integrals, as we now show.

It can be proved that the area of the surface of revolution generated by revolving $y = f(x)$ about the x-axis is given by

$$2\pi \int_{x_1}^{x_2} f \sqrt{1 + (f')^2}.$$

Here x_1 and x_2 are fixed real numbers given in the original statement of the problem (as shown in Figure 44.8), and the value of the integral, which is a real number, will change as the function f changes. What we seek then is the function f that will make the value of this integral the least possible. This problem is certainly not an easy one, and the techniques required for its solution go far beyond calculus. Still, it was solved, partially in the eighteenth century and more completely in the nineteenth century, and it does represent the type of problem treated by the calculus of variations.

As in Example 44.6, even though we cannot give the solution to the problem at hand, we can describe the final answer. The curve giving the answer in typical cases is known as a *catenary* (from the Latin for 'chain'); the resulting surface of revolution is known as a *catenoid*. A catenary can be described most simply as the shape assumed by a flexible chain of uniform construction when it is permitted to hang freely between two fixed points. An example is shown in Figure 44.9, along with the equation in x and y that

Figure 44.9

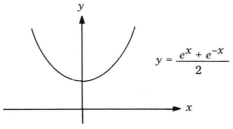

$$y = \frac{e^x + e^{-x}}{2}$$

defines it (which should have more meaning after Example 45.7). Of course chains of different lengths hanging between the same two fixed points will assume different shapes, and part of the solution consists in determining which of the possible catenaries is the appropriate one. In stating above that the catenary gives the solution in typical cases we were implying that in some cases, depending on the relative positions of the two given points (x_1, y_1) and (x_2, y_2), the solution is something other than a catenary; we omit discussion of those cases. Finally, we should remark that there is no apparent reason why the same curve should give the answer to both the problem of minimal surface of revolution and the problem of the shape assumed by a freely hanging cord. But once more, it can be shown that the shape assumed by a hanging cord is given by the solution to a certain minimum problem of physics, and when that problem has been formulated in terms of an integral, one obtains the same integral as in the formulation of the minimal surface problem.

Applications of the calculus of variations to physics and engineering extend to fields such as quantum mechanics, the theory of relativity, hydrodynamics, and electrostatics. The calculus of variations is used in particular to determine optimal designs for objects such as planes and ships, where it is desired that the effect of the resisting medium (air or water) be minimum; this problem was first considered seriously by Newton. Uses of mathematics in the study of maximum and minimum problems, in addition to those already mentioned, include applications to problems outside of geometry and physics, in particular in economics and business. Some of these latter applications are discussed in references [15] and [16].

PROBLEM SET 44

PROBLEM 44.1. Assume two segments to be given, of lengths a and b, respectively. What is the area of the largest triangle that can be constructed with these segments forming two of the sides? Why?

PROBLEM 44.2. A point P is outside a circle.
(a) Describe how to find the point on the circle nearest to P.
(b) Describe how to find the point on the circle farthest from P.

PROBLEM 44.3. What is the shortest segment connecting two skew straight lines? (Lines in three dimensional space are *skew* if they do not intersect and are not parallel.)

PROBLEM 44.4. Assume given a point P in a plane and two intersecting lines l and m in the plane, such that P is on neither l nor m. Assume that points Q and R are chosen on l and m, respectively, such that triangle PQR has minimum perimeter. Explain why the perpendicular to l at Q bisects angle PQR and the perpendicular to m at R bisects angle PRQ.

PROBLEM 44.5. Why do you think something other than the straight line path AB is the solution to the brachistochrone problem in Example 44.6?

PROBLEM 44.6. The ratio $\mu = \sin \alpha_1/\sin \alpha_2$ in Snell's law is called the *index of refraction* of the second medium relative to the first. The index of refraction for water relative to air is about 1.3, and for diamond relative to air is about 2.4.
(a) Assume that a beam of light passes from air into water at an angle of incidence of 30°. Compute $\sin \alpha_2$, where α_2 denotes the angle of refraction. Use Table 35.1 to estimate α_2.
(b) Assume that a beam of light passes from water into air at an angle of incidence of 30°. Compute $\sin \alpha_2$, where α_2 denotes the angle of refraction. Use Table 35.1 to estimate α_2.
(c) Same as part (a) with water replaced by diamond.
(d) Same as part (b) with water replaced by diamond.
(e) The velocity of light in air is 186,000 miles per second. What is the velocity of light in water?
(f) What is the velocity of light in a diamond?

PROBLEM 44.7. (a) Use the formula for the area of a surface of revolution, given in Example 44.7, to compute the area of the cone generated by

revolving around the x-axis the straight line segment cut off by the x-axis and y-axis on $y = 3 - x$ (Figure 44.10). (Suggestion: Use $f(x) = 3 - x$, $f'(x) = -1$, $x_1 = 0$, $x_2 = 3$.)
(b) Same as (a) with $y = 3 - x$ replaced by $y = 2 - 2x$.

Figure 44.10

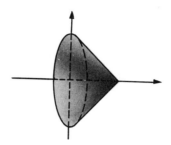

§45. Infinite Series

The importance of functions associated with the set of real numbers should now be apparent. Because of this importance it has been necessary for mathematicians to learn as much as possible about such functions—which ones can be used to describe and solve physical problems, which ones have derivatives, what those derivatives are, and so on. One of the basic problems concerning such functions has been that of finding convenient ways to represent them; we recall that some functions cannot be represented by formulas, for instance. One of the most fruitful ways of representing functions, even functions given by simple formulas, has proved to be that of infinite series. In this section we shall describe one of the ways in which this is done, give a number of examples, and discuss some of the special problems of this area of mathematics. We must begin with infinite series of real numbers, which are of interest in their own right.

With the possible exception of case n, which can be verified from Example 45.1, the correctness of each of the following equations is clear.

$$\tfrac{1}{2} = \tfrac{1}{2}$$
$$\tfrac{1}{2} + \tfrac{1}{4} = \tfrac{3}{4}$$
$$\tfrac{1}{2} + \tfrac{1}{4} + \tfrac{1}{8} = \tfrac{7}{8}$$
$$\cdots$$
$$\tfrac{1}{2} + \tfrac{1}{4} + \tfrac{1}{8} + \cdots + (\tfrac{1}{2})^n = 1 - (\tfrac{1}{2})^n$$

Each of the sums involves only a finite number of terms, and so each has a perfectly well-determined meaning. But we now want to give meaning to expressions involving an infinite number of terms, such as

$$\tfrac{1}{2} + \tfrac{1}{4} + \tfrac{1}{8} + \cdots + (\tfrac{1}{2})^n + \cdots.$$

The appropriate way to do this is through the idea of limit of a sequence. Specifically, we consider the sequence

$$\tfrac{1}{2}, \tfrac{3}{4}, \tfrac{7}{8}, \ldots, 1 - (\tfrac{1}{2})^n, \ldots,$$

whose nth term is the sum of the first n terms of the given series. If this sequence has a limit (real number), then that limit is taken to be the sum of the series. In the present case the sequence has limit 1, and so that is the sum of the series:

$$\tfrac{1}{2} + \tfrac{1}{4} + \tfrac{1}{8} + \cdots + (\tfrac{1}{2})^n + \cdots = 1.$$

In general, by an *infinite series* of real numbers we mean an expression of the form

$$a_1 + a_2 + a_3 + \cdots + a_n + \cdots .$$

As in the example, we form finite sums of increasing lengths, always taking terms from the beginning of the series. We denote the sums by $S_1, S_2, S_3, \ldots, S_n, \ldots$:

$$
\begin{aligned}
a_1 &= S_1 \\
a_1 + a_2 &= S_2 \\
a_1 + a_2 + a_3 &= S_3 \\
&\cdots \\
a_1 + a_2 + a_3 + \cdots + a_n &= S_n \\
&\cdots
\end{aligned}
$$

The numbers $S_1, S_2, \ldots$ are called the *partial sums* of the series, and we consider the sequence

$$S_1, S_2, S_3 \ldots, S_n, \ldots$$

made up of these partial sums. If this sequence of numbers has a limit then we take that limit to be the sum of the given series:

$$a_1 + a_2 + a_3 + \cdots + a_n + \cdots = S$$

if

$$\lim S_n = S \quad \text{as} \quad n \to \infty.$$

Each of the partial sums gives an approximation for the sum of the series, with S_n in general giving a better approximation for larger n.

EXAMPLE 45.1. Let x denote a number between -1 and $+1$, and consider the series

$$x + x^2 + x^3 + \cdots + x^n + \cdots .$$

This is called a *geometric series*, and the series with which we began is the special case of this obtained by taking $x = \tfrac{1}{2}$. In the present case the nth partial sum S_n is

$$S_n = x + x^2 + x^3 + \cdots + x^n.$$

By obtaining a more compact form for S_n we shall be able to see what lim S_n is. We do this by noting that if S_n is as shown, then

$$xS_n = x^2 + x^3 + x^4 + \cdots + x^{n+1}.$$

Therefore, subtracting xS_n from S_n, we obtain

$$S_n - xS_n = x - x^{n+1}$$

because all other terms cancel. Therefore

$$(1 - x)S_n = x - x^{n+1}$$

and so

$$S_n = \frac{x - x^{n+1}}{1 - x}.$$

We are interested in lim S_n as $n \to \infty$, and with x a fixed real number this limit is completely determined once we know what happens to x^{n+1} (the only part involving n). It can be proved that if

$$-1 < x < 1 \quad \text{then}$$
$$\lim x^{n+1} = 0 \quad \text{as} \quad n \to \infty.$$

(This is not hard to believe. For instance, if $x = \frac{1}{2}$ then

$$\lim x^{n+1} = \lim \left(\frac{1}{2}\right)^{n+1} = \lim \frac{1}{2^{n+1}},$$

and $1/2^{n+1}$ clearly approaches 0 as $n \to \infty$.) We conclude that

$$\lim S_n = \frac{x}{1 - x} \quad \text{as} \quad n \to \infty .$$

Thus

$$x + x^2 + x^3 + \cdots + x^n + \cdots = \frac{x}{1 - x}, \quad \text{for} \quad -1 < x < 1 .$$

With $x = \frac{1}{2}$ this gives agreement with our original example. With $x = -\frac{1}{3}$, we get

$$-\frac{1}{3} + \frac{1}{9} - \frac{1}{27} + \frac{1}{81} - + \cdots + \left(-\frac{1}{3}\right)^n + \cdots = -\frac{1}{4}.$$

With $x = 1/10$, we obtain

$$\frac{1}{10} + \frac{1}{100} + \frac{1}{1000} + \cdots + \left(\frac{1}{10}\right)^n + \cdots = \frac{1}{9},$$

from which

$$\frac{9}{10} + \frac{9}{100} + \frac{9}{1000} + \cdots + \frac{9}{10^n} + \cdots = 1 .$$

This in turn is the same as $0.\bar{9} = 1$, in agreement with a result found in Problem 5.2.

EXAMPLE 45.2. Consider the series

$$\frac{1}{1 \cdot 2} + \frac{1}{2 \cdot 3} + \frac{1}{3 \cdot 4} + \cdots + \frac{1}{n(n + 1)} + \cdots .$$

The general term of this series can be written as

$$\frac{1}{n(n+1)} = \frac{1}{n} - \frac{1}{n+1},$$

as can be verified simply by adding the two fractions on the right. It follows, by taking advantage of cancellation, that

$$S_n = \frac{1}{1\cdot 2} + \frac{1}{2\cdot 3} + \frac{1}{3\cdot 4} + \cdots + \frac{1}{n(n+1)}$$

$$= \left(\frac{1}{1} - \frac{1}{2}\right) + \left(\frac{1}{2} - \frac{1}{3}\right) + \left(\frac{1}{3} - \frac{1}{4}\right) + \cdots + \left(\frac{1}{n} - \frac{1}{n+1}\right)$$

$$= 1 - \frac{1}{n+1}.$$

Thus

$$\lim S_n = \lim \left(1 - \frac{1}{n+1}\right) = 1 \quad \text{as} \quad n \to \infty,$$

and so

$$\frac{1}{1\cdot 2} + \frac{1}{2\cdot 3} + \frac{1}{3\cdot 4} + \cdots + \frac{1}{n(n+1)} + \cdots = 1.$$

In contrast with finite series, not every infinite series has a sum. For instance the nth partial sum of the series

$$1 + 1 + 1 + \cdots + 1 + \cdots$$

is n, and so the partial sums increase without bound and certainly do not approach any real number. An infinite series having a sum is said to be *convergent*, and one that does not have a sum is said to be *divergent*. The next example shows that a series may be divergent even though its partial sums do not increase without bound.

EXAMPLE 45.3. The series

$$1 - 1 + 1 - 1 + \cdots + (-1)^{n+1} + \cdots$$

is divergent, because the sequence of partial sums,

$$1, 0, 1, 0, \ldots,$$

does not possess a limit. (Compare Problem 45.9.)

It might be thought that an infinite series will have a sum if its terms approach 0 as n becomes large. The next example shows that this is not necessarily true.

EXAMPLE 45.4. The series

$$1 + \frac{1}{2} + \frac{1}{3} + \cdots + \frac{1}{n} + \cdots$$

is divergent. This can be seen by grouping the terms of the series as follows:

$$1 + \left(\frac{1}{2}\right) + \left(\frac{1}{3} + \frac{1}{4}\right) + \left(\frac{1}{5} + \frac{1}{6} + \frac{1}{7} + \frac{1}{8}\right) + \cdots$$

$$+ \left(\frac{1}{n+1} + \frac{1}{n+2} + \cdots + \frac{1}{2n}\right) + \cdots.$$

Of the n terms beginning with $1/(n+1)$, the smallest is clearly $1/(2n)$; thus the sum of these n terms is greater than $n(1/(2n)) = 1/2$. Therefore the given series with its terms grouped in this way yields a new series having terms greater than the corresponding terms of the series

$$1 + \frac{1}{2} + \frac{1}{2} + \frac{1}{2} + \cdots + \frac{1}{2} + \cdots,$$

which is clearly divergent. Thus the original series is divergent.

EXAMPLE 45.5. In contrast with Example 45.4 it can be shown that the series

$$1 - \frac{1}{2} + \frac{1}{3} - \frac{1}{4} + \cdots + \frac{(-1)^{n+1}}{n} + \cdots$$

is convergent. Its sum is, in fact, $\log_e 2$. A convergent series such as this, which has some positive and some negative terms and for which the corresponding series with all positive terms is divergent (Example 45.4), must be handled with care. In particular the sum of the series may change if the order of the terms is rearranged, something that never happens with finite series and that cannot happen with a convergent infinite series if its terms are all positive. To illustrate this, we first write the given series and then write beneath it the series obtained by multiplying each of the terms of the given series by $\frac{1}{2}$:

$$1 - \frac{1}{2} + \frac{1}{3} - \frac{1}{4} + \frac{1}{5} - \frac{1}{6} + \frac{1}{7} - \frac{1}{8} + - \cdots = \log_e 2$$

$$\frac{1}{2} \quad - \frac{1}{4} \quad + \frac{1}{6} \quad - \frac{1}{8} + - \cdots = \frac{1}{2}\log_e 2.$$

Now add the two sides of these equations to get

$$1 + \frac{1}{3} - \frac{1}{2} + \frac{1}{5} + \frac{1}{7} - \frac{1}{4} + \frac{1}{9} + \frac{1}{11} - \frac{1}{6} + + - \cdots = \frac{3}{2}\log_e 2.$$

The last series is seen to be the same as the original series except for the arrangement of the terms, and yet one has sum $\log_e 2$ while the other has sum $\frac{3}{2}\log_e 2$. Let it be emphasized that there is no contradiction here; both sums are correct in the sense of the meaning of sum of an infinite series. The example simply shows that one cannot safely assume that rules applying to finite series carry over to infinite series. Appropriate theorems reveal when rearrangement and other operations on infinite series are permissible, and in the case of rearrangement these theorems can be easily summarized as follows. A series with positive and negative terms is said to be *absolutely convergent* if the series obtained by making all of its terms positive is convergent. It can be proved that the sum of an absolutely convergent series cannot be altered by rearrangement of the terms of the series. It can also be proved that if a series is convergent, but not absolutely convergent, then the series can be made to have any sum whatsoever by appropriate rearrangement of the terms of the series. Thus our example is a special case of something much more general.

It may be helpful to summarize what we have found thus far. First, the question of whether an infinite series has a sum, and if so, what that sum is, is determined by studying the (finite) partial sums of the series. In specific cases (Examples 45.1 and 45.2) we have been able to compute the sums of infinite series. In other cases (Examples 45.3 and 45.4) we have been able to show that certain series do not have sums, that is, that they are divergent. Finally, we have seen that even if a series has a sum then that sum may change if the terms of the series are rearranged. Thus we have some idea of what is involved in passing from finite series of numbers to infinite series of numbers.

Before moving to the use of infinite series to represent functions, let us give one more collection of infinite series of numbers, these involving the number π. Again we omit the proofs.

EXAMPLE 45.6.

$$\frac{\pi}{4} = 1 - \frac{1}{3} + \frac{1}{5} - \frac{1}{7} + - \cdots$$

$$\frac{\pi^2}{6} = 1 + \frac{1}{2^2} + \frac{1}{3^2} + \frac{1}{4^2} + \cdots$$

$$\frac{\pi^4}{90} = 1 + \frac{1}{2^4} + \frac{1}{3^4} + \frac{1}{4^4} + \cdots$$

Notice that the first of these gives a representation of π with a perfectly well-determined pattern, which contrasts with the apparently random occurrence of digits in its decimal representation. The second two series are given in honor of Euler, who discovered the sums of these two series as well as the sums of the other reciprocal even powers through 26. It is curious that although it is known that the sum of

$$1 + \frac{1}{2^k} + \frac{1}{3^k} + \frac{1}{4^k} + \cdots$$

is a rational multiple of π^k when k is a positive even integer, the sum of the series is unknown for k a positive odd integer. We shall encounter these series again near the end of Section 48.

The geometric series in Example 45.1 can be thought of as defining a function: with each real number between -1 and $+1$ the series associates the real number given by the sum of the series

$$x + x^2 + x^3 + \cdots + x^n + \cdots.$$

In this particular case there is a more compact form for the value of the function, namely the sum $x/(1 - x)$, obtained in Example 45.1. But independent of whether there is such a compact form for the sum of a series involving x, the series can be thought of as defining a function for those values of x for which the series converges. We now want to look at an example of a function presented in this way, and then show how certain functions presented in other ways can be expressed in terms of series.

EXAMPLE 45.7. It can be proved that the series

$$1 + \frac{x}{1!} + \frac{x^2}{2!} + \frac{x^3}{3!} + \cdots + \frac{x^n}{n!} + \cdots$$

converges for every real number x. Thus the series defines a function from the set of real numbers to the set of real numbers. This function, one of the most important in mathematics, is called the *exponential function*, and is denoted by exp x. That is, by definition

$$\exp x = 1 + \frac{x}{1!} + \frac{x^2}{2!} + \frac{x^3}{3!} + \cdots + \frac{x^n}{n!} + \cdots$$

for every real number x. In particular,

$$\exp 1 = 1 + \frac{1}{1!} + \frac{1}{2!} + \frac{1}{3!} + \cdots + \frac{1}{n!} + \cdots,$$

and this series will be recognized as the one used to define the number e in Section 21 and in the discussion of limits. We shall say more about the exponential function in the next section.

By a *power series* in x is meant a series of the form

$$a_0 + a_1 x + a_2 x^2 + \cdots + a_n x^n + \cdots,$$

with $a_0, a_1, a_2, \ldots$ a sequence of real numbers (the name coming from the 'powers' of x: $x, x^2, x^3, \ldots$). The geometric series and the exponential series are power series. Notice that a power series is just like a polynomial except that an infinite number rather than only a finite number of different powers of x are permitted. This extension to an infinite number of powers makes an important difference, however. This can be seen most clearly from a result known as Taylor's Theorem (after the English mathematician Brook Taylor (1685–1731), although used earlier by others). Before illustrating this theorem we introduce some notation for derivatives.

If f denotes a function assigning real numbers to real numbers, so that f' denotes the derivative of f, then f'' is used to denote the derivative of f' and f''' is used to denote the derivative of f''. Thus if $f(x) = \sin x$ and $g(x) = x^5$, then

$$\begin{aligned}
f'(x) &= \cos x & g'(x) &= 5x^4 \\
f''(x) &= -\sin x & g''(x) &= 20x^3 \\
f'''(x) &= -\cos x & g'''(x) &= 60x^2.
\end{aligned}$$

Rather than continue with this notation for further derivatives, it is standard to denote the derivative obtained at the nth stage by $f^{(n)}$. Thus

$$f^{(4)}(x) = \sin x \qquad g^{(4)}(x) = 120x$$
$$f^{(5)}(x) = \cos x \qquad g^{(5)}(x) = 120$$
$$f^{(6)}(x) = -\sin x \qquad g^{(6)}(x) = 0.$$

In words, f' is called the *first derivative* of f, f'' the *second derivative* of f, and so on.

Taylor's Theorem asserts, among other things, that with appropriate restrictions on the function f and the real number x,

$$f(x) = f(0) + \frac{f'(0)}{1!} x + \frac{f''(0)}{2!} x^2 + \cdots + \frac{f^{(n)}(0)}{n!} x^n + \cdots.$$

We shall refer to this as the *Taylor series* for f (it is sometimes called the *Maclaurin series* for f). The 'appropriate restrictions' on x will depend on the particular function f, and yield those values of x for which the series converges. In many important cases, however, this series representation of f is valid for all real numbers x. This is true for the sine and cosine functions, for instance.

EXAMPLE 45.8. If $f(x) = \sin x$, then making use of the derivatives computed above, we have

$$f(0) \ = \sin 0 = 0 \qquad\qquad f^{(4)}(0) = \sin 0 = 0$$
$$f'(0) \ = \cos 0 = 1 \qquad\qquad f^{(5)}(0) = \cos 0 = 1$$
$$f''(0) \ = -\sin 0 = 0 \qquad\quad f^{(6)}(0) = -\sin 0 = 0$$
$$f'''(0) = -\cos 0 = -1 \qquad\text{and so on.}$$

Substituting the values in Taylor's series, we obtain

$$\sin x = x - \frac{x^3}{3!} + \frac{x^5}{5!} - \frac{x^7}{7!} + - \cdots.$$

As stated, this series gives the value of $\sin x$ for every real number x. If x is to represent an angle here, then it must be expressed in radians.

We shall see an illustration of the theoretical importance of this series in the next section. Let us use it now to compute an approximate value for $\sin 55°$. From Table 35.1, we see that $55°$ is approximately 0.96 radian. Therefore using only the first two terms of the series we get

$$\sin 55° \approx \sin 0.96 \approx 0.96 - \frac{(0.96)^3}{3!} \approx 0.96 - \frac{0.8847}{6} \approx 0.814.$$

The symbol $\approx$ means *approximately equal*. The value 0.814 should be compared with the value 0.8192 from Table 35.1. Had we used more than two terms of the series we would have obtained a value nearer that given by the table. But at least we see the potential usefulness of such series for numerical computations. The detailed study of such methods of numerical computation is the province of the branch of mathematics known as numerical analysis. Especially with the availability of electronic computers, which make it possible to carry out computations that would have been unthinkable earlier, numerical analysis has become a very active field of research.

Continuing with the example, we note that because the series for sine converges for each value of x, it can be used to compute $\sin x$ for each value of x, not just $x = 55° \approx 0.96$. The number of terms of the series required to obtain an acceptable approximation for $\sin x$ will depend on the particular value of x. This can be seen clearly from a figure. Denote by $A_1(x)$ the approximation given by the first term of the series, $A_3(x)$ that given by the first and third degree terms, and so on, so that

$$A_1(x) = x$$

$$A_3(x) = x - \frac{x^3}{3!}$$

$$A_5(x) = x - \frac{x^3}{3!} + \frac{x^5}{5!}.$$

Figure 45.1 shows each of these approximations, as well as $y = \sin x$. Notice that for a given approximation, such as A_5, the approximation is closest for

Figure 45.1

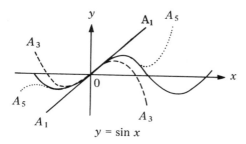

$y = \sin x$

values of x near 0. And for each value of x we get better approximations by using more terms of the series, which is another way of saying that the series converges for each value of x. The theoretical study of these approximations, for different functions, and in particular the way in which the nearness of the approximations depends on x, is an important part of the theory of infinite series.

EXAMPLE 45.9. Using $f(x) = \cos x$ we can follow the same procedure as that in the previous example to obtain

$$\cos x = 1 - \frac{x^2}{2!} + \frac{x^4}{4!} - \frac{x^6}{6!} + - \cdots.$$

We shall make use of the series for sine and cosine near the end of the following section.

We close our discussion of infinite series with a brief outline of the way in which series can be used to represent logarithms and to give meaning to exponents that are not necessarily rational numbers. We continue to omit proofs, but it can indeed be shown that the results in the following examples are consistent with the ideas concerning logarithms and exponents in Section 36. Our first example involves area rather than series.

EXAMPLE 45.10. The function *log* is defined by

$$\log t = \int_1^t \frac{1}{x} \, dx$$

for each real number $t > 0$. Geometrically, $\log t$ is the area in Figure 45.2 (where t has been taken greater than 1). With the meaning of logarithm as an

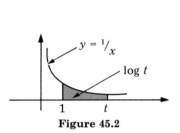

Figure 45.2   **Figure 45.3**

exponent, as it was discussed in Section 36, the function $\log t$ turns out to be $\log_e t$, for the number e given by $e = \exp 1$ in Example 45.7. Notice then that $\log e = \log_e e = 1$, which coincides with the remark accompanying Figure 41.4.

EXAMPLE 45.11. With log defined as in the previous example, it can be proved that

$$\log (1 + x) = x - \frac{x^2}{2} + \frac{x^3}{3} - \frac{x^4}{4} + - \cdots$$

for each value of x in the range $-1 < x \le 1$. In particular, using $x = 1$, we have

$$\log 2 = 1 - \frac{1}{2} + \frac{1}{3} - \frac{1}{4} + - \cdots,$$

which is the relation used in Example 45.5. Notice that this series can be used to compute logarithms (base e) in the same way that the series for sine can be used to compute $\sin x$. There are other series that will represent log for x outside the range $-1 < x \le 1$, but this one example should suffice for us.

EXAMPLE 45.12. For each real number $a > 0$, $\log a$ is given by the integral (area) in Example 45.10. This can be used to define a^x, for *each* real number x, through the series

$$a^x = 1 + x \log a + \frac{(x \log a)^2}{2!} + \frac{(x \log a)^3}{3!} + \cdots.$$

In this way a^x is defined for irrational as well as rational exponents.

The direct connection between the last three examples and the concepts in Section 36 is not apparent. But something of this nature is required if we are to make sense out of things like $2^{\sqrt{2}}$ and e^π. Once more we see the problems created by the existence of irrational numbers.

PROBLEM SET 45

PROBLEM 45.1. What is the difference between a sequence and a series?

PROBLEM 45.2. (a) Can a convergent series be changed into a divergent series by altering the first three terms of the series? What about the first one million terms?

(b) Can a divergent series be changed into a convergent series by altering the first three terms of the series? What about the first one million terms?

(c) Can the sum of a convergent series be changed by altering the first three terms of the series? What about the first one million terms?

PROBLEM 45.3. Obtain the sum of each of the following series by using an appropriate value of x in the geometric series in Example 45.1.

(a) $\dfrac{1}{3} + \dfrac{1}{9} + \dfrac{1}{27} + \dfrac{1}{81} + \cdots$.

(b) $-\dfrac{2}{3} + \dfrac{4}{9} - \dfrac{8}{27} + \dfrac{16}{81} - + \cdots$.

(c) $0.1 + 0.01 + 0.001 + 0.0001 + \cdots$.

(d) $-0.1 + 0.01 - 0.001 + 0.0001 - + \cdots$.

PROBLEM 45.4. To illustrate that the formula in Example 45.1 for the sum of a geometric series is not necessarily valid for x outside the range $-1 < x < 1$, discuss what it yields for $x = 2$.

PROBLEM 45.5. Use Example 45.1 to derive the more general formula

$$a + ax + ax^2 + ax^3 + \cdots + ax^n + \cdots = \frac{a}{1 - x}$$

for $-1 < x < 1$ and a any real number.

PROBLEM 45.6. Obtain the sum of each of the following series by using appropriate values of a and x in Problem 45.5.

(a) $3 + \dfrac{3}{2} + \dfrac{3}{4} + \dfrac{3}{8} + \cdots$.

(b) $\dfrac{1}{10} + \dfrac{1}{10^4} + \dfrac{1}{10^7} + \dfrac{1}{10^{10}} + \cdots$.

(c) $1 - \dfrac{1}{3} + \dfrac{1}{9} - \dfrac{1}{27} + - \cdots$.

(d) $L + \dfrac{L}{4} + \dfrac{L}{4^2} + \dfrac{L}{4^3} + \cdots$.   (Compare Problem 34.16.)

(e) $0.3 + 0.03 + 0.003 + 0.0003 + \cdots$.

PROBLEM 45.7. (a) Evaluate $\dfrac{1}{1 \cdot 2} + \dfrac{1}{2 \cdot 3} + \dfrac{1}{3 \cdot 4} + \dfrac{1}{4 \cdot 5}$.

(b) Evaluate $\dfrac{1}{1 \cdot 2} + \dfrac{1}{2 \cdot 3} + \dfrac{1}{3 \cdot 4} + \cdots + \dfrac{1}{99 \cdot 100}$.

PROBLEM 45.8. Find the sum of the infinite series

$$\frac{1}{1 \cdot 2 \cdot 3} + \frac{1}{2 \cdot 3 \cdot 4} + \frac{1}{3 \cdot 4 \cdot 5} + \cdots + \frac{1}{n(n + 1)(n + 2)} + \cdots.$$

(Suggestion: Verify that
$$\frac{1}{n(n+1)(n+2)} = \frac{1}{2}\left(\frac{1}{n(n+1)} - \frac{1}{(n+1)(n+2)}\right)$$
and use the idea in Example 45.2.)

PROBLEM 45.9. The series in Example 45.3 can be written as either
$$(1-1) + (1-1) + (1-1) + \cdots = 0 - 0 - 0 - \cdots = 0$$
or
$$1 - (1-1) - (1-1) - \cdots = 1 + 0 + 0 + \cdots = 1.$$
Furthermore, using $a = 1$ and $x = -1$ in Problem 45.5 would yield
$$1 - 1 + 1 - 1 + - \cdots = \frac{1}{2}.$$
What conclusion can be drawn?

PROBLEM 45.10. (a) Can rearrangement of the first three terms of a convergent infinite series change the sum of the series? (Compare Example 45.5.)

(b) Can rearrangement of the first one million terms of a convergent infinite series change the sum of the series?

PROBLEM 45.11. Compute the approximations for π obtained from using the first, second, third, fourth, and fifth partial sums of the first series in Example 45.6.

PROBLEM 45.12. It is sometimes possible to obtain the derivative of a function given by an infinite series by using the series obtained from replacing each term of the given series by its derivative. That is, under appropriate conditions, if
$$f(x) = u_1(x) + u_2(x) + u_3(x) + \cdots + u_n(x) + \cdots,$$
where each of the terms $u_1(x), u_2(x), \ldots$ is a function of x, then
$$f'(x) = u_1'(x) + u_2'(x) + u_3'(x) + \cdots + u_n'(x) + \cdots.$$
This is true in particular for the functions exp x defined in Example 45.7. Use this fact to verify that if $f(x) = \exp(x)$, then $f'(x) = \exp x$.

PROBLEM 45.13. Verify that the series for the cosine given in Example 45.9 is correct by computing the terms of the Taylor's series for cos x, as was done in Example 45.8 for sin x.

PROBLEM 45.14. Use the series in Example 45.9 to compute an approximation for cos 55°.

PROBLEM 45.15. Use the series in Examples 45.8 and 45.9 to compute approximations for sin 35° and cos 35°.

PROBLEM 45.16. Use the first four terms of the appropriate series in Example 45.11 to obtain an approximation for the area above the x-axis, below $y = 1/x$, and between $x = 1$ and $x = 1.5$.

PROBLEM 45.17. Use $a = e$ in Example 45.12, simplify, and compare with the series in Example 45.7.

PROBLEM 45.18. Using the approximation 3.14 for π, and the first four terms of the series in Example 45.7, compute an approximation for e^π.

§46. Complex Numbers

One of the morals of Chapter I was that the system of real numbers arose from smaller systems through necessity. A simple example will show that for the purposes of algebra the system of real numbers must, through necessity, be enlarged still further.

Suppose that we want to solve the equation $x^2 + 1 = 0$; that is, to find a number x such that $x^2 = -1$. This cannot be done with a real number, for the square of any real number is either positive or zero. For this reason mathematicians developed a system of numbers, called the system of complex numbers, that is larger than the system of real numbers and in which the equation $x^2 + 1 = 0$ does have a solution. This system, which evolved during the period from the sixteenth century through the early nineteenth century, gives a great deal more than a solution to $x^2 + 1 = 0$, as we shall come to see. But we must first give an explicit description of the complex numbers.

The first step in the construction of the system of complex numbers is the invention of a new 'number', denoted i, with the property that $i^2 = -1$. The next step is to build a system containing, among other things, all of the real numbers as well as the new number i, and to introduce operations of addition and multiplication into the system in a way that preserves in the system the usual properties of the operations of algebra (such as $x + y = y + x$, $x(yz) = (xy)z$, and so on). Before continuing with this second step let us look at a similar construction that is more familiar.

If the natural numbers and zero were the only numbers available, and if we wanted to solve the equation $x + 1 = 0$, we could do it by introducing a new 'number', denoted -1, with the property that $(-1) + 1 = 0$. We could then build a system containing all of the natural numbers and zero as well as this new number, and we could introduce operations of addition and multiplication into this system in a way that would preserve the usual properties of the operations of algebra. This new system would turn out to be the system of all integers, which we would now be meeting for the first time. The set of numbers in this system of integers would be $\{0, 1, 2, 3, \ldots, 1(-1), 2(-1), 3(-1), \ldots\}$: zero together with the natural numbers together with each of the natural numbers 'multiplied' by -1.

The system of complex numbers is constructed by a process similar to that just described.

The system of complex numbers *consists of all 'numbers' of the form* $a + bi$, *where* a *and* b *are real numbers.*

Thus $\sqrt{2} + 3i$, $2 - 5i$ and $\frac{1}{2} + \pi i$ are examples of complex numbers. Each real number is a complex number ($a = a + 0i$) and i is a complex number ($i = 0 + 1i$). We operate with these numbers using the usual operations of algebra $(x + y = y + x, x(yz) = (xy)z$, and so on), with the extra convention that i^2 can always be replaced by -1. In particular if $a + bi$ and $c + di$ are any two complex numbers then

$$(a + bi) + (c + di) = (a + c) + (b + d)i$$

and

$$\begin{aligned}
(a + bi) \cdot (c + di) &= a(c + di) + bi(c + di) \\
&= ac + adi + bci + bdi^2 \\
&= (ac - bd) + (ad + bc)i.
\end{aligned}$$

EXAMPLE 46.1. Here are some computations with complex numbers.

$(2 + i) + (1 + i) = 3 + 2i \qquad (-i)^2 = (-1)^2(i)^2 = i^2 = -1$

$(2 + i) + (3 - i) = 5 \qquad (2i)^2 = 4i^2 = -4$

$i^3 = i^2 \cdot i = (-1)i = -i \qquad (1 + i)(1 - i) = 1 - i^2 = 1 - (-1) = 2$

Just as the system of real numbers can be represented geometrically as the set of points on a line, the system of complex numbers can be represented geometrically as the set of points in a plane. This is done by letting $a + bi$ correspond with the point having x-coordinate a and y-coordinate b: $a + bi \leftrightarrow (a, b)$. Several examples are shown in Figure 46.1. Addition and multiplication of complex numbers can be described

Figure 46.1

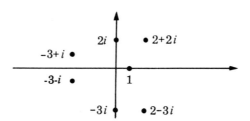

geometrically in terms of these representations, and for any extensive work with complex numbers the geometry becomes very useful. This usefulness became evident with the doctoral thesis of Gauss, published in 1799, in which we find the geometric interpretation of complex numbers used in the first satisfactory proof of the following important theorem.

FUNDAMENTAL THEOREM OF ALGEBRA
  Every algebraic equation

$$a_n x^n + a_{n-1} x^{n-1} + \cdots + a_1 x + a_0 = 0,$$

which is of degree at least one and whose coefficients $a_n, a_{n-1}, \ldots, a_1, a_0$ are complex numbers, has at least one root in the system of complex numbers.

The existence of a root (the number i) for $x^2 + 1 = 0$ is a special case of the Fundamental Theorem of Algebra ($n = 2$, $a_2 = 1$, $a_1 = 0$, $a_0 = 1$). The significant thing about the theorem is that it tells us that the system of complex numbers is large enough so that it will never be necessary to enlarge the system further in order to find a root for an algebraic equation having coefficients in the system. Contrast the case of each of the smaller systems we have encountered: to find a root for $x + 1 = 0$ (coefficients natural numbers) it is necessary to go to the negative integers; to find a root for $2x + 1 = 0$ (coefficients natural numbers) it is necessary to go to the rational numbers; to find a root for $x^2 - 2 = 0$ (coefficients integers) it is necessary to go to the real numbers; to find a root for $x^2 + 1 = 0$ (coefficients natural numbers) it is necessary to go to the complex numbers. The Fundamental Theorem of Algebra asserts that not only a root for any algebraic equation with *integer* coefficients exists in the system of complex numbers, but that a root for any algebraic equation with *complex* coefficients exists in the system of complex numbers.

Notice that the Fundamental Theorem states only that every algebraic equation *has* a root; it does not give a root, and it says nothing about how to go about finding one. This should be contrasted with the comments in Section 27 when discussing the role of group theory in the study of algebraic equations. It was stated there that there cannot exist a formula for expressing the roots of a general algebraic equation of degree higher than four in terms of the coefficients of the equation by use of the fundamental operations of arithmetic. Those results are completely independent of the Fundamental Theorem of Algebra, and the distinction is an important one. The Fundamental Theorem of Algebra is an example of what is known in mathematics as an existence theorem: the theorem guarantees the existence of something without giving any information about how to find it. Existence theorems are common in mathematics, and they can be very useful; progress is often made from the mere knowledge that a solution to a problem exists, whether or not an actual solution is known.

Functions assigning complex numbers to complex numbers are the subject of an extensive branch of mathematics known as complex analysis. Such things as limits, derivatives, integrals, sequences, and series are studied in complex analysis, just as they are in calculus, and the results have proved to be widely applicable in mathematics, science, and engineering. We shall encounter such an application in discussing the distribution of primes, in Section 48. For the present we give a remarkable result generally known as Euler's formula. We stress that this is only a special formula and should not be taken as indicative of the depth or extensive character of modern complex analysis; but we shall need the formula in the next section, and in any case it leads to one of the most curious facts in all of mathematics.

We begin by recalling that

$$e^x = 1 + \frac{x}{1!} + \frac{x^2}{2!} + \frac{x^3}{3!} + \cdots + \frac{x^n}{n!} + \cdots,$$

$$\sin x = x - \frac{x^3}{3!} + \frac{x^5}{5!} - \frac{x^7}{7!} + - \cdots,$$

and

$$\cos x = 1 - \frac{x^2}{2!} + \frac{x^4}{4!} - \frac{x^6}{6!} + - \cdots,$$

each relation holding for every real number x (Examples 45.7, 45.8, 45.9). It is proved in complex analysis that each of these relations is in fact meaningful for every complex number x (if x is not real then $\sin x$ and $\cos x$ lose their original geometrical meaning, but as long as x is real they can be thought of with that meaning). Thus we can consider each series for a complex number of the form iy. Remembering that $i^2 = -1$, $i^3 = -i$, $i^4 = 1$, and so on, we see that

$$e^{iy} = 1 + \frac{iy}{1!} + \frac{(iy)^2}{2!} + \frac{(iy)^3}{3!} + \frac{(iy)^4}{4!} + \frac{(iy)^5}{5!} + \frac{(iy)^6}{6!} + \frac{(iy)^7}{7!} + \cdots$$

$$= 1 + i\frac{y}{1!} - \frac{y^2}{2!} - i\frac{y^3}{3!} + \frac{y^4}{4!} + i\frac{y^5}{5!} - \frac{y^6}{6!} - i\frac{y^7}{7!} + \cdots$$

$$= \left(1 - \frac{y^2}{2!} + \frac{y^4}{4!} - \frac{y^6}{6!} + - \cdots\right) + i\left(y - \frac{y^3}{3!} + \frac{y^5}{5!} - \frac{y^7}{7!} + - \cdots\right)$$

$$= \cos y + i \sin y.$$

This is Euler's formula:

$$e^{iy} = \cos y + i \sin y.$$

The case of most interest comes with $y = \pi$, for then $\cos y = -1$ and $\sin y = 0$, and we obtain a single surprising equation relating the numbers e, i, π, and 1:

$$e^{i\pi} = -1.$$

Which is indeed one of the most curious facts in all of mathematics.

PROBLEM SET 46

PROBLEM 46.1. Simplify each of the following expressions. That is, reduce each to the form $a + bi$ with a and b real numbers, as in Example 46.1.

(a) i^4 (b) i^5 (c) i^6

(d) i^{19} (e) $(-i)^3$ (f) $(7 + i) + (3 - i)$

(g) $(1 + i)^2$ (h) $(2 - i)(3 + 2i)$ (i) $(2 - i)^2$

(j) $(4 + 2i)(4 - 2i)$ (k) $[(\sqrt{2}/2) + (\sqrt{2}/2)i]^2$ (l) $[(\sqrt{3}/2) + (1/2)i]^3$

PROBLEM 46.2. Verify that if a and b denote real numbers then
$$(a + bi)(a - bi) = a^2 + b^2.$$

PROBLEM 46.3. Verify that if a and b denote real numbers then
$$\frac{1}{a + bi} = \frac{a}{a^2 + b^2} - \frac{b}{a^2 + b^2} i.$$

(Suggestion: Multiply by $(a - bi)/(a - bi)$, and use Problem 46.2.)

PROBLEM 46.4. Use the idea in Problem 46.3 to simplify each of the following expressions, as in Problem 46.1.

(a) $1/(1 + i)$ (b) $1/(1 - i)$ (c) $1/(2 + i)$
(d) $7/(4 + 2i)$ (e) $(2 + i)/(3 + i)$ (f) $1/i$
(g) $(1 + 2i)/(1 - i)$ (h) $i/(2 - i)$ (i) $[(1 + i)/(i - 1)]^2$

PROBLEM 46.5. Verify that if $x = 2 + i$ or $x = 2 - i$, then $x^2 - 4x + 5 = 0$. Thus $2 + i$ and $2 - i$ are solutions of $x^2 - 4x + 5 = 0$.

PROBLEM 46.6. Which of the numbers $1, -1, 2, i, -i, 3 + i, 3 - i$ are solutions of the equation $x^3 - 8x^2 + 22x - 20 = 0$?

PROBLEM 46.7. Verify by direct computation that the two expressions given by the quadratic formula,
$$x = \frac{-b \pm \sqrt{b^2 - 4ac}}{2a},$$
are solutions of the general quadratic equation,
$$ax^2 + bx + c = 0.$$

PROBLEM 46.8. Use the quadratic formula, given in the preceding problem, to find the solutions of each of the following equations.

(a) $x^2 - x - 1 = 0$ (b) $x^2 - 6 = 0$
(c) $x^2 + 4 = 0$ (d) $4x^2 + 4x - 3 = 0$
(e) $x^2 - 6x + 10 = 0$ (f) $x^2 + 4x + 4 = 0$
(g) $x^2 + ix = 0$ (h) $x^2 + 2ix - 1 = 0$
(i) $x^2 + 3ix + 4 = 0$ (j) $ix^2 + 2x - i = 0$

PROBLEM 46.9. (a) Use Euler's formula to compute $e^{i\pi/2}$.
(b) Use Euler's formula to compute e^i.

PROBLEM 46.10. If you have read Chapter IV, explain why the set of complex numbers has the same cardinal number as the set of real numbers.

PROBLEM 46.11. The Fundamental Theorem of Algebra asserts that the equation
$$a_n x^n + a_{n-1} x^{n-1} + \cdots + a_1 x + a_0 = 0$$
has at least one root in the system of complex numbers. It can also be proved that the equation has at most n roots. If the roots are $x_1, x_2 \cdots, x_n$, then
$$a_n x^n + a_{n-1} x^{n-1} + \cdots + a_1 x + a_0 = a_n(x - x_1)(x - x_2) \cdots (x - x_n).$$
(a) Illustrate the facts stated by verifying that $1, -1, i, -i$ are roots of $x^4 - 1 = 0$, and that also
$$x^4 - 1 = (x - 1)(x + 1)(x - i)(x + i).$$

(b) Illustrate the facts stated by verifying that 2, $2i$, $-2i$ are roots of $x^3 - 2x^2 + 4x - 8 = 0$, and that also

$$x^3 - 2x^2 + 4x - 8 = (x - 2)(x - 2i)(x + 2i).$$

(c) Why is it impossible to have complex numbers $a_n, a_{n-1}, \ldots, a_1, a_0$ such that $\sin x = a_n x^n + a_{n-1} x^{n-1} + \cdots + a_1 x + a_0$ for each x?

§47. Algebraic and Transcendental Numbers

In Section 34A we introduced three famous problems of Greek geometry:

I.   The duplication of the cube.
II. The trisection of an arbitrary angle.
III. The quadrature of the circle.

We now want to discuss the sense in which any such problem is equivalent with a corresponding problem in algebra. Then we shall learn why the Greeks had been unable to solve the three problems, and in the process we shall be led in a natural way to the two kinds of numbers in the title of this section. This will furnish an excellent example of how problems in one area of mathematics can sometimes be properly understood, and settled, only after being considered from the viewpoint of a different area of mathematics. Recall that for the duplication of the cube, the requirement is to construct the edge of a cube having twice the volume of a given cube. Taking the edge of the given cube to be the unit of length, 1, so that the volume of the given cube is 1 $(= 1^3)$, we see that if the edge of the required cube is x then we must have $x^3 = 2$ (the volume of the required cube, x^3, equal to twice the volume of the given cube). Thus the problem of the duplication of the cube can be rephrased as follows.

I′. Given a segment of length 1, construct a segment of length x with $x^3 = 2$.

For the second problem we require a formula from trigonometry connecting an angle with its trisected angle through the cosine function:
If A is any angle, then

$$\cos A = 4[\cos (A/3)]^3 - 3[\cos (A/3)].$$

In particular, using $\cos 60° = \frac{1}{2}$ (Table 35.1), we see that with $A = 60°$ and $x = \cos (A/3)$ this equation becomes

$$\tfrac{1}{2} = 4x^3 - 3x$$

or

$$8x^3 - 6x - 1 = 0.$$

We can consider an acute angle as given by its cosine, and so the problem of the trisection of a 60° angle can be put as follows.

II'. *Given a segment of length 1, construct a segment of length x with $8x^3 - 6x - 1 = 0$.*

Notice that II refers to an arbitrary angle while II' came from consideration of an angle of 60°; we shall see later why it is sufficient to consider the special case of 60°.

For the quadrature of a circle we can take the radius of the circle to be the unit of length, 1, and then the problem becomes that of constructing a square with area π, because that is the area of the circle ($\pi \cdot 1^2 = \pi$). The side of such a square will have length $\sqrt{\pi}$, and so problem III can be restated as follows.

III'. *Given a segment of length 1, construct a segment of length x with $x = \sqrt{\pi}$.*

With I', II', and III', each of the original problems becomes a problem of whether a certain multiple of a given length can be constructed. The key to whether such problems can be solved is in the following theorem. The rational operations referred to here are addition, subtraction, multiplication, and division.

THEOREM 47.1

A necessary and sufficient condition that a segment of length x can be constructed with unmarked straightedge and compass, beginning with a segment of length 1, is that x can be obtained from 1 by a finite number of rational operations and square roots.

We omit the proof of the theorem but outline in the problems how the basic constructions involved can be carried out. It follows from the theorem that segments with lengths such as the following can be constructed:

$$1 + 1 = 2 \qquad\qquad 3 \cdot \tfrac{1}{2} = \tfrac{3}{2}$$
$$1 + 1 + 1 = 3 \qquad \sqrt{3}$$
$$1{,}000{,}000{,}000 \qquad 4 - \sqrt{3}$$
$$\tfrac{1}{2} \qquad\qquad\qquad \sqrt{4 - \sqrt{3}}$$

Theorem 47.1 reduces the three problems to the question of whether the quantities x in I', II', and III' can be obtained in this way. In particular the theorem translates the original geometric problems into algebraic problems.

The problems were finally settled in their algebraic form: it is now known that the constructions in the three problems are impossible. The Greeks did not succeed in solving the three problems because it was logically impossible to do so. Thus with these problems the Greeks and later geometers were in the same hopeless situation they were in with regard to Euclid's Fifth Postulate (Chapter II). The case of the three famous problems is somewhat different, however, in the sense that they are known to be impossible only through use of methods of algebra, or, in the case of the quadrature of the circle, both algebra and analysis. These methods were developed only in the nineteenth century, the algebra from the theory of equations (the work underlying Galois theory, discussed in Section 27), and the analysis from work related to complex numbers.

We can now see why in translating problem II into problem II′ it sufficed to consider the special case of a 60° angle. We have said that II′ is impossible, and it follows that II is impossible, for if a particular angle cannot be trisected then certainly not every angle can be trisected. Some angles, such as 90° angles, can in fact be trisected with unmarked straightedge and compass.

We shall now leave the first two problems and say more about what was involved in settling the problem of the quadrature of the circle. To do this we must introduce algebraic and transcendental numbers, the unifying concepts of this section.

An *algebraic number* is a complex number that satisfies a polynomial equation

$$a_n x^n + a_{n-1} x^{n-1} + \cdots + a_1 x + a_0 = 0$$

in which the coefficients $a_n, a_{n-1}, \ldots, a_1, a_0$ are all integers. Thus $\frac{1}{2}$ is an algebraic number because it is a solution of $2x - 1 = 0$, and $\sqrt{2}$ is an algebraic number because it is a solution of $x^2 - 2 = 0$. More generally, any rational number is algebraic, because a/b is a solution of $bx - a = 0$; and the square root of any rational number is algebraic, because $\sqrt{a/b}$ is a solution of $bx^2 - a = 0$. A complex number that is not algebraic is called a *transcendental number*. A number is algebraic if we can exhibit one equation, of the appropriate type, of which the number is a root; to know that a number is transcendental we must assure that it is a root of none of the equations of the appropriate type. Before giving examples of transcendental numbers let us see what this has to do with geometrical constructions.

It can be proved that if a number x is of the type in Theorem 47.1, then x must be an algebraic number. The converse of this is not true: for instance the solutions of the equations in I′ and II′ are algebraic, but we have already said they do not yield lengths of constructible segments and thus they are not of the type in Theorem 47.1. But in any case, since every number of the type in Theorem 47.1 is algebraic, it follows that a number which is not algebraic (that is, which is transcendental) cannot be of the type in Theorem 47.1. This gives the connection between transcendental numbers and geometrical constructions. In

particular, it gives the method by which the quadrature of the circle
was proved to be impossible, for it was proved in 1882 that π is transcendental, and it follows that a segment of length π cannot be constructed and thus a segment of length $\sqrt{\pi}$ cannot be constructed, so that
the quadrature of the circle is impossible. The story behind the proof
of the transcendence of π is of separate interest and so we shall look at
it. But first let us note clearly that the problem of the quadrature of the
circle, recorded and attempted in ancient Greece, was not settled until
the late nineteenth century, and then, as we shall see, only with help
of the most surprising kind.

The first known transcendental numbers were constructed in
1844 by the French mathematician Joseph Liouville (1809–1882), who
developed a method for producing transcendental numbers at will. The
method itself is much too complicated to be described here, but a sample
of the numbers it revealed to be transcendental is given by

$$\frac{1}{10^1} + \frac{1}{10^2} + \frac{1}{10^6} + \frac{1}{10^{24}} + \frac{1}{10^{120}} + \cdots,$$

or more generally any number

$$\frac{1}{k^{1!}} + \frac{1}{k^{2!}} + \frac{1}{k^{3!}} + \frac{1}{k^{4!}} + \frac{1}{k^{5!}} + \cdots$$

for k a real number greater than 1. While Liouville was able to produce
transcendental numbers, he did not succeed in proving that any particular number previously given was transcendental. The first proof of
the latter kind came in 1873 when another Frenchman, Charles Hermite
(1822–1901) proved the transcendence of the number e. The next significant example, and the one which interests us now, came nine years later
when the German C. L. F. Lindemann (1852–1939) proved the transcendence of π. Lindemann did this by first proving that no algebraic
number k can be a solution of

$$e^{ix} = -1.$$

But by Euler's formula (Section 46)

$$e^{i\pi} = -1.$$

Thus π cannot be algebraic, and so it must be transcendental!

While we cannot give a complete proof of the transcendence of
any particular number, either of the kind produced by Lindemann or the
more difficult cases such as e and π, we can prove that transcendental
numbers do exist in profusion. This is shown by the following theorem,
which was published by Cantor in 1874. The terminology is that of
Chapter IV.

THEOREM 47.2

The cardinal number of the set of algebraic real numbers is equal to the cardinal number of the set of natural numbers.

Before proving the theorem we point out that it does show that transcendental real numbers exist, for otherwise every real number would be algebraic, which would imply that the set of real numbers possesses the same cardinal number as the set of algebraic real numbers; this would contradict Theorem 47.2 in light of Example 23.1. In fact, the cardinal number of the set of transcendental real numbers is the same as the cardinal number of the set of all real numbers (Problem 47.6 indicates how to prove a weakened form of this statement).

Proof of Theorem 47.2

It suffices to establish that the set of algebraic real numbers can be put in a sequence, for then we can put 1 in correspondence with the first, 2 in correspondence with the second, and so on.

We first observe that if each polynomial

$$a_n x^n + a_{n-1} x^{n-1} + \cdots + a_1 x + a_0$$

is paired with the set

$$\{a_n, a_{n-1}, \ldots, a_1 a_0\},$$

then there is established a one-to-one correspondence between the set of all such polynomials and the set of finite subsets of the set of natural numbers. It follows from Problem 24.6(d) that the set of all polynomials of the above form can be arranged in a sequence, such as

$$p_1(x), p_2(x), p_3(x), \ldots, p_n(x), \ldots.$$

Now we make use of the fact, which is proved in the theory of equations, that if such a polynomial is of degree k then it has at most k roots. Thus we can replace each polynomial in the sequence by a list of its roots. For example, $x^2 - 1$ would be replaced by $+1$, -1. If we then remove all repetitions from the new sequence, there will result a sequence consisting precisely of the algebraic numbers. Thus the set of all algebraic numbers can be put in a sequence, and so certainly the set of algebraic real numbers can be put in a sequence. □

Notice once more that on the basis of Theorem 47.2 we cannot say that any particular number is transcendental; we can simply say that there are transcendental numbers. This is another example of an existence theorem, like the Fundamental Theorem of Algebra, given in Section 46. The problem of proving particular numbers transcendental remains a difficult one. In addition to e and π, it is known for instance that the numbers

$$e^\pi,\ 2^{\sqrt{2}},\ \log_e 2$$

are transcendental, but it is not known whether the numbers

$$\pi^e,\ 2^e,\ e + \pi$$

are transcendental. This leads us to the seventh problem posed by Hilbert in his address to the International Congress of Mathematicians in 1900 (Section 33):

> *If a and b are algebraic, a is not 0 or 1, and b is irrational, is a^b necessarily transcendental?*

A special case of this problem had been raised by Euler in 1748. Hilbert's question was answered affirmatively by A. O. Gelfond (Russian) in 1934. In 1935 T. Schneider (German) gave a simpler proof. It is by the Gelfond-Schneider result that the numbers e^π and $2^{\sqrt{2}}$ above are known to be transcendental: the case of $2^{\sqrt{2}}$ follows directly, while the case of e^π follows because of $e^\pi = i^{-2i}$, another surprising result originally discovered by Euler.

The story does not stop with the solution to Hilbert's seventh problem, however. An improvement of the result of Gelfond and Schneider was obtained in the 1960's by the English mathematician Alan Baker. One of the new transcendental numbers coming out of Baker's work is the number

$$\pi + \log_e 2.$$

For his work in this area Baker was awarded one of the four Fields prizes at the International Congress of Mathematicians in 1970. To merely quote that the number $\pi + \log_e 2$ is transcendental hardly conveys the depth of the mathematics involved in proving it. With this acknowledgment of the range between the statements of the results we have been quoting and the proofs of some of those results, we end our discussion of algebraic and transcendental numbers.

PROBLEM SET 47

PROBLEM 47.1. Give an example of each of the following, or state why such does not exist.
(a) A complex number that is not algebraic.
(b) A complex number that is not transcendental.
(c) A rational number that is not algebraic.
(d) A rational number that is not transcendental.
(e) An algebraic number that is not transcendental.

(f) A transcendental number that is not algebraic.
(g) An algebraic number that is not rational.
(h) A transcendental number that is rational.
(i) A transcendental number that is irrational.
(j) An algebraic number that is not real.

PROBLEM 47.2. Indicate which of the following are algebraic and which are transcendental, giving a reason in each case.

(a) 7   (b) $\sqrt{3}$ (c) i

(d) $3^{\sqrt{2}}$ (e) e (f) π

(g) $\sqrt[3]{2}$ (h) $\sqrt{\sqrt{2}-1}$ (i) $(\tfrac{1}{2})^{\sqrt{3}}$

PROBLEM 47.3. Indicate which of the following represent lengths of segments that can be constructed with unmarked straightedge and compass, in light of Theorem 47.1 and other information in this section.
(a) A positive integer.
(b) A rational number.
(c) The square root of a positive integer.
(d) The square root of the square root of a rational number.
(e) The number e.
(f) The number π.
(g) Every algebraic number.
(h) Some transcendental numbers.

PROBLEM 47.4. (a) The text states that the sum of the series $10^{-1!} + 10^{-2!} + 10^{-3!} + \cdots$ is transcendental. Write the first thirty places of the decimal representation of this number.
(b) In contrast with the sum in part (a), the sum of the series $10^{-1} + 10^{-4} + 10^{-7} + 10^{-10} + \cdots$ is algebraic. Why? (See Problem 45.6(b).)

PROBLEM 47.5. The text states that if a segment of length π cannot be constructed with straightedge and compass then neither can a segment of length $\sqrt{\pi}$. Why? (Suggestion: Use Problem 47.10 and *reductio*.)

PROBLEM 47.6. Prove that the set of transcendental numbers has cardinal number larger than that of the set of natural numbers. (Suggestion: Use Theorem 47.2, Problem 23.4, and *reductio*.)

PROBLEM 47.7. Describe how to construct segments of lengths $x + y$ and $x - y$, given segments of lengths x and y.

PROBLEM 47.8. Figure 47.1 suggests how to construct a segment of length $x/3$, given a segment of length x. Answer the questions indicated.

Figure 47.1

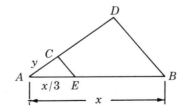

(a) Mark $AB = x$ on a line and mark AC of any length y on any other line through A.

(b) Extend AC to D so that $AD = 3y$. Why can this be done? (See Problem 47.7.)

(c) Draw DB and construct a line through C parallel to DB, intersecting AB at E.

(d) $AE = x/3$. Why? (Consider similar triangles.)

PROBLEM 47.9. Figure 47.2 suggests how to construct a segment AE of length x/y given segments of lengths x, y, and 1. The procedure to be followed is similar to that outlined in Problem 47.8. Describe it in detail.

Figure 47.2

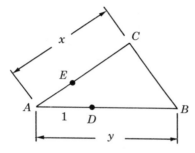

PROBLEM 47.10. Figure 47.3 suggests how to construct a segment AE of length xy given segments of lengths x, y, and 1. The procedure to be followed is similar to that outlined in Problem 47.8. Describe it in detail.

Figure 47.3

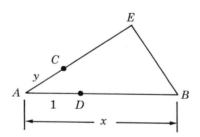

PROBLEM 47.11. Figure 47.4 suggests how to construct a segment of length $\sqrt{x}$ given a segment of length 1 and a segment of length x. Answer the questions indicated.

(a) Mark $AB = x$ and $BC = 1$ on a straight line.

(b) Construct a circle with AC as diameter.

Figure 47.4

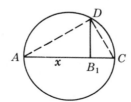

(c) Construct the perpendicular to AC at B, intersecting the circle at D. Complete triangle ADC.

(d) Angle ADC is a right angle. Why?

(e) Therefore angle ADB = angle BCD. Why?

(f) Therefore triangles ADB and BCD are similar. Why?

(g) Let $y = BD$. Then $x/y = y/1$. Why?

(h) Therefore $y = \sqrt{x}$, and so BD has the proper length.

§48. Distribution of Primes

In this section we work our way from one of the most famous proofs in mathematics to one of the most famous unsolved problems in mathematics. In the process we shall, once more, pass from the ancient to the modern, and from the elementary to the advanced.

The proof we refer to is that of Euclid's Theorem. Before getting to that, however, let us make sure of some elementary facts about prime numbers and divisibility. An integer m is said to be *divisible* by an integer n if there is an integer q (for quotient) such that $m = nq$. Thus 6 is divisible by 2 because $6 = 2 \cdot 3$; and 5 is not divisible by 2 or 3 or 4. An integer p is said to be a *prime* if $p > 1$ and p is divisible by no positive integer other than 1 and p itself. Thus the primes are

$$2, 3, 5, 7, 11, 13, 17, 19, 23, \ldots .$$

An integer that is greater than 1 and is not a prime is said to be *composite*. Our goal is to say as much as we can about primes.

The following theorem shows that the primes are in a sense the building blocks of the integers; this gives the primes much of their special importance.

FUNDAMENTAL THEOREM OF ARITHMETIC
Each integer greater than 1 can be written as a product of primes, and, except for the order in which these primes are written, this can be done in only one way.

Thus $12 = 2^2 \cdot 3 = 2 \cdot 3 \cdot 2 = 3 \cdot 2^2$, $30 = 2 \cdot 3 \cdot 5$, $31 = 31$, $32 = 2^5$, and $30031 = 59 \cdot 509$. The reason behind the first part of the theorem is simple: if an integer (such as 180) is not a prime, then it can be factored in at least one way (such as $10 \cdot 18$); if the two factors are primes, stop; if either factor is not a prime, factor it ($10 = 2 \cdot 5$ and $18 = 2 \cdot 9$); repeat this as often as necessary ($180 = 2^2 \cdot 3^2 \cdot 5$). The complete proof of the theorem is not difficult but its technical details outweigh its interest, and so we shall not give it.

We are now ready for the oldest known significant fact about the set of primes itself. Both the theorem and its proof go back to Proposition 20 of Book IX of Euclid's *Elements*.

EUCLID'S THEOREM

There are infinitely many primes.

Proof

The proof will be *reductio ad absurdum*, and so we begin by assuming there to be only finitely many primes. Under this assumption there must be a largest prime, which we denote by p. Thus the primes are $2, 3, 5, \ldots, p$. Consider the integer $q = (2 \cdot 3 \cdot 5 \cdots p) + 1$, where $2 \cdot 3 \cdot 5 \cdots p$ is the product of the primes. The integer q, just as all other integers greater than 1, must be divisible by at least one prime, that is, by at least one of $2, 3, 5, \ldots, p$. But each prime divides $2 \cdot 3 \cdot 5 \cdots p$, and so a prime dividing q will necessarily divide $q - (2 \cdot 3 \cdot 5 \cdots p) = 1$. No prime divides 1, and so we have reached a contradiction. $\square$

By Euclid's Theorem the set of primes is an infinite set of integers, and by the Fundamental Theorem of Arithmetic it is one of the most important such sets. It is also one of the most mysterious. Compare the set of primes with the set of positive even integers, for instance: given an integer we can determine at a glance whether it is even, but determining whether it is prime can be much more difficult. Is 9379 even? Clearly not. Is 9379 prime? The answer is not obvious. The only apparent way to test whether a number is prime is to search for divisors, and that can be very tedious. It does help to realize that only primes need be tried as divisors, for if a number has a divisor other than 1 and itself then it must have a prime divisor. It also helps to realize that in searching for a divisor of m there is no need to test primes greater than $\sqrt{m}$, for if $m = nq$ then either $n \le \sqrt{m}$ or $q \le \sqrt{m}$ (otherwise $nq > \sqrt{m} \sqrt{m} = m$). Thus in the case of 9379 it certainly suffices to test divisibility by primes less than 100. This particular case shows the kind of bad luck one can have; for $9379 = 83 \cdot 113$, and so although the number 9379 is not a prime, a systematic search trying $2, 3, 5, 7, \ldots$ in order would require 23 trials (83 being the 23rd prime). And of course it could be worse.

Another important contrast between the set of positive even integers and the set of primes concerns the distribution or density of the two sets among the set of positive integers. The even integers appear regularly as we move through the positive integers, but a glance at Table 48.1 will reveal that the primes appear irregularly, and less and less frequently. Some surprising things can be said about the way the sequence of primes behaves in this respect, and we shall look at them after saying more about locating individual primes.

The most famous method for determining primes systematically is the Sieve of Eratosthenes, which is described in Problem 48.9. If it is desired to find all primes up to some particular integer n, and if n is not

TABLE 48.1

Primes Between 1 and 1,000

2	101	211	307	401	503	601	701	809	907
3	103	223	311	409	509	607	709	811	911
5	107	227	313	419	521	613	719	821	919
7	109	229	317	421	523	617	727	823	929
11	113	233	331	431	541	619	733	827	937
13	127	239	337	433	547	631	739	829	941
17	131	241	347	439	557	641	743	839	947
19	137	251	349	443	563	643	751	853	953
23	139	257	353	449	569	647	757	857	967
29	149	263	359	457	571	653	761	859	971
31	151	269	367	461	577	659	769	863	977
37	157	271	373	463	587	661	773	877	983
41	163	277	379	467	593	673	787	881	991
43	167	281	383	479	599	677	797	883	997
47	173	283	389	487		683		887	
53	179	293	397	491		691			
59	181			499					
61	191								
67	193								
71	197								
73	199								
79									
83									
89									
97									

Primes Between 1,000,001 and 1,001,000

1,000,003	1,000,117	1,000,211	1,000,303	1,000,403	1,000,507	1,000,609	1,000,721	1,000,829	1,000,907
1,000,033	1,000,121	1,000,213	1,000,313	1,000,409	1,000,537	1,000,619	1,000,723	1,000,847	1,000,919
1,000,037	1,000,133	1,000,231	1,000,333	1,000,423	1,000,541	1,000,621	1,000,763	1,000,849	1,000,921
1,000,039	1,000,151	1,000,249	1,000,357	1,000,427	1,000,547	1,000,639	1,000,777	1,000,859	1,000,931
1,000,081	1,000,159	1,000,253	1,000,367	1,000,429	1,000,577	1,000,651	1,000,793	1,000,889	1,000,969
1,000,099	1,000,171	1,000,273	1,000,381	1,000,453	1,000,579	1,000,667			1,000,973
	1,000,183	1,000,289	1,000,393	1,000,457	1,000,589	1,000,669			1,000,981
	1,000,187	1,000,291	1,000,397			1,000,679			1,000,999
	1,000,193					1,000,691			
	1,000,199					1,000,697			

Primes Between 10,000,001 and 10,001,000

10,000,019	10,000,103	10,000,223	10,000,303	10,000,439	10,000,511	10,000,609	10,000,721	10,000,813	10,000,931
10,000,079	10,000,121	10,000,229	10,000,339	10,000,451	10,000,537	10,000,643	10,000,723	10,000,819	10,000,943
	10,000,139	10,000,247	10,000,349	10,000,453	10,000,583	10,000,651	10,000,733	10,000,831	10,000,961
	10,000,141	10,000,253	10,000,357	10,000,457	10,000,591	10,000,657	10,000,741	10,000,849	10,000,967
	10,000,169	10,000,261	10,000,363	10,000,481		10,000,667	10,000,747	10,000,867	10,000,987
	10,000,189	10,000,271	10,000,379			10,000,687	10,000,759	10,000,871	10,000,993
						10,000,691	10,000,763	10,000,873	
							10,000,769	10,000,877	
							10,000,789	10,000,891	
							10,000,799		

too large, then the Sieve of Eratosthenes is an efficient method for finding them.

It would be preferable to have a formula for producing primes, and many attempts have been made in that direction. There is a simple formula for producing positive even integers: substitute $1, 2, 3, \ldots$ successively for n in the expression $2n$. The most desirable kind of formula for primes would be of the same type: it would produce all of the prime numbers and no other numbers. There is no reasonable formula of that kind. (There do exist complicated expressions that could be thought of as formulas for primes, but in reality they say only that the nth prime is the nth prime.) Another possibility would be a formula giving only prime values—not all primes, but in any case only primes. The most famous attempt in this direction involved so-called Fermat numbers. These numbers are defined by

$$F_n = 2^{2^n} + 1,$$

so that

$$F_0 = 3, F_1 = 5, F_2 = 17, F_3 = 257, F_4 = 65537.$$

These first five Fermat numbers are prime, and Fermat conjectured that all Fermat numbers are prime. But in 1732 Euler discovered that

$$F_5 = 641 \cdot 6700417,$$

and so F_5 is not prime. Further, in 1880 Landry discovered

$$F_6 = 274177 \cdot 67280421310721.$$

Since then many other F_n have been shown to be composite, and none has been shown to be prime. Fermat primes (Fermat numbers that are prime) were shown by Gauss to be related to geometrical constructions (Section 47): a regular polygon of N sides can be constructed using unmarked straightedge and compass if and only if $N = 2^m p_1 p_2 \cdots p_k$, where m is zero or a positive integer, and the p's are distinct Fermat primes.

A third possible type of formula for producing primes would be one giving infinitely many primes—composite numbers as well, perhaps, but in any case infinitely many primes. This can be done with the trivial formula $f(n) = n$: substitute $1, 2, 3, \ldots$ successively for n and we get $1, 2, 3, \ldots$, so in particular we get all primes. But we certainly want to be more selective than that. An only slightly better formula in this sense is $g(n) = 2n + 1$: substitute $1, 2, 3, \ldots$ and we get $3, 5, 7, \ldots$, which is the sequence of all positive odd integers, which includes the sequence of all odd primes. The most remarkable result of this kind is a famous theorem of Dirichlet, the proof of which is extremely difficult.

DIRICHLET'S THEOREM

If a and b are positive integers having no common divisor, then there are infinitely many primes of the form an + b.

With $a = 3$ and $b = 5$, for instance, the theorem guarantees that there are infinitely many primes in the sequence

$$3 + 5, 6 + 5, 9 + 5, 12 + 5, \ldots, 3n + 5 \ldots.$$

Any such sequence will also contain composite numbers (Problem 48.15). And if a and b have a common divisor, then there are no primes of the form $an + b$ (Problem 48.14).

Let us return to the question of the distribution of the primes among the positive integers. We begin with three statements concerning gaps in the sequence of primes. The first, Theorem 48.1, asserts that there are arbitrarily large gaps, and we shall prove it. The second, Bertrand's Postulate (which is really a theorem rather than a postulate), asserts that although there may be arbitrarily large gaps, one must go reasonably far out to find them. And the third, the Twin Prime Conjecture, which has never been proved, asserts that one will always return to small gaps no matter how far one has gone. We must be more precise.

THEOREM 48.1

For each positive integer n, there is a sequence of n consecutive composite integers.

Proof

This is best seen from a special case. Choose $n = 99$, and consider the sequence*

$$100! + 2, 100! + 3, 100! + 4, \ldots, 100! + 100.$$

The first of these is divisible by 2, the second by 3, the third by 4, and so on, so that none is prime.

To obtain a sequence of n consecutive composite integers, we can use the sequence

$$(n + 1)! + 2, (n + 1)! + 3, (n + 1)! + 4, \ldots, (n + 1)! + (n + 1). \ \square$$

Bertrand's Postulate was stated as a conjecture by Bertrand and proved in 1850 by the Russian mathematician Tchebycheff (1821–1894). Its proof is much more difficult than that of Theorem 48.1.

BERTRAND'S POSTULATE

For each positive integer n, there is a prime p such that $n < p \leq 2n$.

---

* The notation $n!$ (n factorial) is explained in Section 18.

Thus, for instance, there is at least one prime between 30000000 and 60000000.

For our third result we require the following definition: primes p and q are said to be *twin primes* if $p + 2 = q$. Here are some twin primes:

$$3, \quad 5$$
$$5, \quad 7$$
$$11, \quad 13$$
$$17, \quad 19$$
$$29, \quad 31$$
$$\vdots$$
$$8537, \quad 8539.$$

TWIN PRIME CONJECTURE
There are infinitely many twin primes.

As we have said, the Twin Prime Conjecture has not been proved (or disproved). It rates with Goldbach's Conjecture (Problem 2.8) and Fermat's Last Theorem (Section 3) among easy to state and difficult to solve problems in number theory.

The three statements just given show a high degree of irregularity in the distribution of the primes among the integers. We now show that in spite of this irregularity, there is, in another sense, a high degree of regularity.

Let us recall an important function: for each real number x, $\pi(x)$ denotes the number of primes that do not exceed x. In particular, if p_n denotes the nth prime, so that $p_1 = 2, p_2 = 3, p_3 = 5, p_4 = 7, \ldots,$ then $\pi(p_n) = n$ for each n. The graph of the function π is shown in Figure 38.2. (The three statements about gaps can be interpreted in terms of the segments making up this graph: Theorem 48.1 asserts that the graph contains segments arbitrarily long; Bertrand's Postulate asserts that there is always at least one jump between n and $2n$; and the Twin Prime Conjecture asserts that beyond any point there will remain segments of length 2.)

As x increases, $\pi(x)$ also increases. But the rate at which $\pi(x)$ increases tends to decrease as x becomes larger—this is simply another way of saying that the primes appear less and less frequently as we move through the positive integers. Late in the eighteenth century Gauss and the French mathematician Legendre (1752–1833) conjectured results that were very close to what is now known as the Prime Number Theorem. This remarkable theorem states that $\pi(x)$ increases at roughly the same rate as $x/\log x$.*

---

* Recall that $\log x$ means $\log_e x$ (Example 45.10).

PRIME NUMBER THEOREM

$$\lim \frac{\pi(x)}{x/\log x} = 1 \quad \text{as} \quad x \to \infty.$$

In explaining the theorem let us first concentrate on $x/\log x$. Although $\log x$ increases, in a way that can be seen most clearly from its graph (Figure 45.3), it does not increase as rapidly as x itself. In particular $x/\log x$ increases as x increases because the denominator does not increase as fast as the numerator. The Prime Number Theorem reveals that the function π increases on the average in the same way as $x/\log x$, in the sense that the ratio of $\pi(x)$ to $x/\log x$ approaches 1 as x becomes large. We can consider the function $x/\log x$ to be well understood; thus the function π, which is so unpredictable in its detailed behavior, is on the average very predictable.

An indication of the way in which the ratio of $\pi(x)$ to $x/\log x$ does approach 1 can be seen from Table 48.2. Notice that although their ratio approaches 1 their difference does not approach 0. If we think of $x/\log x$ as an approximation for $\pi(x)$, then $\pi(x) - x/\log x$ is the amount we are in error. Although the Prime Number Theorem asserts that this error becomes arbitrarily small in relative terms, it does not become small in absolute terms. Number theorists have spent a large amount of time attempting to estimate this error, and also in studying functions that yield slightly better approximations than $x/\log x$.

TABLE 48.2

x	$\pi(x)$	$x/\log x$*	$\dfrac{\pi(x)}{x/\log x}$	$\pi(x) - x/\log x$*
100	25	22	1.15 ...	3
1,000	168	145	1.16 ...	23
10,000	1,229	1,086	1.13 ...	143
100,000	9,592	8,686	1.10 ...	906
1,000,000	78,498	72,382	1.08 ...	6,116
10,000,000	664,579	620,420	1.07 ...	44,159

* Rounded to the nearest integer.

Neither Gauss nor Legendre succeeded in proving the Prime Number Theorem. The first significant step in this direction was taken by Tchebycheff, who proved in 1848 that if the ratio in the theorem approaches a limit at all then that limit must be 1. Tchebycheff made other contributions to the problem in 1850, but the final key to the proof of the theorem was given by Riemann in 1859. Riemann's idea has proven to be of such great importance that we have chosen to close by describing what has developed from it.

Consider the infinite series

$$1 + \frac{1}{2^s} + \frac{1}{3^s} + \frac{1}{4^s} + \cdots.$$

We have already encountered this series for special values of s. In Example 45.4 we saw that it is divergent if $s = 1$. In Example 45.6 we saw that for $s = 2$ it is convergent with sum $\pi^2/6$, and for $s = 4$ it is convergent with sum $\pi^4/90$, both sums being due to Euler. In 1737 Euler discovered the following identity involving this series:

$$1 + \frac{1}{2^s} + \frac{1}{3^s} + \frac{1}{4^s} + \cdots$$

$$= \left(1 - \frac{1}{2^s}\right)^{-1} \left(1 - \frac{1}{3^s}\right)^{-1} \left(1 - \frac{1}{5^s}\right)^{-1} \left(1 - \frac{1}{7^s}\right)^{-1} \cdots.$$

The product here is an infinite product with one factor corresponding to each prime, and such products can be given a precise meaning in terms of limits in much the same way as infinite series. The point of Euler's identity is that for each real number $s > 1$ the series and the product represent equal real numbers; furthermore, it establishes a direct relationship between the series and the set of prime numbers.

Because the series determines a real number (its sum) for each real number $s > 1$, it defines a function of s. This function has come to be denoted by ζ (Greek letter zeta). Thus for each real number $s > 1$,

$$\zeta(s) = 1 + \frac{1}{2^s} + \frac{1}{3^s} + \frac{1}{4^s} + \cdots.$$

Riemann's basic idea was to show that there is a reasonable way to give meaning to this function for complex numbers as well as for real numbers. In this way he obtained what is now known as the Riemann zeta function: for each complex number $s \neq 1$, $\zeta(s)$ is also a complex number, and for each real number $s > 1$, the value of $\zeta(s)$ is that given by the series. Riemann was therefore able to move questions about primes into the domain of complex analysis, which we have already encountered in discussing transcendental numbers; in particular the problem of proving the Prime Number Theorem now became connected with the zeta function. It might be thought that nothing could be gained in moving from a question about primes to questions in complex analysis, which is apparently a much deeper branch of mathematics. The moral is that there may be nothing in the statement of a problem to reveal what may be involved in its solution.

Riemann was able to prove a number of important theorems about the zeta function and he sketched a proof of the Prime Number Theorem. This proof was incomplete, however, and the matter was not settled until

1896 when Jacques Hadamard (French, 1865–1963) and C. J. de la Vallée-
Poussin (Belgian, 1866–1962) independently proved the Prime Number
Theorem.   Their proofs made use of Riemann's methods.   Number
theorists were not content with a proof requiring complex analysis,
however, and in 1947 A. Selberg and P. Erdös finally succeeded, independently, in obtaining proofs without the tools of complex analysis;
but their proofs are by no means easy.   Selberg was awarded a Fields
medal at the 1950 International Congress of Mathematicians for his
work in this area.

The proofs of Selberg and Erdös did not free the Prime Number
Theorem from complex analysis, however.   There remains always the
question of the error $\pi(x) - x/\log x$, and efforts to estimate this are still
closely tied to complex analysis, and in particular to the Riemann zeta
function.   There could be no more fitting way to end than by returning
to this function, and to a problem that has defeated many of the greatest
mathematicians since Riemann.

The zeta function has infinitely many roots.   That is, there are
infinitely many different complex numbers s such that $\zeta(s) = 0$.   We have
met two other functions with the same property: sin x has roots $\ldots$,
$-2\pi, -\pi, 0, \pi, 2\pi, \ldots$; and cos x has roots $\ldots, -3\pi/2, -\pi/2, \pi/2, 3\pi/2, \ldots$.
It was known to Riemann that the roots of the zeta function fall into two
classes.   The first class consists of the negative even integers: $\ldots$,
$-2n, \ldots, -6, -4, -2$.   The second class consists of infinitely many
complex numbers of the form $x + iy$ with $0 < x < 1$.   Geometrically the
numbers in the second class all lie in the infinite strip that is shaded in
Figure 48.1.   Riemann made a conjecture, now known as the Riemann
hypothesis, about the roots in the second class, and it has still been
neither proved nor disproved.   The problem of settling this conjecture
was the eighth on Hilbert's list of problems presented to the International
Congress of Mathematicians in 1900 (Section 33).   We cannot hope to
convey the apparent difficulty of this problem, or the amount of mathematics that has been developed in attempts to answer it—much of which
has found application in other contexts.   Still, as a symbol of the vitality
of modern mathematics, we shall close by stating one of its most chal-
lenging problems: to prove, or disprove, the Riemann hypothesis.

RIEMANN HYPOTHESIS

*All roots of the zeta function, other than the negative even integers,
lie on the line $x = \frac{1}{2}$.*

Figure 48.1

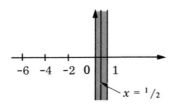

PROBLEM SET 48

PROBLEM 48.1. Write each of the following as a product of primes.
  (a) 18   (b) 93   (c) 111
  (d) 137   (e) 217   (f) 611
  (g) 1024   (h) 1703   (i) 3611

PROBLEM 48.2. One of the following equations is incorrect. Apply the Fundamental Theorem of Arithmetic to decide which, without multiplying.

$$7 \cdot 7 \cdot 31 = 11 \cdot 139 \qquad 21 \cdot 84 = 9 \cdot 196$$

PROBLEM 48.3. Find an example to show the following statement false: If k, m, and n are integers and k divides mn, then k divides m or k divides n. (The statement is true if k is a prime.)

PROBLEM 48.4. Determine the number of positive integer divisors of each of the following integers.
  (a) 3^5 (b) 3^{200}
  (c) $2^5 \cdot 3^5$ (d) 21^{10}
  (e) $p^m q^n$, p and q different primes, m and n positive integers.

PROBLEM 48.5. List all primes that divide 20!.

PROBLEM 48.6. Prove or disprove: If n is a natural number, and $p_1, p_2, \ldots, p_n$ denote the first n primes, then $p_1 p_2 p_3 \cdots p_n + 1$ is a prime. (Compare the proof of Euclid's Theorem.)

PROBLEM 48.7. (a) Does the proof of Euclid's Theorem remain valid if $q = (2 \cdot 3 \cdot 5 \cdots p) + 1$ is replaced by $q = (2 \cdot 3 \cdot 5 \cdots p) - 1$?
  (b) What if $q = (2 \cdot 3 \cdot 5 \cdots p) + 1$ is replaced by $q = (2 \cdot 3 \cdot 5 \cdots p) + 2$?
  (c) What if $q = (2 \cdot 3 \cdot 5 \cdots p) + 1$ is replaced by $q = (2 \cdot 3 \cdot 4 \cdot 5 \cdots p) + 1$, where $2 \cdot 3 \cdot 4 \cdot 5 \cdots p$ is the product of all integers from 2 through p?

PROBLEM 48.8. (a) Prove that if m and n are integers both divisible by an integer k, then $m + n$ and $m - n$ are also divisible by k.
  (b) Part of (a) was used without explicit reference in the proof of Euclid's Theorem. Where?

PROBLEM 48.9. The Sieve of Eratosthenes (c. 250 B.C.) is a method for determining all primes less than any number n. Write all of the integers from 2 to n, in order. Circle 2 and then mark out all integers in the list that are greater than 2 but divisible by 2 (they cannot be primes since they are divisible by 2). Next circle 3 and then mark out all integers in the list that are greater than 3 but divisible by 3 (they cannot be primes since they are divisible by 3). Continue, each time circling the smallest number neither circled nor marked out previously, and then marking out all other integers in the list that are divisible by the number last circled. Stop the process when a number greater than $\sqrt{n}$ has been circled. The primes less than n are the numbers in the list that have been either circled or not marked out. Use this method to determine all primes less than 50.

PROBLEM 48.10. A prime of the form $2^p - 1$, where p is also a prime, is called a *Mersenne prime*. Examples are $2^2 - 1 = 5$ and $2^3 - 1 = 7$.
  (a) Are $2^5 - 1$ and $2^7 - 1$ primes? (Use Table 48.1.)
  (b) Determine all Mersenne primes less than 4,000.
  (The number $2^p - 1$ is prime for twenty of the primes p less than 5,000.

The number $2^{11213} - 1$ is a Mersenne prime, containing 3,376 digits. See also Problem 48.11. Mersenne lived 1588–1648.)

PROBLEM 48.11. A natural number is said to be *perfect* if it is the sum of its positive divisors, excluding itself. Thus 6 is perfect because $6 = 1 + 2 + 3$, but 8 is not perfect because $8 \neq 1 + 2 + 4$.
(a) Verify that 28 is perfect.
(b) Verify that 496 is perfect.
(c) Verify that 6 is the only perfect number less than 20.
(d) Euclid proved that if $2^p - 1$ is prime then $2^{p-1}(2^p - 1)$ is perfect. Use this to verify that 8128 is perfect. (Use $p = 7$. See Problem 48.10(a).) (Euler proved that all even perfect numbers have the form $2^{p-1}(2^p - 1)$ for p and $2^p - 1$ primes. It is unknown whether there are any odd perfect numbers, or if there are infinitely many even perfect numbers.)

PROBLEM 48.12. For which N less than 100 can a regular polygon of N sides be constructed using unmarked straightedge and compass.

PROBLEM 48.13. (a) Use Table 48.1 to find the primes less than 500 and of the form $20n + 3$. (Compare Dirichlet's Theorem.)
(b) Use Table 48.1 to find the primes less than 500 and of the form $10n + 17$. (Compare Dirichlet's Theorem.)

PROBLEM 48.14. Prove that if a and b have a common divisor greater than 1, then there are no primes of the form $an + b$. (Compare Dirichlet's Theorem.)

PROBLEM 48.15. Prove that if a and b are positive integers, then there are infinitely many composite numbers of the form $an + b$. (Compare Dirichlet's Theorem.)

PROBLEM 48.16. Use Euclid's Theorem to prove the following special case of Dirichlet's Theorem: If b is any positive odd integer, then there are infinitely many primes of the form $2n + b$.

PROBLEM 48.17. Using Table 48.1, list all twin primes in each of the following ranges.
(a) Between 1 and 100.
(b) Between 1 and 1,000.
(c) Between 1,000,001 and 1,001,000.
(d) Between 10,000,001 and 10,001,000.

PROBLEM 48.18. (a) Use the Prime Number Theorem to compute an approximate value for log 1,000,000,000, given that $\pi(1,000,000,000) = 50,847,478$.
(b) Compute log 1,000,000,000 using log 10 = 2.30259 and $\log 10^9 = 9 \log 10$ (Problem 36.8). Compare the result in part (a).

PROBLEM 48.19. Given $\pi(100,000,000) = 5,761,455$ and log 10 = 2.30259 and $\log 10^8 = 8 \log 10$ (Problem 36.8), complete the row that would correspond to 100,000,000 in Table 48.2.

REFERENCES

1. ALEKSANDROV, A. D., et al., eds., *Mathematics: Its Content, Methods, and Meaning*, 3 vols., The MIT Press, Cambridge, Mass., 1969. (English translation of 1956 Russian edition.)

2. BELL, E. T., *Men of Mathematics*, Simon and Schuster, New York, 1937.

3. BOYER, C. B., *History of the Calculus*, Columbia University Press, New York, 1939; paperback edition, Dover, New York, 1959.

4. BOYER, C. B., *A History of Mathematics*, John Wiley & Sons, New York, 1968.

5. CAJORI, FLORIAN, 'History of Zeno's Arguments on Motion', American Mathematical Monthly, vol. 22, 1915, pp. 1–6, 39–47, 77–82, 109–115, 145–149, 179–186, 215–220, 253–258, 292–297.

6. COHEN, M. R., and I. E. DRABKIN, *A Source Book in Greek Science*, Harvard University Press, Cambridge, Mass., 1958.

7. COURANT, R., and H. ROBBINS, *What is Mathematics?*, Oxford University Press, London, 1941.

8. EVES, HOWARD, *An Introduction to the History of Mathematics*, rev. ed. Holt, Rinehart and Winston, New York, 1964.

9. HEATH, T. L., *The Works of Archimedes*, Cambridge University Press, Cambridge, 1897; paperback edition, including Archimedes' *Method*, New York.

10. HEATH, T. L., *Manual of Greek Mathematics*, Oxford University Press, London, 1931; paperback edition, Dover, New York, 1963.

11. HILBERT, D., 'Mathematical Problems', trans. by M. W. Newson, Bulletin of the Americal Mathematical Society, vol. 8, 1902, pp. 437–445, 478–479. (Reprinted in part in [18].)

12. KLEIN, F., *Famous Problems of Elementary Geometry*, Chelsea Publishing Company, New York, 1955.

13. KLINE, MORRIS, *Mathematical Thought from Ancient to Modern Times*, Oxford University Press, London, 1972.

14. LEHMER, D. N., *List of Prime Numbers from 1 to 10,006,721*, Hafner Publishing Company, New York, 1956.

15. *The Mathematical Sciences*, The MIT Press, Cambridge, Mass., 1969.

16. *Mathematical Thinking in Behavioral Sciences*, readings from Scientific American with introductions by David M. Messick, W. H. Freeman, San Francisco, 1968.

17. *Mathematics in the Modern World*, readings from Scientific American with introductions by M. Kline, W. H. Freeman, San Francisco, 1968.

18. NEWMAN, J., ed., *The World of Mathematics*, 4 vols., Simon and Schuster, New York, 1956.

19. POLYA, G., *Mathematics and Plausible Reasoning*, 2 vols., Princeton University Press, Princeton, 1954.

20. REID, C., *Hilbert*, Springer-Verlag, New York, 1970.

21. SMITH, D. E., *A Source Book in Mathematics*, McGraw-Hill, New York, 1929; paperback edition, Dover, New York, 1958.

APPENDIX

Answers to Selected Problems

Answers are given only to serve as a check on the understanding of certain basic points. For problems with multiple parts, the answers are in most cases chosen from among parts (a). (d), and (g).

Problem Set 1

1.1. **(a)** 9. **(d)** 1/9. **(g)** 243. **1.2.** **(a)** 2. **(d)** 9. **(g)** 1/16. **1.5.** **(a)** 5. **(d)** $\sqrt{5}$ **1.6.** **(a)** 3. **(d)** 3. **1.8.** **(a)** Requires use of the converse of the Pythagorean Theorem. **(b)** Requires use of the Pythagorean Theorem and anticipates the method of *reductio ad absurdum*, discussed in Section 4. **1.15.** **(a)** Statement true, converse false. **(d)** Statement true, converse false. **(g)** Statement true, converse false.

Problem Set 2

2.1. **(a)** 8 + 4 + 1. **(d)** 32 + 16 + 8 + 4. **2.2.** **(d)** 16 = 2^4, so to multiply a number by 16, double 4 times: 12, 24, 48, 96, <u>192</u>. **2.3.** **(d)** 20 · 15 = 20 · (1 + 2 + 4 + 8) = (20 · 1) + (20 · 2) + (20 · 4) + (20 · 8), so we add the following terms: <u>20</u>, <u>40</u>, <u>80</u>, <u>160</u>. This gives 300. **2.4.** **(a)** 1001. **(d)** 100001. **2.5.** **(a)** 9. **(d)** 64. **(g)** 44. **2.10.** **(a)** $V_c = 180 \frac{2}{3}$, $V_B = 180 \frac{1}{2}$.

Problem Set 3

3.1. **(a)** Pythagorean triple. **(d)** Not a Pythagorean triple. **(g)** Not a Pythagorean triple because the numbers are not natural numbers. **3.3.** **(c)** There are four of them.

Problem Set 4

4.3. **(a)** $a = 1$ and $b = 1$ will do because $4 \neq 2$. **(d)** $a = 1$ and $b = 1$ will do because $\sqrt{2} \neq 2$.

Problem Set 5

5.1. **(a)** $0.\overline{09}$. **(d)** $0.\overline{153846}$. **5.2.** **(a)** 1/9. **(d)** 182/99. **5.3.** **(a)** True, 1. **(d)** False, $r/2s$ is smaller than r/s.

Problem Set 6

6.5. **(b)** If $\sqrt{wz} = x$, then $w + z > 2x$. **(d)** The arithmetic mean of 1 and 4 is 2.5, and the geometric mean of 1 and 4 is 2.

Problem Set 7

7.1. **(a)** Consistent. **(d)** Consistent. **(g)** Consistent. **7.2.** **(a)** Consistent. **(d)** Inconsistent. **(g)** Consistent. **7.3.** **(a)** II. **(d)** II. **(g)** II. **7.4.** **(a)** II. **(d)** III. **(g)** II. **7.7.** **(c)** The sum can be anything between two and four right angles.

Problem Set 8

8.1. **(a)** III. **(d)** I. **(g)** II. **(j)** III (Theorem 12.2). **8.5.** One of the first twenty-eight propositions will suffice. Which one? **8.7.** Use I 17 and Theorem 8.1(b).

Problem Set 15

15.1. **(a)** There are six possible outcomes. **(b)** The probability is 2/3 that the number selected is greater than 200. **15.2.** **(a)** 1/4. **(d)** 1. **15.5.** **(a)** 1/36. **(d)** 1/4. **(g)** 5/6. **15.6.** Probabilities of sums 2, 5, 8, and 11 are 1/36, 4/36, 5/36 and 1/18, respectively. **15.7.** **(a)** 1/2. **(d)** See Problem 15.11. **15.8.** **(a)** 1/4. **(d)** 12/13. **15.9.** **(a)** 3/8. **(d)** 1/8. **(g)** 1/2 (including the outcome *BBB*). **15.10.** **(a)** 1/4. **(d)** 1/16. **(g)** 5/16 (including the outcome *BBBB*).

Problem Set 16

16.3. **(a)** 1/216. **(d)** 1/72. **16.6.** **(a)** Forty. **(d)** Sixty-five. **16.8.** **(a)** 720. **(d)** 2/3. **16.9.** **(a)** $21^2/26^2$. **(d)** The probability of obtaining no vowels is 42/65. **16.10.** **(a)** 20. **(d)** 1/2. **(g)** 0.

Problem Set 17

17.3. **(a)** 1/8. **(d)** 1/8. **17.4.** **(a)** 1/4. **17.5.** **(a)** No. **(d)** Yes. **(g)** No.

Problem Set 18

18.1. **(a)** 720. **(d)** 120. **(g)** 21. **(j)** 4950. **18.2.** **(a)** 28. **(d)** -960. **18.6.** **(a)** $C(52, 13)$. **(d)** $C(48, 9)$. **18.7.** **(a)** $C(39, 13)/C(52, 13)$. **(d)** $C(26, 13)/C(52, 13)$. **18.8.** **(a)** $C(9, 2)/C(90, 2)$. **(d)** $45^2/C(90, 2)$. **18.9.** **(a)** $C(9, 3)/C(90, 3)$. **(d)** $45^2 \cdot 22/$ $C/90, 3)$.

Problem Set 19

19.1. **(a)** 35/128. **(d)** 11/32. **(g)** 0.8684 (approximately). **19.2.** **(a)** 5/16. **19.4.** **(a)** The probability is 1/2. **19.5.** **(a)** 0.0098. **(d)** 0.0010. **(g)** $11/2^{10}$ (including the outcome all boys). **19.6.** **(a)** 1/64. (Assume the precinct large enough so that selection without replacement is essentially the same as selection with replacement.) **19.7.** **(a)** $C(20, 10)$. **(d)** $C(10, 5) \cdot C(10, 5)/C(20, 10)$.

Problem Set 20

20.2. **(a)** $(1/5)^{10}$. **(d)** $(4/5)^{10} + 10(1/5)(4/5)^9 + 45(1/5)^2(4/5)^8$. **20.3.** **(a)** $15(5/26)(21/26)^{14}$. **(d)** The probability that exactly one is a vowel is $C(5, 1) \cdot$ $C(21, 14)/C(26, 15)$. **20.5.** **(a)** $10(1/216)(215/216)^9$. **20.6.** **(a)** $10(1/4)^2(3/4)^3$. **(d)** $(3/4)^5 + 5(1/4)(3/4)$. **20.7.** **(a)** $(19/20)^{10}$. **(d)** $C(10, 6)(1/20)^6(19/20)^4 + C(10, 7) \cdot$ $(1/20)^7(19/20)^3 + C(10, 8)(1/20)^8(19/20)^2 + C(10, 9)(1/20)^9(19/20) + C(10, 10) \cdot$ $(1/20)^{10}$. **20.8.** **(a)** $(1/4)^{10}$. **(d)** $C(10, 5)(3/4)^5(1/4)^5$.

Problem Set 21

21.1. **(a)** 0.0175. **(d)** 0.1841. **(g)** 0.3413. **(j)** 0.9974. **21.2.** 0.0287. **21.5.** Approximately 0.1. **21.7.** **(a)** Approximately 0.68. **21.8.** **(a)** 0.34. **21.9.** **(a)** 0.02. **(d)** 0.98.

Problem Set 22

22.1. **(a)** Pair 1, 2, 3, ... with $-1, -2, -3, ...$ respectively. **(d)** Pair 1, 2, 3, 4, 5, 6, ... with 0, 2, -2, 4, -4, 6, ... respectively. **22.2.** **(a)** No. **(d)** No. **22.7.** **(a)** ϕ, $\{x\}$, $\{y\}$. **22.8.** **(a)** The pairing given by $n \leftrightarrow n + 1$ will suffice. **22.10.** **(a)** The set of all powers of 2 (2, 4, 8, ...) and the set of all powers of 3 (3, 9, 27, ...). (There are many other possibilities on most of these problems.)

Problem Set 23

23.1. **(a)** 0.51.

Problem Set 24

24.1. **(a)** Apply Problem 22.1(d). **(d)** Apply Problem 22.1(e). **24.6.** **(a)** Use the scheme in Example 22.1, replacing each fraction r/s by the pair $\{r, s\}$ and making omissions as needed.

Problem Set 25

25.1. **(a)** Let R denote any infinite set, S the power set of R, and T the power set of S. **25.3.** **(a)** $T = \phi$. **25.4.** **(a)** 1. **(d)** ϕ. **25.5.** **(a)** 0.75. **(d)** 0.078125. **25.6.** **(a)** 0.1. **(d)** 100.1.

Problem Set 27

27.1. **(a)** Group. **(d)** Not a group, only 1 and -1 have inverses. **(g)** Not a group, the associative law fails. **27.3.** **(a)** The rule given is an operation that is associative, with -1 as an identity element. **(d)** The rule given is an operation that is associative, but there is no identity element. **(g)** The rule is not an operation on the set of integers. **27.4.** **(a)** Commutative. **(d)** Commutative. **(g)** Not an operation. **27.7.** **(a)** 16. **27.8.** $a^2 = a, b^3 = a$. **27.10.** **(a)** 1.

Problem Set 28

28.1. **(a)** $\begin{pmatrix} 1 & 2 & 3 & 4 \\ 3 & 2 & 1 & 4 \end{pmatrix}$. **(d)** $\begin{pmatrix} 1 & 2 & 3 & 4 \\ 4 & 1 & 3 & 2 \end{pmatrix}$. **(g)** $\begin{pmatrix} 1 & 2 & 3 & 4 \\ 3 & 1 & 2 & 4 \end{pmatrix}$. **(j)** $\begin{pmatrix} 1 & 2 & 3 & 4 \\ 3 & 4 & 1 & 2 \end{pmatrix}$

28.4. **(a)** P_1. **(d)** P_1. **28.6.** **(a)** The element shown together with the identity permutation. **28.7.** **(a)** $\{P_1, P_5\}$. **(d)** $\{P_1, P_5\}$. **28.8.** **(a)** The subgroup has order six. **(d)** The same group as in part (a). **28.10.** **(a)** 1. **(d)** 2. **28.11.** **(a)** 1/2. **(d)** 1/6.

Problem Set 29

29.4. **(a)** M_1. **(d)** M_1, M_2, M_3, M_4. **29.8.** **(a)** IV.

Problem Set 30

30.2. **(a)** $y * z = w, y * w = x, z * y = w, z * z = x, z * w = y, w * y = x, w * z = y, w * w = z$. **30.5.** **(a)** For the first part, multiply both sides of $x * y = z$ on the left by x^{-1}.

Problem Set 31

31.1. **(a)** 1, 2, 5, 10. **(d)** 1, 17. **31.2.** There are five subgroups. **31.4.** There are four subgroups. **31.7.** **(a)** The orders are 1, 3, 3, 2, 2, 2.

Problem Set 32

32.7. There are two automorphisms. **32.11.** **(a)** One of the groups is cyclic, and the other is not. Moreover, one is finite while the other is infinite.

Problem Set 35

35.1. **(a)** $20°$. **(d)** $10°$. **35.2.** **(a)** $\pi/6$. **(d)** $-\pi$. **35.4.** **(a)** 1. **(d)** -1. **35.5.** **(a)** $0, \pm\pi, \pm 2\pi, \pm 3\pi, \ldots$. **(d)** $\pi/6, 5\pi/6$, and any angle differing from one of these by $\pm 2\pi, \pm 4\pi, \pm 6\pi, \ldots$. **35.6.** **(a)** $\pi/2$ and any angle differing from this by $\pm \pi, \pm 2\pi, \pm 3\pi, \ldots$. **(d)** $\pi/3, -\pi/3$ and any angle differing from one of these by $\pm 2\pi, \pm 4\pi, \pm 6\pi, \ldots$. **35.7.** **(a)** $0 < x < \pi$. **(d)** $0 \le x < \pi/2$ and $3\pi/2 < x \le 2\pi$.

Problem Set 36

36.3. **(a)** 3. **(d)** 216. **(g)** 1/25. **36.4.** **(a)** 1. **(d)** 5. **(g)** -3. **36.5.** **(a)** 1.17609. **36.7.** **(a)** -0.30103. **36.9.** **(a)** 3.0103.

Problem Set 37

37.6. (a) $x = 2$. **(d)** $x^2 + y^2 = 5$.   **37.9. (a)** Each of the three types. **(d)** Only the third type.

Problem Set 38

38.1. (a) 2. **(d)** 83.   **38.2. (a)** 1. **(d)** 0.   **38.5. (a)** 0. **(d)** 7.   **38.7. (a)** 1, 4, 9, 16, 25. **(d)** 1, 1/4, 1/9, 1/16, 1/25. **(g)** $-1, 1, -1, 1, -1$.

Problem Set 39

39.1. (a) Limit 0. **(d)** Limit 7. **(g)** No limit, alternate terms are always at least one unit apart.   **39.2. (a)** No limit, the successive terms get further apart rather than closer together. **(d)** Limit 0. **(g)** No limit, alternate terms are always two units apart.   **39.3. (a)** Limit 25. **(d)** Limit 2π. **(g)** Limit 8.   **39.4. (a)** No limit, $\pi(x) \le 4$ if $x < 11$, but $\pi(x) \ge 5$ if $x > 11$.   **39.5. (a)** 2.9, 2.99, 2.999, ...   **39.8. (a)** 100.

Problem Set 40

40.1. (a) The average velocity over the interval $t = 0$ to $t = 2$ is 3.   **40.3. (a)** Position $\frac{1}{2}g = 16.1$ feet below the top of the building, velocity $g = 32.2$ feet per second.   **40.4. (a)** $f'(x) = 10x^9, f''(x) = 90x^8$. **(d)** $f'(x) = x^4 + x^3 + x^2 + x + 1, f''(x) = 4x^3 + 3x^2 + 2x + 1$.   **40.5. (a)** 2. **(d)** 1.   **40.6. (a)** 0. **(d)** 0.   **40.8. (a)** Minimum at $x = 3$. **(d)** Maximum at $x = -2$, minimum at $x = 1$.

Problem Set 41

41.1. (a) 14. **(d)** 9. **(g)** $9[1 - (3/2n) + (1/2n^2)]$.   **41.4. (a)** 25/4. **(d)** 4. **(g)** $4[1 - (2/n) + (1/n^2)]$.   **41.6. (a)** $\int_{-\pi/4}^{0} \cos x \, dx$.

Problem Set 42

42.1. (a) x. **(d)** $x^4/4$.   **42.2. (a)** 4. **(d)** 31/5. **(g)** 24/35.   **42.3. (a)** 21/2.   **42.7. (a)** $h(x) = x^2 + 1$ will do.

Problem Set 43

43.1. (a) $v(t) = 2t + 1; a(t) = 2$.   **43.2. (a)** Not a possibility because $d'(t) = 2t \ne v(t)$.   **43.3. (a)** Not a possibility because $d''(t) = 0 \ne a(t)$.   **43.5. (a)** 40 feet below the top of the building. **(d)** 40 feet per second.

Problem Set 44

44.1. The segments given should be perpendicular to produce the largest triangle.   **44.6. (a)** $\sin \alpha_2 = 0.1991, \alpha_2 = 11°$.

Problem Set 45

45.3. (a) 1/2.   **45.6. (a)** 6.   **45.11.** The first partial sum gives 4; the second partial sum gives 8/3.

Problem Set 46

46.1. **(a)** 1. **(d)** $-i$. **(g)** $2i$. **46.4.** **(a)** $(1 - i)/2$. **(d)** $(14 - 7i)/10$. **(g)** $(-1 + 3i)/2$. **46.8.** **(a)** $(1 \pm \sqrt{5})/2$. **(d)** $1/2, -3/2$. **(g)** $0, -i$.

Problem Set 47

47.1. **(a)** π or e will do. **(d)** Any rational number will do. **47.2.** **(a)** Algebraic. **(d)** Apply the solution to Hilbert's seventh problem.

Problem Set 48

48.1. **(a)** $2 \cdot 3^2$. **(d)** 137. **48.4.** **(a)** 6. **48.6.** No. Try $n = 6$ and compare the factorizations following the statement of the Fundamental Theorem of Arithmetic. **48.13.** **(a)** There are eleven of them. **48.17.** **(a)** There are eight pairs less than 100.

Index

Abel, N. H., 155, 182
Absolute value, 226
Acceleration, 254–261
  defined, 254–255
Ahmes, 10
  Ahmes Papyrus (*see* Rhind
    Papyrus)
Aleksandrov, A. D., 190, 306
Alexandria, 13
Algebraic equations:
  and geometric constructions,
    290
  and groups, 153–155
Algebraic numbers, 288–294
  defined, 290
Al-Khowarizmi, 193
Analysis, 191–307
  characterized, 194
Analytic geometry, 194, 216–222
Angle:
  acute, 40
  obtuse, 40
  of parallelism, 66

  right, 40
  trisection, 196, 288–290
Antiderivative, 251–252
Apollonius, 192, 198, 201
Arabic mathematics, 154, 193
Archimedes, 192, 198, 201–202,
    254, 307
Area:
  parabolic segment, 201–202
  rhombus, 6
  triangle, 7
  surface of revolution, 268–269
  (*see also* Integrals; Method of
    exhaustion)
Aristaeus, 200
Aristarchus, 210, 256
Aristotle, 12, 258
Associative law, 152, 157
Astronomy, 208, 211, 254–262
Automorphism, 188–189
Axiom of choice, 139, 148
Axioms of Euclidean geometry,
    39–41

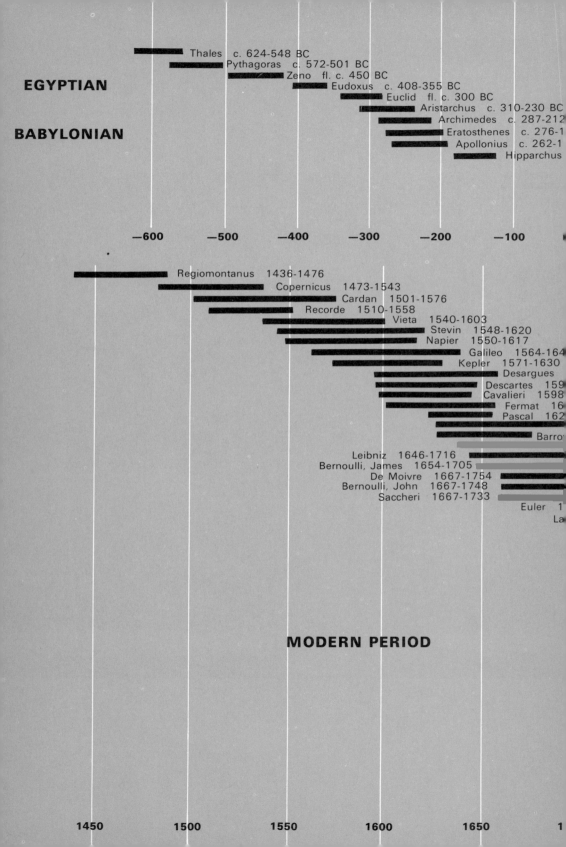

EGYPTIAN

BABYLONIAN

Thales   c. 624-548 BC
Pythagoras   c. 572-501 BC
Zeno   fl. c. 450 BC
Eudoxus   c. 408-355 BC
Euclid   fl. c. 300 BC
Aristarchus   c. 310-230 BC
Archimedes   c. 287-212
Eratosthenes   c. 276-1
Apollonius   c. 262-1
Hipparchus

−600   −500   −400   −300   −200   −100

Regiomontanus   1436-1476
Copernicus   1473-1543
Cardan   1501-1576
Recorde   1510-1558
Vieta   1540-1603
Stevin   1548-1620
Napier   1550-1617
Galileo   1564-164
Kepler   1571-1630
Desargues
Descartes   159
Cavalieri   1598
Fermat   16
Pascal   162
Barro
Leibniz   1646-1716
Bernoulli, James   1654-1705
De Moivre   1667-1754
Bernoulli, John   1667-1748
Saccheri   1667-1733
Euler   1
La

MODERN PERIOD

1450   1500   1550   1600   1650